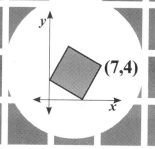

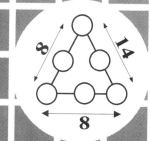

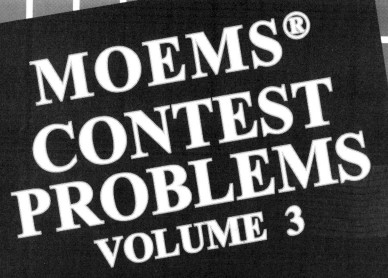

MOEMS® CONTEST PROBLEMS
VOLUME 3

RICHARD KALMAN &
NICHOLAS J. RESTIVO,
EDITORS

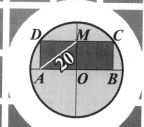

About the Math Olympiads

The Mathematical Olympiads for Elementary and Middle Schools (MOEMS®) was created by Dr. George Lenchner, then the Director of Mathematics for the Valley Stream High School District on Long Island, NY. He created four pilot Olympiads for the elementary schools in 1978-79 before formally organizing MOES (Mathematical Olympiads for Elementary Schools) for all Long Island elementary schools in the fall of 1979. Serving as its first Executive Director until his retirement in 1996, he oversaw the growth of MOES into an international competition. Dr. Lenchner wrote all the problems for those first 16 years.

In subsequent years, his successor, Richard Kalman, who joined MOEMS in 1994 became its second Executive Director, and for three years wrote all the problems; but later, large committees chaired by Grant Duffrin were created to formulate and polish the problem sets. In 1998 Division M was created to serve students in grades 7 and 8, allowing its veteran mathletes to continue to compete after grade 6. During these years the introduction of several innovations took place: the naming of strategies for all solutions; providing extensions for about half of the problems; the start-up of two Web sites (one highly informative for the general public and the other a secure communication system for MOEMS® coaches); the creation of two end-of-year tournaments; and establishing a popular presence at mathematics teachers' conferences.

Nicholas J. Restivo began his service as the third Executive Director in 2010. A tradition of a strong presence at mathematics teachers' conferences, professional development workshops in problem solving, regional mathematics tournaments separate from the Olympiads, and the number of foreign affiliates has continued to grow.

Publisher:

MOEMS® - Mathematical Olympiads for Elementary & Middle Schools, Inc., Bellmore NY, USA
Web site: http://www.moems.org   Phone: 516-781-2400

Editors:

Grant Duffrin, Contest Editor
Richard Kalman and Nicholas J. Restivo, Book Editors

Layout, Graphics, and Additional Material:

Richard Kalman

Cover Design:

Nicholas J. Restivo and Richard Kalman

Printer:

Tobay Printing Company, Inc. Copaigue, NY

Printed in U.S.A., published in Bellmore, N.Y. 2013.

Library of Congress Catalog Number: 2014914482
ISBN: 978-1-882144-12-0

Dr. George Lenchner
(1917 - 2006)

This book is dedicated to the memory of Dr. George Lenchner, who created the Math Olympiads out of his pure love for students and learning. His entire career was an inspiration for thousands of teachers and students.

TABLE OF CONTENTS

Preface

Learning to compute efficiently is the lesser part of learning mathematics, although in the earlier grades the focus is primarily on arithmetic. Learning to reason logically is the major skill students must develop. Learning to solve authentic problems is the most important tool students can use toward this end.

This book is a collection of 400 challenging and interesting problems authored for the *Mathematical Olympiads for Elementary & Middle Schools* (*MOEMS®*) over an eight-year period from 2005 to 2013. Over 150,000 students participate every year, representing about 7500 teams worldwide. Approximately two-thirds of those teams are within the United States.

The problems in this book for Division M were created by Gene Vetter, and those for Division E by the team of George Reuter and Jason Mutford. Additional problems were contributed by J. Bryan Sullivan, Grant Duffrin and Richard Kalman. The Problem Writing Committees, which polished the questions and wrote the solutions, was chaired by Grant Duffrin, who also performed as contest editor. Special appreciation is due all of the above for their masterful contributions to the MOEMS® contests.

Committee members who contributed significantly to the polishing and previewing of the contest problems included in this book are: Randi Albertelli, Mary Altieri, Carol Babcock, Dr. Elliott Bird, Jay Blackman, Curt Boddie, Sandy Cohen, James Connelly, Michael Curry, Barbara Duffrin, Grant Duffrin, David Hankin, Art Kalish, Richard Kalman, Joanne Lufrano, Mary Ann Mansfield, Lisa Minerva, Donna Milgrom, Dennis Mulhearn, Jason Mutford, Cheryl Novick, Eric O'Brien, Oana Pascu, Cheriese Pemberton, David Phillips, Jerald Resnick, George Reuter, Marj Rubin, Arthur Samel, Gene Vetter, Jean Wahlgren, and Harry Witkin.

We owe them great thanks for their skill and judgment in making recommendations with respect to appropriateness, problem placement, level of difficulty, clarity, and ambiguity.

We are also indebted to the following people for their careful review of all or part of the manuscript for this book: Dorothy Hess, Mary Ann Mansfield, Dennis Mulhearn, Sue Norton Scott, Dot Steinert, Jeanne Swierkowski, Harry Witkin, and Nicole Wong.

We all enjoyed creating the problems and solutions and increasing our insights into mathematical principles significantly in the process. I hope you experience the same in testing yourself against them.

Richard Kalman

Nicholas J. Restivo

June, 2014

CONTEST PROBLEM TYPES

Many but not all contest problems can be categorized. This is useful if you choose to work with several related problems even if they involve different concepts.

KEY: problems are organized by type and are coded by **page number and problem placement** on that page. For example, "**Long division: 36BD, 84A, 165E**" refers to four questions, each involving long division: problems B and D on page 36, problem A on page 84, and problem E on page 165.

Note: Pages 24-64 refer to Division E contest problems and pages 66-106 refer to Division M contest problems. Each _FOLLOW-UP_ problem is located after a model solution to a contest problem, is related conceptually to it, and usually extends or expands an aspect of it.

A

Addition patterns — see _Patterns_

Age problems: 30C, 31B, 34E

Algebraic thinking: 24A; 28C, 29B, 30C, 31A, 34B, 35A, 43AE, 46B, 47B, 49D, 50AD, 51A, 52A, 54B, 55C, 56D, 57B, 58C, 61A, 68A, 70C, 72A, 74A, 75E , 77B, 78A , 79B, 83C, 84B, 85AD, 87BC, 90AD, 92C, 95B, 97B, 98BE, 99C, 100B, 101C, 103B, 105AC

———— Also see _Digit problems_; _Coin problems_; _Age problems_

Alphanumeric problems —see _Cryptarithms_

Angles: 87A, 93E, 100D, 104BD, 105E

Area: 24C, 26C, 28C, 30D, 31C, 35D, 38D, 40D, 46D, 60E, 62D, 66E, 75D , 77D, 78D , 79BE, 83E, 91E, 95C, 96C, 102B, 103E

———— **and perimeter:** 25D, 29D, 36C, 39C, 45D, 53C, 55D, 56E, 71D, 76C, 78D , 79D, 80B

———— _Also see Circles and area_

Arithmetic sequences and series — see _Sequences and Series_

———— Also see _Patterns_

Averages (arithmetic means) ———— see _Statistics_

B

Binary numbers:

Business problems: 28D, 46B, 47B, 52A, 58B, 73D, 74C, 75A, 85A, 87E, 95B, 104C, 105, 105D

C

Calendars: 26A, 32A, 37A, 102A

———— Also see _Cycling numbers_; _Remainders_

Certainty problems: 24E, 43D, 44C

Circles: 30A, 59E, 72B

———— **and area:** 69D, 70D, 74E, 75D , 79E, 88D, 89C, 94D, 100E

———— **Circumference:** , 68E

Clock problems: 44D, 51C, 74B, 93E

Coin problems: 29E, 36B, 41B, 42A,71C, 91B

Combinations:

Common multiples — see _Multiples_

Congruent figures:

Consecutive numbers: 25E, 29B, 33A, 57B, 66A, 70B, 76E, 82C, 84D, 89B, 93A, 101B

———— **Consecutive odd or even numbers:** 25C, 48E, 78E , 79B, 97C

Coordinates — see _Graphs_

Cryptarithms: 24B, 32B, 37E, 43C, 45A, 54E, 56C, 57D, 60B, 61E, 67A , 77C, 79A, 89D, 98A, 100A

Cubes and rectangular solids: 44E, 47E, 48D, 77A, 82E, 83E

———— **Painted cube problems:** 27D, 40E, 57E, 97D, 101E

Cubic numbers — _see Square and cube numbers_

Cycling numbers: 27A, 30A, 41E, 49A, 55B, 66D, 73A, 92D, 100C, 105B

———— Also see _Calendars_; _Remainders_

D

Decimals — see *Fractions*

Digit problems: 25AE, 32E, 33C, 35E, 39D, 44D, 46D, 49B, 56A, 70E, 73B, 81B, 83B, 84D, 88A, 95A, 99ACD

—— Also see *Cryptarithms*; *Divisibility*

Distance problems — see *Motion problems*

Distributive property: 44A,60A, 81C, 83D, 87B, 99B

Divisibility: 27E, 39B, 41A, 46E, 57D, 58A , 77C

—— Also see *Factors*; *Multiples; Cycling numbers*

Draw a diagram: 27A, 30B, 31C, 32D, 33B, 35B, 37BC, 38D, 41C, 42CE, 43A, 46CD, 47C, 49E, 50D, 51D, 52BE, 54D, 55C, 59E, 61D, 62E, 70A, 72B, 75D, 78B, 86D, 88D, 90E, 91E, 94ACE, 96C, 97D, 100D, 101CE, 103AE, 104AD

—— Also see *Graphs*

E

Even vs. odd numbers — see *Parity*

Exponents: 41E, 83B, 88B, 100C

F

Factorials: 88B, 98E

Factors: 24D, 31AE, 33C, 35C, 42D, 46E, 67D, 69B, 71E, 75B, 91D

—— **Common Factors:** 45D, 83A

—— Also see *Divisibility*; *Multiples*

Fractions, decimals, percents: 27B, 28B, 31D, 37C, 50D, 52D, 58BE, 62E, 63A, 66D, 67DE, 68D, 69A, 70C, 71E, 73D, 74D , 77B , 79C, 80A, 82A, 83CD, 87BE, 88E, 90BD, 92A, 93C, 95C, 97B, 97E, 99B, 102E, 104E, 105D

—— Also see *ratios and proportions*

G

Graphs: 82B, 84C, 85C, 86E, 89E, 93D, 95E, 98D, 101C, 103E, 104A

L

Logic: 28A, 29C, 30B, 33E, 35B, 36A, 40A, 52B, 53B, 63D, 66C, 67C, 81A, 94A, 96E, 99A, 103A

Least Common Multiple — see *Multiples*

M

Magic Squares: 25C, 56B, 85E

Mean, Median, Mode — see *Statistics*

Memorable problems:

Border Problem, the: 26D

Clover Problem, the: 53E

Fence-Post Problem 70A

Funny Numbers: 35C

Palimage Problem, the: 25A

Three Intersecting Figures: 32D

Traffic Flow 68D

Turnover Card Problem, the: 43D

Twinners: 45B

Up-and-down numbers: 77E

Motion problems: 37D, 47C, 51E, 66B, 74B, 76D, 79C, 80D, 84C, 100D, 102D

Multiples: 39E, 42D, 48C, 49B, 50B, 60D, 76E, 86C, 89B

—— **Common multiples:** 27B, 38C, 40B, 47D, 51B, 68C, 81C

—— Also see *Divisibility*; *Factors*

N

Number patterns — see *Patterns*

Number sense: 28E, 29A, 31A, 34AD, 37B, 38A, 39A, 44A, 45A, 48A, 53AB, 54AC, 55A, 59AB, 62A, 71A, 76A, 86AC, 88A, 89A, 91A, 93B, 96A, 97A, 101A

—— Also see *Cryptarithms*

O

Odd vs. even numbers — see *Parity*

Order of operations: 44A, 60A

Organizing data: 29B, 32C, 34C, 42B, 43D, 44D, 45C, 47B, 49E, 52E, 53D, 54D, 57A, 59D, 60D, 61BCD, 67B, 72D , 77E, 81E, 82D, 94E, 95D, 96E, 104B

P

Painted cube problems — see *Cubes and rectangular solids*

Palindromes: 42D

Parity (*odd vs. even numbers*): 27E, 31E, 32C, 41E, 47D, 49D, 50E, 51B, 56D, 57D, 62C, 67A, 75C, 76E, 78C, 80D, 85B, 86C, 93D, 95E

INTRODUCTION

For the Reader

This book was written for both the participants in the MOEMS® - Mathematical Olympiads for Elementary & Middle Schools and their advisors. It is suitable for mathletes who wish to prepare well for the contests, students who wish to develop higher-order thinking, and teachers who wish to develop more capable students. All problems were designed to help students develop the ability to think mathematically, rather than to teach more advanced or unusual topics. While a few problems can be solved using algebra, nearly all problems can be solved by other, more elementary, methods. In other words, the fun is in devising non-technical ways to solve each problem.

The 400 Math Olympiad contest problems contained in this book are organized into 16 sets of five contests each. Every set represents one year's competition. The first eight sets were created for Division E, which originated in 1979 for students in grades 4-6, and the other eight for Division M, which was added in 1998 for students in grades 7-8. These problems exhibit varying degrees of difficulty and were written for contests from November 2005 through March 2013, inclusive.

This introduction is arranged into three parts. Sections 1 through 5, written for all readers, contain discussions of problem solving in general. Sections 6 through 8 offer many suggestions for getting the most out of this book. Sections 9 through 14, designed for the advisor, called the Person-In-Charge-of-the-Olympiads (PICO), include recommendations related to the various aspects of organizing a Math Olympiad program.

1. HOW TO USE THIS BOOK

Establishing a Study Schedule

A little learning every day is more effective than large chunks of learning once a month for two reasons. The mind needs time to absorb each new thought, and constant practice allows frequent review of previously learned concepts and skills. Together, these foster retention. Try to spend 10 or 15 minutes daily doing one or two problems. This approach should help you minimize the time needed to develop the ability to think mathematically.

You might want to track growth over time by recording success rates for these problem sets. Since you are probably changing the way you think about mathematics, your growth needs time to become apparent. Before long, you are likely to find solving problems increasingly and intensely rewarding.

Choosing Problems

What criteria can help you choose problems from this book? You might pick those that appeal to you, or those of a specific type, or you might go through all contests in order. You might want to select the easiest problems or the most difficult. Section 6 contains suggestions to help you select problems according to need and preference. Section 7 offers ways to get started on those problems that stump you. Section 8 describes the most commonly used strategies. Ultimately, you should test yourself against each and every problem. If you are stuck, see the hint for that problem on pages 107-124.

Using the Solutions in This Book

Whether you solve a problem quickly or you are baffled, it is worth studying the solutions in this book, because often they offer unexpected insights that can help you understand the problem more fully. After you have spent time — actually, after you have *invested* time — trying to solve each problem any way you can, reviewing our solutions is very effective. Think of each problem as a small doorway that opens into a large room of mathematical thought. You want to be in that room. There you will find a wealth of concepts bundled together into one or more solutions to that problem. There you learn to think mathematically.

Many of the problems in this book can be solved in more than one way. There is always a single answer, but there can be many paths to that answer. Once you solve a problem, go back and see if you can solve it by another method. See how many methods you can find. Then check our solutions to see if any of them differ from yours. *Most veteran problem-solvers agree that the solutions usually teach much more than the questions do.*

Each solution in this book is the result of *hours* of consideration and discussion. This book usually omits common, brute-force ways such as guess-check-and-revise or make-a-list whenever thoughtful, conceptual approaches are available. However, if, on your own, you don't see a mathematically efficient solution, try any method that promises to work. Even if your approach to a problem, under time pressure, takes the same path as ours, there still may be much that you can learn from ours. We tried to polish each solution in this book to be direct, concise, and elegant.

There is a saying: "All of us together are smarter than any of us alone." Attempting a problem as part of a study group enables you to benefit not only from your insights but also to learn from others. While you may want to test yourself as an individual, consider working with others on problems or, alternatively, comparing solutions aloud after each of you worked separately on the same questions.

2. WHY WE STUDY PROBLEM SOLVING

Most people, including children, love puzzles and games. It is fun to test ourselves against challenges. The continuing popularity of crossword, jigsaw, and sudoku puzzles, as well as of board, card, and video games, attests to this facet of human nature.

Problem solving builds on this foundation. A good problem is engaging in both senses of the word. Child or adult, we readily accept the challenge, wanting to prove to ourselves that "I can do this." To many of us, a problem is fun more than it is work. A good problem captures our interest, and once you have our interest, you have our intelligence.

A good problem contains within it the promise of the thrill of discovery, that magic "Aha!" moment. It promises that deep satisfaction, if we solve it, of knowing we've accomplished something. It promises growth, the realization that we will know more today than we did yesterday. It speaks to our universal desire for mastery. Babies reach continually for their toes until they succeed in grasping them. Toddlers fall continually until they succeed in walking. Children swing continually at a baseball until they succeed in hitting it frequently. A good problem promises us many things, all of them worthwhile.

The history of mathematics is a history of problem-solving efforts.

It is said that perhaps all mathematics evolved as the result of problem solving. Often, one person challenged another, or perhaps himself, to handle an unexpected question. Sometimes the solution extended the range of knowledge in a well-known field or even led to the creation of a new field.

Very little of the knowledge we have today is likely to have developed in the way we study it. What we see in many books is the distilled material, whose elegant, economical organization and presentation obscure the struggling and false starts that went into polishing it. That which grabbed and held the imagination has been scrubbed out.

A typical example of this is high school geometry. The ancient Greek mathematicians enjoyed challenging each other. "Alpha" would ask "Beta" to find a way to perform a specific construction using only a straightedge and a pair of collapsible compasses. But it wasn't enough for Beta to merely create a method. He also had to convince Alpha that his method would always work. Thus, proofs were born, as a result of problem solving. Slowly, the Greeks built up a whole body of knowledge. Euclid's genius was in collecting all the properties into an organized reference book in which most of them grew logically from a very few basic properties.

For centuries we have taught geometry according to Euclid, instead of tracing the journey taken to arrive at the knowledge. This removed the thought-provoking elements of problem solving mentioned above and with it, much of the involvement for many students.

Therefore…, why should we learn math through problem solving? To put the magic back into math.

3. CHARACTERISTICS OF GOOD PROBLEMS

Problems and exercises are quite different from each other. An exercise presents a familiar situation to which we apply a known procedure. A problem presents an unfamiliar situation for which we need to devise a procedure. For most readers, few of the problems in this book are exercises, if any. A problem is said to be good if it contains some or all of the following ten characteristics.

1. A good problem is engaging and interesting to students. They want to see "how it ends."

2. A good problem illustrates useful principles. The mathematics should not only *be* meaningful, but also should *appear* meaningful to the solver. It should involve important topics, whether past, present, or future. Puzzles are fun, but they may or may not fit this criterion.

3. A good problem allows creative or subtle solutions. Some unexpected solutions may prove startling.

4. A good problem allows a fresh look at situation. Familiar skills and principles may be used in unfamiliar ways.

5. A good problem can trigger more than one method of solution. It is not unusual to solve one in three or four different ways. For example, one **DIVISION E** problem was solved by one group of fourth and fifth grade students in a workshop 11 different ways!*

6. A good problem can combine more than one topic. It is not simple and it allows the student to see a connection between two apparently different topics.

7. A good problem can be expanded or extended. Often, the situation presented in a problem turns out to be part of a much larger picture. A concept may be seen as a special case of a more general concept. Think of it as a camera zooming out to reveal unexpected additional things.

8. A good problem is related to other problems. Two apparently different problems may turn out to have many elements in common.

9. A good problem is challenging, but not intimidating, and should appear accessible to everyone. It should not demand specialized knowledge not possessed by the solver. It is more important that we develop the desire to continue to try problems.

10. A good problem is clear to all students after explanation. This provides both closure to the problem and a sense of satisfaction, even to those who did not solve it correctly on their own.

---

*Kalman, R. "Revisiting the Sum of Odd Natural Numbers", *Mathematics Teaching in the Middle School* (NCTM), (September 2003: 58-61).

4. WHAT EVERY YOUNG MATHLETE SHOULD KNOW

I. Vocabulary and Language

The following explains, defines, or lists some of the terms in **bold** that may be used in Olympiad problems. To be accepted on an Olympiad, an answer must be consistent with both this section and the wording of the related problem. When referring to an ascending or descending order of a set of numbers or the digits of a number, it is understood that the digits or numbers are read *from left to right*.

A. Basic Terms
Sum, difference, product, quotient, remainder, ratio, square of a number (also, **perfect square**), **factors of a number.** The **value** of a number is the simplest name for that number. "**Or**" is inclusive: "*a or b*" means "*a or b or both*."

⟹ **DIVISION M: Square root** of a number, **cube** of a number (also, **perfect cube**).

B. Reading Sums
An ellipsis (…) means "and so on":
Read "1 + 2 + 3 + …"   as "one plus two plus three and so on, without end."
Read "1 + 2 + 3 + … + 10"   as "one plus two plus three and so on up to ten."

C. Writing Whole Numbers
The **standard form of a number** refers to the form in which we usually write numbers (also called Hindu-Arabic numerals or positional notation).

A **digit** is any one of the ten numerals 0, 1, 2, 3, 4, 5, 6, 7, 8, 9. Any numeral is written by assigning a place value to each of its digits. A number may be described by the number of digits it contains: 358 is a three-digit number. The "**lead-digit**" (leftmost digit) of a number is not counted as a digit if it is 0: i.e., 0358 is a three-digit number. **Terminal zeroes** of a number are the zeroes to the right of the last nonzero digit: i.e., 30,500 has two terminal zeroes because to the right of the digit 5 there are two zeroes.

D. Sets of Numbers
1. **Whole Numbers** = {0, 1, 2, 3, …}.
2. **Counting Numbers** = {1, 2, 3, …}.

   Note: The term natural numbers is no longer used in Olympiad contests because in some fields of mathematics, the definition of natural numbers is the same as that of counting numbers while in other fields it is the same as that of whole numbers.

3. ⟹ **DIVISION M: Integers** = {…, –3, –2, –1, 0, +1, +2, +3, …};

   Positive numbers, negative numbers, nonnegative numbers, and nonpositive numbers. These terms may appear in Division M problems, but not in Division E problems.

4. **Consecutive Numbers** are counting numbers that differ by 1, such as 83, 84, 85, 86, and 87. **Consecutive Even Numbers** are multiples of 2 that differ by 2, such as 36, 38, 40, and 42. **Consecutive Odd Numbers** are nonmultiples of 2 that differ by 2, such as 57, 59, 61, and 63.

E. <u>Multiples, Divisibility, and Factors</u>

The product of any two or more whole numbers is called a **multiple** of each of the whole numbers. Zero is considered a multiple of every whole number. *Examples*: The first five multiples of 6 are 0, 6, 12, 18, and 24.

Note: Many but not all authorities expand the definition of multiples to include all integers. To them, −24 (also ⁻24) is a multiple of 6. For Olympiad problems, no multiples will be negative.

A whole number *a* is said to be **divisible by** a counting number *b* if *b* divides *a* with a remainder of zero. In such instances: (1) their quotient is also a whole number, (2) *b* is called a **factor** of *a*, and (3) *a* is called a **multiple** of *b*.

F. <u>Number Theory</u>
1. A **prime number** (also, a **prime**) is a counting number greater than 1, which has *exactly two* different factors, namely the number itself and the number 1. *Examples*: 2, 3, 5, 7, 11, 13, …

2. A **composite number** is a counting number which has *three or more* different factors, namely number itself, the number 1, and at least one other factor. *Examples*: 4, 6, 8, 9, 10, 12, …

3. The number 1 is neither prime nor composite since it has *exactly one* factor, namely the number 1. Thus, there are 3 separate categories of counting numbers: prime, composite, and the number 1.

4. A number is **factored completely** when it is expressed as a product of only prime numbers. *Example*: $144 = 2 \times 2 \times 2 \times 2 \times 3 \times 3$. It may also be written as $144 = 2^4 \times 3^2$.

5. The **Greatest Common Factor (GCF)** of two counting numbers is the largest counting number that divides each of the two given numbers with zero remainder. *Example*: GCF (12,18) = 6.

6. If the GCF of two numbers is 1, then we say the numbers are **relatively prime** or **co-prime**.

7. The **Least Common Multiple (LCM)** of two counting numbers is the smallest number that each of the given numbers divides with zero remainder. *Example*: LCM (12,18) = 36.

8. **Order of Operations**. When computing the value of expressions involving two or more operations, the following priorities must be observed from left to right:

1) do operations in parentheses, braces, or brackets first, working from the inside out,

2) do multiplication and division from left to right, and then

3) do addition and subtraction from left to right.

$$\begin{aligned} \textit{Example:} \quad & 3 + 4 \times 5 - 8 \div (9 - 7) \\ = & 3 + 4 \times 5 - 8 \div \quad 2 \\ = & 3 + \quad 20 \quad - \quad 4 \\ = & 19 \end{aligned}$$

Introduction

G. Fractions

1. A **common** (or **simple**) **fraction** is a fraction (of the form $\frac{a}{b}$) where the **numerator** and **denominator** are whole numbers, except that the denominator cannot be 0. Its operational meaning is that the numerator is divided by the denominator.

2. A **unit fraction** is a common fraction with numerator 1. *Examples*: $\frac{1}{3}$, $\frac{1}{8}$, $\frac{1}{25}$

3. A **proper fraction** is a common fraction in which the numerator is less than the denominator. Its value is more than 0 and less than 1. *Examples*: $\frac{2}{3}$, $\frac{5}{8}$, $\frac{15}{25}$

4. An **improper fraction** is a common fraction in which the numerator is equal to or more than the denominator. Its value is 1 or greater than 1. *Examples*: $\frac{3}{3}$, $\frac{6}{5}$, $\frac{23}{8}$, $\frac{25}{25}$

   A fraction whose denominator is 1 is equivalent to an integer.

5. A **complex fraction** is a fraction whose numerator or denominator contains a fraction.

   Examples: $\dfrac{\frac{2}{3}}{5}$, $\dfrac{2}{\frac{3}{5}}$, $\dfrac{\frac{2}{3}}{\frac{5}{7}}$, $\dfrac{2+\frac{3}{5}}{5-\frac{1}{2}}$

   Complex fractions are often simplified by using the operational meaning. Divide the numerator by the denominator.

   Example: $\dfrac{\frac{2}{3}}{5} = \frac{2}{3} \div 5 = \frac{2}{3} \times \frac{1}{5} = \frac{1}{15}$.

6. The fraction $\frac{a}{b}$ is **simplified** ("**in lowest terms**") if the only common factor of the numerator a and the denominator b is 1 [**GCF**(a,b) = 1].

7. A **decimal** or **decimal fraction** is a fraction whose denominator is a power of ten. The decimal is written using decimal point notation. *Examples*: $0.07 = \frac{7}{100}$, $0.153 = \frac{153}{1000}$, $6.4 = 6\frac{4}{10}$ or $\frac{64}{10}$.

8. ⟹ DIVISION M: A **percent** or **percent fraction** is a fraction whose denominator is 100. The percent sign represents the division by 100. *Examples*: $9\% = \frac{9}{100}$, $125\% = \frac{125}{100}$, $0.3\% = \frac{0.3}{100}$ or $\frac{3}{1000}$.

H. Statistics and Probability

The **average (arithmetic mean)** of a set of N numbers is the sum of all N numbers divided by N. The **mode** of a set of numbers is the number listed most often. A set with every number listed once is said to have no mode. The **median** of an *ordered set* of numbers is the middle number if N is odd or it is the mean of the two middle numbers if N is even.

Examples: For the set $\{5, 5, 7, 11\}$, the mean is $28 \div 4 = 7$, the mode is 5, and the median is $(5 + 7) \div 2 = 6$.

The **probability of an event** is a value between 0 and 1 inclusive that expresses how likely an event is to occur. It is often found by dividing the number of times an event *does* occur by the total number of times the event can possibly occur. *Example*: The probability of rolling an odd number on a die is $\frac{3}{6}$ or $\frac{1}{2}$. Either $\frac{3}{6}$ or $\frac{1}{2}$ will be accepted as a correct probability on an Olympiad contest.

I. Geometry

   1. Angles: **degree-measure, vertex** (plural: **vertices**), **congruent; acute, right, obtuse, straight, reflex.**

   2. **Congruent segments** are two or more **line segments** of equal length.

   3. **Polygons and circles:**

       a. Parts: **side, angle, vertex, diagonal, midpoint; interior region, exterior region; diameter, radius, chord.**

       b. **Triangles: acute, right, obtuse; scalene, isosceles, equilateral.**
           Note: All equilateral triangles are isosceles, but only some isosceles triangles are equilateral.

       c. **Quadrilaterals: parallelogram, rectangle, square, trapezoid, rhombus.**
           Note: a square is one type of rectangle with all four sides congruent. It is also a rhombus with all four angles congruent.

       d. Other polygons: **pentagon, hexagon, octagon, decagon, dodecagon, icosagon.**

       e. **Perimeter:** the number of unit lengths in the boundary of a **plane figure.**

       f. **Area:** the number of **unit squares** (also, **one-unit squares**) contained in the interior of a region. A unit square is a square each of whose sides measures 1 unit. The area of each unit square is **one square unit.** *Example:* The area of a **5-cm square** is 25 sq cm.

       g. **Circumference:** the perimeter of a circular region.

       h. **Congruent figures:** two or more plane figures whose **corresponding** pairs of sides are congruent and whose **corresponding** pairs of angles are congruent.

       i. **Similar figures:** two or more plane figures whose shape is the same but whose size may be different. *Note: All squares are similar; all circles are similar.*

   4. **Geometric Solids:**

       a. **Cube, rectangular solid; face, edge, vertex** (plural: **vertices**).
           ⟹ DIVISION M: **right circular cylinder.**

       b. ⟹ DIVISION M: **volume:** the number of **unit cubes** contained in the interior of a solid. A **one-unit cube** is a cube each of whose edges measures 1 unit. The volume of each 1-unit cube is **1 cubic unit.** *Example:* The volume of a **5-km cube** is 5^3 or 125 cu km.

       c. ⟹ DIVISION M: **surface area:** the sum of the areas of all the faces of a geometric solid. *Example:* The surface area of a **5-cm cube** is 6×5^2 or 150 square cm.

II. SKILLS

1. Computation

   The tools of arithmetic are needed for problem solving. Competency in the basic operations on whole numbers, fractions, and decimals is essential for success in problem solving at all levels.

   ⟹ **DIVISION M:** Competency in basic operations on signed numbers should be developed.

2. Answers to contest questions

   On a contest, any answer different from the "official" answer should be marked as incorrect. Such a "wrong" answer can be appealed to contest officials, but the panel of appeal judges will grant credit only if the wording of the problem allows for an alternate interpretation or if the wording of the problem makes every answer impossible. Correct answers must satisfy *all* the conditions in the problem.

   Units of measure are rarely required in answers — but if a student labels an answer, the label must be correct. More generally, an answer in which any part is incorrect is not acceptable. To avoid being denied credit students should be careful to include *only* required information.

   Unless otherwise specified in a problem, equivalent numbers or expressions should be accepted. For example, $\frac{7}{2}$, 3.5, and $3\frac{1}{2}$ are equivalent.

   After reading a problem, a wise procedure is to indicate the nature of the answer at the bottom of a worksheet before starting the work necessary for solution. Examples: "A = ___, B = ___"; "The largest number is ___"; "The perimeter is ___ sq cm". Another worthwhile device in practice sessions is to require the student to write the answer in a simple declarative sentence *using the wording of the question itself.* Example: "The average speed is 54 miles per hour." This device usually causes the student to reread the problem and answer the question actually asked, rather than the question he or she wishes were asked.

3. Measurement

   The student should be familiar with units of measurement for time, length, area, and weight (and for **DIVISION M**, volume) in both English and metric systems. Within a system of measurement, the student should be able to convert from one unit to another.

   Measures of area are usually written as square units, sq. units, or units². For example, square centimeters may be abbreviated as sq cm, or cm × cm, or cm².

   ⟹ **DIVISION M:** cubic measures are treated in a like manner.

   Because there was no year 0, the first century spanned the years 1 to 100 inclusive. Accordingly, the 20th century spanned the years 1901 to 2000 and the 21st century spans the years 2001 to 2100, all inclusive.

5. SOME COMMON PROBLEM SOLVING STRATEGIES

The most commonly used general strategies include the following:

A. **Guess-check-and-revise.** This is the most basic method. Rarely is it quick or the one that the problem writer had in mind, but it can help you find the answer. Still, even if your answer is right, you should ask other people or check the "official solution" to understand the mathematics behind the problem. After all, the long-term goal is to improve mathematically, not merely to score points.

B. **Find a pattern.** Mathematics is sometimes described as the science of patterns. Studying how the numbers behave in a given problem can allow you to predict the result.

C. **Make an organized list.** Listing every possibility in an organized way is an important tool. How you organize your data often reveals additional information.

D. **Build a table.** This is a special case of making an organized list. Seeing the numbers laid out in an organized way allows you to comprehend the patterns within.

E. **Solve a simpler related problem.** Many hard problems are merely easy ones that have been extended to larger numbers. Replacing the large number by at least three of the smallest possible numbers can introduce patterns that allow you to solve the original problem. Strategies B through E are often used together in various combinations.

F. **Eliminate all but one possibility (process of elimination).** Deciding what a quantity is *not* can narrow the field to a very few possibilities. Test each remaining possibility against all conditions of the problem.

G. **Handle one condition at a time.** In a problem with many conditions, selecting one yields many results. As in strategies E and F, each additional condition then removes all but one result.

H. **Work backward.** If a problem describes a procedure and then specifies the final result, this method usually makes the problem much easier to solve.

I. **Draw a picture or diagram.** One picture is worth a thousand words. In a geometry problem, always draw a diagram. In a non-geometry problem, try to represent the amounts by a diagram; it often makes the solution much easier to understand. Label it with all given measurements and see what other numbers you can figure out.

J. **Draw a convenient segment in a geometric figure.** Sometimes you can divide an unusual shape into two or more common shapes by drawing one or more convenient line segments. Other times you can transfer a known length to a much more usable location.

K. **Make a change and compensate.** There are times when changing some of the conditions of a problem make a solution clearer or more convenient. However, to return to the original overall conditions of the problem requires either an additional change or the reversal of the first change. For an example of the former, change 45×16 to 90×8 or change $488 + 756$ to $500 + 744$. For an example of the latter, to find the 50th odd number, shift each member of the sequence 1, 3, 5, … up by 1 to find the 50th even number, 100, and then reverse the shift, getting 99.

Encourage students to guess-check-and-revise when no other method presents itself. With time and practice, more efficient strategies should start to present themselves.

Thorough discussions of these and many other useful topics may be found in *Creative Problem Solving in School Mathematics*. Visit _www.moems.org_ for information.

6. SELECTING PROBLEMS FOR A PURPOSE

There are many ways to use this book. Some examples follow.

Beginning problem-solvers often need a little more help getting started. They may want to choose easier problems (those of high percentage) in order to get the "feel" of our problems and build up confidence, eventually building up to the harder problems (those of low percentage). It takes time for people to understand what is expected of them and to adopt a mode of thought. It is a good idea to minimize pressure by ignoring the given time limits at first. On the other hand, experienced problem solvers might take the opposite approach in order to sharpen existing skills, by dealing with the most difficult problems and trying the FOLLOW-UPS.

As an Olympiad contest date approaches, some readers might wish to simulate the Olympiad under actual contest conditions, like a dress rehearsal. During earlier practices though, there is value in ignoring time limits and having small groups work cooperatively. This removes the pressure of time, allows the mathletes to review more concepts and to help each other, and involves everyone in the problem-solving process more fully. During later practices, adhering to time limits is advisable.

The reader may want to focus on one specific type of problem at a time, using the contest problem types on pages vii-x. This strategy for studying can be extended by combining a topic from *Creative Problem Solving in School Mathematics* (MOEMS, 2005) with related problems taken from this book. This permits an investigation of that topic in depth and perhaps a shoring up of a perceived weakness. With this approach, however, many interesting one-of-a-kind problems will be missed.

Each method of study mentioned above has its strengths and its limitations, but an overall plan incorporating each in turn may be the most effective preparation for the Olympiads.

7.   ATTEMPTING TO SOLVE A PROBLEM

Solving a problem is comparable to driving with insufficient directions in a strange neighborhood. As we search for a route from point A to point B, we probe different roads hoping to find a landmark. Whenever we realize that a particular road won't get us to our destination, we go back to a previous spot and try another road. We believe that if we continue probing, we are bound to find point B. The next time we drive from A to B, we are likely to make fewer false turns, resulting in a much quicker, more efficient drive. If we continue driving from A to B, we eventually find the shortest, most efficient route.

When faced with an unfamiliar complex problem, we try different routes to a solution. If one approach does not work, we try another. We probe and probe on scrap paper, each time learning something else. We hope to find a route that takes us to an answer. If we then write out our solution or explain it orally, we eliminate many false starts, our understanding becomes fuller, and our solution becomes more direct. This is an unexpected benefit provided by rewriting a solution. The more frequently we explain it to other people, the deeper our comprehension and the sharper our explanation is likely to be.

A common saying is, "Problem solving is *what* you do when you don't *know* what to do."

Perhaps the most important quality that problem solvers develop is that of persistence. We believe that with each attempt, we will discover something more. On our first try we are likely to see some of the thinking behind the solution. With each subsequent attempt, we gain additional insights, encouraging us to try again. Without realizing it, this persistence gives us two major benefits: our ability to think mathematically improves, and our capacity to handle frustrations increases.

8. SOLVING PROBLEMS IN A CONTEST SETTING

Picture yourself in the middle of a math contest. Unfortunately, not only does the problem appear to be different from any you have seen before, but you are told you have only five minutes to solve it. *How* do you proceed?

Start by reading the problem through twice. The first time, look for the overall picture: Where does the problem start? Where does it finish? What is the general situation or type? The second time, notice as many details as possible. Can you draw any conclusions from any given fact? Can you connect any two facts together? Spending a little extra time at the start can save you much time afterwards.

It pays to focus on each fact and each number given in the problem. The author probably chose them for a reason. In fact, changing any fact or number often changes the nature of the problem. Ask yourself *how* you can use any or all of the given facts or numbers.

Next, decide on a course of action, using all or some of the following approaches.

- **Is the problem similar to a more familiar problem?** Can you apply the same general method that worked before? What changes are needed to make the method more appropriate for the current problem?

- **Work forward from the beginning.** Can you use any fact in the problem to learn something more? Can the second thing in turn reveal a third thing? How far can you extend this chain of reasoning? This course is similar to a toddler putting one foot in front of the other when learning to walk. Call it Toddler Math.

- **Work backward from the end.** Does the desired answer suggest a step *before* it? Is there a fact or number you must find before you can reach the concluding step? Is there a step before that which will lead you to the next to last step? How far back from the conclusion can you trace the chain of reasoning?

- **Combine the two approaches.** Many problems are solved by working from both the beginning and the end towards some middle point. At best, the two will meet. At worst, you could have a much simpler problem to solve.

- **Guess-check-and-revise.** As mentioned on page 9, this may be the most inefficient method of solving problems, but it is the easiest way to reach the correct answer. It often has the strength of revealing things about the problem with each guess and just as often the weakness of hiding the concept underlying the problem. This is the method to use if you see no other way to solve a problem; it gets you started. Beginners in particular are urged to use guess-check-and-revise often, until they catch the "feel" of solving problems. In time, as you learn to think mathematically, you grow into using more sophisticated and efficient approaches.

- **Get to know many of the most common strategies.** In Section 5, several were discussed. Become comfortable with them to allow you to see ways to handle many problems.

Every Math Olympiad problem is built to encourage mathematical thought on the part of the student. Nevertheless, for purposes of entering scores, it makes no difference how the answer was obtained, only that the students found the correct answer. Of course, to improve your problem solving abilities, examine the "official solution" after you try each of the problems.

9. WHY WE *TEACH* PROBLEM SOLVING

"When am I ever going to use this?" Contrary to common belief, these words are rarely uttered by a student intent on discussing the future. Rather, they seem to be a statement of frustration, an indirect way of saying, "I don't know what I'm doing, and I don't like feeling uncertain." Cataloging careers that use mathematics or listing high school math courses does not seem likely to reassure such a student. Reassurance comes best from giving the student ownership of the skill or concept, and by helping the student become comfortable with the work.

Teachers can provide ownership by posing a good problem and then by allowing the student to find his or her own way to solve it. Teachers can use that innate love of a challenge to engage the student's interest, and therefore the student's intelligence, as discussed in Section 2. The student, responding to the challenge, sees reasons to focus on the problem. If the problem is well chosen and constructed, the student learns something important.

How does teaching through problem solving help the teacher to develop stronger students?

1. **Interest:** Good problems tap into something deep within all of us. Assigning them to students engages their interest and focus.

2. **Meaning:** Embedding a concept or skill into a good problem provides more meaning to students than merely stating or demonstrating it; students can see a purpose. Skills are not learned just for their own sake, but are seen as tools to be used, not as ends in themselves.

3. **Complexity:** Life is not simple. Life's problems are not simple. We do students no favor by making mathematical problems simple. Most good problems require more than one concept to solve. Assigning good problems may help students develop the ability to see the interplay between different concepts.

4. **Creativity and flexibility:** Many of the problems in this book show multiple solutions. The more ways a student can see to solve a problem, the freer he or she may feel to try an unusual approach to a puzzling problem. Some of the problems in this book have triggered highly inventive methods.

5. **Developing mathematical thinking:** Over time, continued exposure to thoughtful solutions leads students to think mathematically. Subsequent math courses in high school and college entrance examinations will require this ability.

6. **Retention:** A good problem often allows for many strategies and may require several principles and skills with each strategy. Continually tackling problems and discussing solutions allows the student to revisit most concepts and procedures frequently, each time from a fresh perspective. This disguised practice builds in reinforcement while it clarifies the concept.

*<u>P</u>erson <u>I</u>n <u>C</u>harge of <u>O</u>lympiad

7. **Building student confidence:** Each demanding problem the teacher assigns reflects a respect for the students' abilities, which students may well appreciate. With each successful solution, the student realizes, "I can do this!" Since nothing builds self-confidence like accomplishment, these two things can stimulate intellectual growth.

8. **Empowerment:** When the teacher allows students to tackle problems on their own with no more than an occasional hint and then asks several students to present different approaches aloud, the students assume ownership of the problems. Students are likely to accept that the responsibility for learning is theirs, not the teacher's. Each student becomes an active partner in the learning process. The problem, the solution, the principles involved all become his or her property and are more likely to be available when needed.

10. WHY SHOULD WE DO MOEMS CONTESTS?

As discussed in Section 2, various puzzles, games, and sports leagues are immensely popular among both children and their parents, and have been so for many generations. In fact, children seem to turn almost any situation into a game. Why is this so? The most basic answer is that we love to compete, to test ourselves against arbitrary standards, our potential, or our peers. All we require is a reasonable chance of succeeding. Why do we keep at it if we are not doing well? We have an innate belief that with practice we will continually improve. In most of the above we compete less against other people than against our own abilities. This is a valuable source of true growth.

Contests such as spelling bees and the Math Olympiads use this fundamental human characteristic to entice students into mastering skills or developing a way of thinking. Children (and sometimes the adults) may assume they are competing in order to win awards or to show they can do well on a national scale. The real purpose, however, is to get them to want to tackle richer, more demanding problems than those they may be used to. As with all education, the goal is growth. Adults should be careful to keep the students' sense of competition low-key. To maximize growth, the children should not feel pressured or threatened.

Students usually want two things out of any activity: to feel they belong on this level and to maintain a sense of progress.

To fill the first need and to satisfy most students, the Math Olympiad contests are scaled so that the average student correctly solves about 40% of the problems during the year. Each contest includes problems specifically designed for both ends of the spectrum. Some problems are uncomplicated (even though they involve mathematical thinking) and their solutions can easily be understood by all. Such problems enable beginners to expect to solve their fair share of the problems within the time limits. Moreover, a student's scoring typically improves from year to year. Meanwhile, other problems challenge even the strongest mathletes. Success is quite attainable, but perfection is rare. In fact, less than one-third of one per cent of all participants correctly solve every problem for the year!

To fill the second need, all Olympiad problems involve higher order thought. Those who use guess-check-and-revise will be shown more elegant and efficient solutions immediately afterwards when the PICO reviews the problem. Even the best mathletes will learn new ways to apply familiar concepts inasmuch as the 25 problems may employ 40 or more principles, some in very subtle ways. The variety itself presents a challenge. Each time students learn something new, their sense of accomplishment is reinforced.

There are two completely separate divisions, **DIVISION E** (for students in grade 6 and below) and **DIVISION M** (for students in grade 8 and below). The Math Olympiads consist of five monthly contests, stretching from November to March. This provides constant reinforcement of mathematical thinking and problem solving, and helps to keep student interest high. Contests are conducted under strict standard testing conditions. All team members take the contests together. There are no make-ups. Each team can have as many as 35 students and a school can have as many teams as it wants; interested students should not be turned away.

Practices are important. Beginners develop a comfort level with contest problems and all mathletes improve their problem solving skills. Towards this end MOEMS provides 50 practice problems with detailed solutions prior to the first Olympiad. Each solution also names the strategy employed; about half of the problems offer extensions to help the teacher develop each problem into a mini-lesson.

An individual's score is just the number of problems answered correctly. While in general work should be shown, it is not required on our contests. The team score, compiled after the last Olympiad, is simply the sum of the ten highest individual scores. Large teams and small teams are therefore on a fairly equal footing. No traveling is required; contests are held in the school.

Further, the generous awards structure enables the school to provide ample recognition. The awards package sent to each team includes a Certificate of Participation for every mathlete reported, embroidered felt patches for about 50% of all mathletes nationally, a variety of other awards for the high scorers on each team, and assorted team awards for about 25% of all teams. Further information is available at our Website *www.moems.org*.

11. BUILDING A PROGRAM

So you want to start a math team.

Any successful program requires solid support from many elements. Your students must be enthusiastic about the activity, their parents must see potential benefits for their children, and the school administration must feel they can justify the expenditure easily to central administration and others. Experienced Math Olympiad coaches have used the following suggestions successfully. Few people do everything mentioned below, but the more you do, the more effective you are likely to be.

One way to build a program is to meet with the school principal and the director of mathematics to map out your procedures for devising a philosophy, recruiting students, building parental support, training students, conducting contests, and recognizing accomplishments.

Devising a philosophy: Many decisions need to be made, including the following:

- Will the activity be open to all students or only to those in a gifted program?
- Will it be embedded in classes, done as a pull-out program, or offered as a club that meets outside of class time?
- Will it be run by a faculty member or by one or more parents?
- Will funding come from the school, from the parents' association, or from another source?
- Will students be given study and practice sheets as needed or will contest books be issued to all members?
- Will homework and outside projects be assigned?

Recruiting students: If participation in the contests is to be voluntary, you, the PICO, should devise a campaign to encourage students to join the new math team. You may speak to several classes, ask your colleagues to talk it up in class, place posters around the school, send announcements home, write one or more articles for the school district newsletter or a local newspaper, and/or make a brief morning announcement for several consecutive days ("Only 4 more days until …"). You might ask fellow teachers to recommend names of students. Approaching one person at a time face-to-face is usually very effective. You might even sit down with the student and parent together. If you call a meeting for all interested students and their parents, be sure to leave time for them to ask you questions.

Involving students: There is value in assigning productive roles to your mathletes. You may want to hold elections for your math team officers, assigning specific duties to each office. The president and vice-president, and maybe others, might prepare and run some of the practices, with guidance from you. A team publicist might write bulletins for the school's morning announcements after each contest and perhaps also for the community newspaper or district newsletter. A recording secretary might keep track of attendance, completed assignments, and results of each contest and practice problems. Other possible student jobs include decorating bulletin boards with team news and announcements, providing snacks at practices, and scheduling social get-togethers. Holding elections for several productive positions can supply students with a vested interest in the success of the team. Your mathletes will own the activity.

Building parental support: Parental support helps build a popular ongoing program. The better informed that parents are, the more their enthusiasm is felt by their children. Like Johnny Appleseed, parents of current mathletes are likely to "spread the word" to parents of future mathletes. Think of it as having a score of publicists working for you free. Some may volunteer to write articles for local newspapers after each contest and after special occasions, such as elections of officers and award ceremonies. In some schools parents are used to keep records and submit contest results, to open their homes to all team members for periodic social events such as barbecues, and to conduct team outings to such as ballparks or beaches. In certain cases, the parents' association or individual parents have supplied the PICO and/or paid the enrollment fee.

The next few sections discuss ways to conduct practices and contests and to recognize student accomplishments.

12. CONDUCTING PRACTICE SESSIONS

What does a practice session look like?

You will have to decide how you will choose problems, how you will configure your mathletes, and how you will utilize the students. Some of this will arise from the nature of rich problems. Mathletes do not practice a single action repetitively, because almost every problem differs from those before it. Instead, they typically need to apply more than one skill and more than one concept sequentially as they attempt to handle new and novel sets of conditions. Often they have to use familiar tools in a completely unexpected way. Your teaching will need to be geared to developing problem solving skills, not procedures. Naturally, you will personalize the routines utilized during practice, selecting appealing features from others, and adding touches of your own.

Problem selection: Your team may spend an hour investigating a variety of problems that utilize a single concept in sharply different settings. Or it may spend the time exploring a set of completely unrelated problems. The former provides depth for one concept while the latter allows for broadness, embracing many one-of-a-kind situations. Problems are assigned, either singly or in sets. You might select the problems and run the practices yourself or you might have individual team members do it. There is much of value to the latter approach.

Time and homework: We generally recommend practice sessions of at least an hour a week, but naturally, more is better. You can maximize your efforts by assigning problem sets to do at home between practices. Make sure your mathletes know that they are expected to solve some of the problems, but not all. Homework, even about problem solving, has several benefits. It extends significantly the amount of practice for each student without increasing your workload; it communicates to the student how serious you are about learning; it allows parents to see what is expected of their children; and it shows respect to the student by implying that you think he or she can handle difficult work.

Organizing your team: You can treat your team as a whole or you can split it into mini-groups. You can employ the format of a formal lesson or you can have several independent study groups work simultaneously.

Some of the practices may take the form of small in-school contests, whether team or individual, with small prizes such as candies or stickers offered as awards. Some problems may be solved by using manipulatives or acting them out, and others by guess-check-and-revise or by thought-filled reasoning. You may wish to use several of these techniques.

Trusting students: One approach that has worked well is to assign a set of problems as homework, giving the students the problems *and* the detailed solutions. This allows the student to practice problem solving more frequently, which in turn can help them develop the quality of thinking mathematically. Suggest that they attempt one or two contest problems every day, adhering to time limits and test conditions.

The student tries the problems, and then, using the printed solutions, determines the number of problems solved correctly. At the next practice you record their numbers. This keeps them on task. Most students are likely to hold themselves to higher standards than anyone else could. With solutions available, many will opt to see how MOEMS handled a troublesome problem; suggest it yourself if students don't think of it. Others, even though they solved the problem, may look at our solution to verify their approach or to see if our solution contains anything unexpected.

Cooperative solving: Form your team into small groups of three or four mathletes and let them discuss the problem. Problem solving often involves discovering the correct solution a piece at a time; it requires getting past false starts and turns. A given or implied fact is overlooked at first, or a small careless error changes the nature of the question. Discussions in a group allow members to continually correct and teach each other, moving ever closer to a complete solution. Try to devise ways to prevent one student from dominating a group, perhaps by frequent reorganization. Circulate, monitoring each group's discussion continuously. Have some, occasionally all, groups share their discussions with the whole team.

Multiple solutions: Many problems can be solved two or more different ways. A powerful technique is to allow several mathletes to explain several different methods of solution. After each explanation, ask if anyone used a different approach. After everyone has had the opportunity to speak, then you can add, "You know, there's still another way." By explaining more methods aloud, more concepts are reviewed and more students receive recognition.

Giving students ownership: As stated above, let the students explain their solutions aloud. Let teammates correct errors, where possible. Do not offer your solution unless it provides an insight not stated by the mathletes. There are many reasons why it is more effective for several youngsters to explain solutions than for the teacher to do so: Most people remember what they say better than what they hear; students listen more closely to friends than to adults; when explaining, a student revisits a problem, often seeing aspects not noticed before; students recognize that the teacher has shown them the respect of asking them what they think. At first this practice of allowing many students to comment on a problem is much slower than lecturing; you cover less material. But as students take ownership of the learning process, their ability to think mathematically increases, resulting in a faster learning process. By the end of the year, your team will have covered more material than if you had lectured, and they would have done so more thoroughly.

13. CONDUCTING REVIEWS AFTER EACH CONTEST

"Practice makes perfect." As a rule, the more frequently your mathletes practice, the more they learn and the more capable they become. Cramming for a once-a-year test or contest helps to some extent, but not nearly as much as preparing for it on a regular basis. In fact, *working for a few minutes every day is more effective than working for several hours periodically.* Learning is reinforced while it is fresh and forgetting is minimized. That said, most mathletes practice for an hour every week, as a compromise between the ideal and other demands. PICOs can supplement the formal practice, though, by assigning homework.

It is best to review solutions at the time of the contest itself, while the problems are freshest in the mathletes' minds. The first practice after a contest can be used to extend some contest problems. You might combine *FOLLOW-UP* problems chosen from the contest with other related problems selected from this book or other sources. It is recommended that, when possible, you try to choose problems that involve the same concept as the contest problem. These should use the concept in a different way or combine it with another principle.

There are two ways to go with practices, in general. You might want to cover a wide range of topics, concepts, and types. This book and the prior two volumes of the *Math Olympiad Contest Problems* are ideal sources because each offers at least 80 complete contests (400 problems with detailed solutions). Or you might want to focus on fewer concepts, examining each in depth. *Creative Problem Solving in School Mathematics* offers approximately 400 more problems, arranged by topics. Many PICOs prefer to mix the two approaches.

14. TOPPING OFF THE YEAR

Once the last contest is done, two things remain to do: distribute awards and set up the team for the following year.

Distributing awards: Your mathletes have worked hard and have grown significantly. They have earned recognition. Towards this end, many teams create a special awards assembly. It may occur during school, after school, in the evening, or on a weekend. It may be attended by the entire student body, by parents and guests, or by team members only. It may take place in the school auditorium, in a classroom, or at a team barbecue or dinner. What is important is that students are honored publicly.

A special school-wide assembly or an evening ceremony might contain any of the following: Parents and a guest speaker can be invited. The speaker might be a member of the board of education, the district superintendent, the high school chairman of mathematics, or a professor of mathematics from a local college. This can help the students see how this year's activities can lead to future activities or how they fit into a larger picture. It also acknowledges the importance of the activity. During the ceremony the PICO might alternate past Olympiad problems with the awards and elicit solutions aloud from the mathletes. This provides a public way to let parents see what their children can do.

Setting up the team for the following year: Make sure each officer's responsibilities are clear and well understood. Increase the vested interest each mathlete has in the new team by having them elect the new officers. This would give the officers time to plan ahead. Also, by holding the vote at this point, you limit the officers to those with at least one year's experience as mathletes.

Training the returning members of next year's team: The school year extends several weeks after the "season" is over. This time can be used to sharpen the problem solving abilities of your "veterans-to-be" and perhaps to go into selected topics more deeply. After several months of straightforward practices, a change of pace can be very effective. Messages from PICOs have described some ingenious activities. You may want next year's leaders to actually plan and teach the lessons. A lot can be learned just from the act of choosing problems to fit a plan. Rotating the responsibilities among many students strengthens more than just one or two of them.

Team competitions: Split the team into small, nearly equal groups. Give them a sheet of 5 problems and a time limit of 10 or 15 minutes and have them work cooperatively on the set. A tight time limit may force them to use teamwork: each problem might be tackled by a different team member, who, when done, checks a teammate's answer. Give the team one point for every correct answer and a bonus point if all five answers are correct. Keep a running total for a few sessions.

Scavenger hunt: Starting in one room, the scavenger hunt quickly spreads to many parts of the building. The team is split into several small groups. Past problems are chosen or rewritten so that the answer indicates a specific location in the school. As a group solves a problem, it goes to the location indicated by the answer. The person posted there accepts the answer and gives the group a new problem, which can lead the group to another location. This continues until the last problem, which leads the group to the finish point. The winner is the first group to get to the finish point.

Relay race: Again, the team is split into small groups. A problem is distributed to each group, which then shows its answer to the PICO. If the answer is correct, the group receives the next problem. The first group to solve the last question correctly wins. A variation is for the PICO to accept answers regardless of correctness. In this case, the team with the most correct answers wins, and if there is a tie, the faster team wins.

Tournament: The current team might participate in a three-way contest. A second team can be formed from the parents of the mathletes and a third team from past members of the team. Holding the contest in the evening or on a weekend allows many people to attend. This also allows parents and friends to witness "their mathlete" in action, and adds to the excitement.

Alternately, your local teacher organization or school district might host a full-day face-to-face tournament for five-member teams from several schools. The tournament should consist of more than one event and include problems like those found in this book, solution-review sessions, and presentation of awards.

For a moderate fee, MOEMS would supply fresh camera-ready problems and solutions, and a detailed booklet walking your tournament committee through every step from preparation to execution. The latter includes camera-ready masters for all paperwork and a computer-ready scoring spreadsheet. If any per-team fees are set, your organization or district would set and keep them, and would control every step of the way. Moreover, the name of your tournament is chosen by your organization or district and can appear in large print in the heading of every sheet of paper.

Any of these events provides a cap to the year, allowing the students to finish on a high note. If you've successfully employed activities not expressed in this book, please contact us at *office@moems.org* with a detailed description. We would *love* to know about it and perhaps share it with our PICOs.

Key to Shaded Rectangles
pages 23 – 106

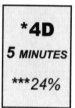

```
*4D
5 MINUTES
***24%
```

The references in this shaded box represent:

*   The question placement on a particular Olympiad Contest within a Set of Contests.

**   The time allocated for a particular problem.

***The percentage of correct responses as reported by PICOs.

In the above example, the box contains the following information about one problem from a given set. On Olympiad contest 4 (out of five that year) this was problem D (out of the five problems A through E). Students were given 5 minutes to solve it. After all reports were received from PICOs, it was determined that 24% of the students received credit for the correct answer.

OLYMPIAD PROBLEMS

DIVISION E
SETS 1-8

SET 1

OLYMPIAD 1

1A
3 MINUTES
79%

What number can replace the square to make the statement true?

$$5 \times 11 = \square + 12$$

1B
6 MINUTES
16%

The sum of the 3-digit number AAA and the 2-digit number BB is the 4-digit number CD6E. A, B, C, D, and E are different digits. What 4-digit number does CD6E represent?

```
    A  A  A
 +     B  B
 ----------
    C  D  6  E
```

1C
7 MINUTES
47%

What is the area, in square meters, of the shaded part of the rectangle?

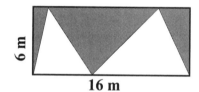

6 m

16 m

1D
5 MINUTES
6%

In simplest form, the fraction $\frac{60}{N}$ represents a whole number. N is also a whole number.
What is the total number of different values that N can be?

1E
5 MINUTES
24%

A bowl contains 100 pieces of colored candy: 48 green, 30 red, 12 yellow, and 10 blue. They are all wrapped in foil, so you do not know the color of any piece of candy. What is the least number of pieces you must take to be certain that you have at least 15 pieces of the same color?

Solutions start on page 132.

SET 1
OLYMPIAD 2

2A
4 MINUTES
81%

If two different counting numbers have the same digits but in reverse order, each number is called the palimage of the other. For example, 738 and 837 are palimages of each other; so are 1234 and 4321. What two different numbers between 40 and 60 are palimages of each other?

2B
4 MINUTES
50%

A cricket chirps 6 times every 8 seconds. At that rate, how many times does the cricket chirp in 2 minutes?

2C
6 MINUTES
39%

The odd numbers from 1 through 17 are placed in the magic square so that the sum of the numbers in each row, column and diagonal are equal. What number goes in the square marked "X"?

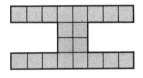

2D
5 MINUTES
15%.

Each small region in the figure shown is a square. The area of the entire figure is 320 sq cm. What is the number of cm in the perimeter of the entire figure?

2E
6 MINUTES
7%

The pages of a book are numbered consecutively, beginning with 1. The digit 7 is printed 25 times in numbering the pages. What is the largest number of pages the book can have?

Solutions start on page 133.

SET 1

OLYMPIAD 3

3A **4 MINUTES** 61%	What is the greatest number of Mondays that can occur in 45 consecutive days?
3B **5 MINUTES** 49%	The arithmetic mean (average) of five numbers is 8. Two of the numbers are 2 and 5. The other three numbers are equal. What is the value of one of the three equal numbers?
3C **6 MINUTES** 46%	Each figure shown is formed by surrounding one row of black squares with white squares. How many white squares will surround one row of 50 black squares? 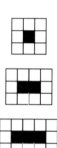
3D **6 MINUTES** 6%	A picture frame is 20 cm by 30 cm. This includes a border (the shaded region) 5 cm wide surrounding the picture itself. What is the area of this shaded border in sq cm? 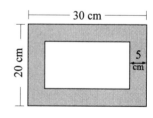
3E **6 MINUTES** 11%	Two standard dice (number cubes) are rolled. One is red and one is green. What is the probability that the product of the two numbers on top is divisible by 3?

Solutions start on page 135.

Division E

SET 1

OLYMPIAD 4

4A
4 MINUTES
82%

Five students (Amy, Beth, Corey, Diego, Emily) sit in that order in a circle, counting down to 1. Amy starts by saying, "34". Then Beth says, "33", and so on. They continue around the circle to count down by ones. Who says, "1"?

4B
5 MINUTES
61%

What whole number may be used in place of to make this statement true?

$$\frac{3}{5} < \frac{\square}{7} < \frac{4}{5}$$

4C
6 MINUTES
32%

Bay Street has from 2 through 15 houses, numbered 1, 2, 3, and so on. Mr. Sullivan lives in one of the houses. The sum of all the house numbers less than his equals the sum of all the house numbers greater than his. How many houses are there on Bay Street?

4D
6 MINUTES
13%

Eight cubes are glued together to form the figure shown. The length of an edge of each cube is 3 centimeters. The entire figure is covered in paint. How many square centimeters are covered in paint?

4E
7 MINUTES
9%

The whole number N is divisible by 7. If N is divided by 2 or 3 or 4 or 5, the remainder is 1 in each case. What is the smallest value that N can be?

Solutions start on page 137.

SET 1
OLYMPIAD 5

5A
6 MINUTES
34%

Mr. Red, Mr. White, Mr. Blue, and Mr. Gray each wears a shirt that is the same color as the name of one of the other three men. Each man wears a different color. Mr. Red and Mr. White are older than the man in gray. The man in red is next to Mr. White. Which man wears a white shirt?

5B
4 MINUTES
17%

A, B, and C represent three different numbers. Each is chosen from the set {3, 5, 7, 9}. What is the least possible value of $\frac{A}{B+C}$? Express your answer as a simple fraction.

5C
5 MINUTES
48%

Two rectangles with equal heights are cut from a rectangular piece of paper as shown. The area of the remaining piece of paper is 980 sq cm. What is the height of each cut, in cm?

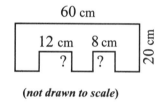

(not drawn to scale)

5D
7 MINUTES
10%

Alexis bakes 90 identical pizzas. Each pizza is cut either into 8 small slices or 6 large slices. There are 5 small slices for every 3 large slices. How many of the 90 pizzas are cut into small slices?

5E
5 MINUTES
20%

Lin has 8 marbles. Each marble weighs either 20 grams or 40 grams or 50 grams. He has a different number of marbles (at least one) of each weight. What is the smallest possible total weight of Lin's marbles?

Solutions start on page 139.

Division E

1A
3 MINUTES
71%

Choose any number between 32 and 56.
Add 20. Subtract 17. Add 13. Subtract your original number.
What is the resulting number?

1B
5 MINUTES
41%

The sum of three consecutive counting numbers is 15 more than the greatest of them. What is the greatest of the three numbers?

1C
6 MINUTES
56%

Each of three colored cups covers one of three objects.
  1) The red cup is somewhere to the left of the white cup.
  2) The coin is somewhere to the left of the bean.
  3) The gray cup is somewhere to the right of the shell.
  4) The bean is somewhere to the right of the gray cup.
Under which color cup is the shell?

1D
5 MINUTES
20%

A rectangle has a perimeter of 2 meters and a length of 70 centimeters.
Find the area of the rectangle in square centimeters.

1E
6 MINUTES
12%

Asha has 5 more 40¢ stamps than 30¢ stamps. The total value of her 40¢ stamps is $5.20 more than that of her 30¢ stamps. How many of the 40¢ stamps does Asha have?

Solutions start on page 141.

SET 2
OLYMPIAD 2

2A
3 MINUTES
84%

An ant travels around the circle in the direction shown. It touches each of the labeled points in order. The first three points that the ant touches are A, B, and C, in that order. What is the 28th point that the ant touches?

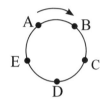

2B
4 MINUTES
92%

Gina is taller than Henry but shorter than Jennie. Ivan is taller than Katie but shorter than Gina. Who is the tallest of these five people?

2C
5 MINUTES
42%

Mr. Jackson was born on January 1, 1970. His daughter Lea was born on January 1, 1992. In what year was Mr. Jackson exactly three times as old as Lea?

2D
6 MINUTES
16%.

Rectangle *ABCD* is split into four smaller rectangles as shown. Each side of each rectangle is a whole number of centimeters. The areas of three of the small rectangles are shown. What is the area of rectangle *ABCD*, in square centimeters?

A		*B*
21 sq cm	48 sq cm	
35 sq cm		
D		*C*

Not drawn to scale.

2E
7 MINUTES
20%

Amy began with 5 marbles for every 3 marbles that Tara had. After Amy gave 1 marble to Tara, Amy ended with 3 marbles for every 2 that Tara had then. How many marbles did Amy begin with?

Solutions start on page 143.

Division E

3A

4 *MINUTES*

56%

One counting number is 4 times as great as a second counting number. The product of the two numbers is 36. What is the sum of the two numbers?

3B

5 *MINUTES*

63%

Mrs. Saada is between 50 and 80 years old. If you divide her age by 9, the remainder is 1. If you divide her age by 4, the remainder is 1. How old is Mrs. Saada?

3C

5 *MINUTES*

46%

The floor of a rectangular room is completely covered with square tiles. The room is 9 tiles long and 5 tiles wide. Find the number of tiles that touch the walls or door of the room.

3D

6 *MINUTES*

24%

One day Kevin counts 50 cars that pass his house. One-fifth of the cars contain more than one person. Of the cars containing only one person, three-fifths are driven by women. Of the cars containing just one person, how many cars are driven by men?

3E

7 *MINUTES*

39%

What is the least prime number that is a divisor N?
$$N = (13 \times 17) + (19 \times 23)$$

Solutions start on page 146.

SET 2

4A
4 MINUTES
67%

Suppose today is Tuesday. In all, how many Fridays are there in the next 53 days?

4B
5 MINUTES
51%

In the addition at the right, different letters represent different digits. What is the two-digit number HA?

```
    A
    A
 +  H
 H  A
```

4C
6 MINUTES
26%

The room numbers on one side of a hotel hall are odd. They are numbered from 11 through 59 inclusive. Kristen is in one of these rooms. Express as a fraction the probability that Kristen's room number is divisible by 5.

4D
6 MINUTES
5%

A circle, a rectangle, and a triangle are drawn on the same sheet of paper. No side of the rectangle is also all or part of a side of the triangle. What is the greatest possible number of points of intersection?

4E
6 MINUTES
12%

The pages of a book are numbered consecutively, starting with page 1. It takes 258 digits to number all the pages. What is the last page number?

Solutions start on page 147.

Division E

SET 2

OLYMPIAD 5

5A
4 MINUTES

77%

My book is open. I see two pages. The sum of the page numbers is 245. What is the next page number?

5B
5 MINUTES

44%

The average height of four adults is 180 centimeters. Two of the adults are each 170 centimeters tall, and the third is 185 centimeters tall. How tall, in centimeters, is the fourth adult?

5C
7 MINUTES

37%

The number on Mr. Kay's license plate has three digits. The product of the digits is 216. Their sum is 19. What is the greatest three-digit number that could be on the license plate?

5D
7 MINUTES

38%

Ana starts with 8 and counts by 5s. Her first three numbers are 8, 13, and 18. Josh starts with a whole number other than 8 and counts by a whole number other than 5. Some of his numbers are 11, 32, and 46, but he does not start with 11. 24 is not one of his numbers. What number does Josh start with?

5E
5 MINUTES

69%

The table shown is filled so that each row and each column contains each of the numbers 1, 2, 3, and 4 exactly once. Find the number in the square marked "X".

			1
	2		
		X	
1			4

Solutions start on page 149.

1A

3 MINUTES

78%

What is the sum?

$$81 + 18 + 72 + 27 + 63 + 36 + 54 + 45 + 4$$

1B

5 MINUTES

41%

There are a total of 100 men and women on an airplane. There are 12 more women than men. What is the number of women on the airplane?

1C

5 MINUTES

9%

What is the total number of rectangles of all sizes that can be traced using the lines in this diagram?

1D

6 MINUTES

32%

Each of the 6 circles contains a different counting number. The sum of the 6 numbers is 21. The sum of the 3 numbers along each side of the triangle is shown in the diagram. What is the sum of the numbers in the shaded circles?

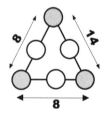

1E

6 MINUTES

33%

Rebekah's mother is 4 times as old as Rebekah is now. In 6 years, Rebekah's mother will be 3 times as old as Rebekah will be then. What is Rebekah's age now, in years?

Solutions start on page 151.

SET 3

OLYMPIAD 2

2A
3 MINUTES
67%

What number makes the statement true?

$$220 - 22 = \underline{} \times 22$$

2B
4 MINUTES
68%

Five students sit around a circular table. Their chairs are numbered in order from 1 through 5. Abby sits next to both Ben and Colin. Dalia sits next to both Ben and Sarah. The numbers on Abby's and Colin's chairs add up to 6. Who sits in chair number 3?

2C
5 MINUTES
12%

Suppose we call a number funny if it is the product of three prime factors, of which exactly two are the same. (For example: $12 = 2 \times 2 \times 3$, so 12 is funny.) What is the total number of funny numbers between 30 and 60?

2D
6 MINUTES
11%.

In the figure, all angles are right angles and all distances are in meters. What is the area of the figure, in square meters?

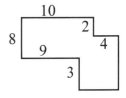

2E
6 MINUTES
42%

The counting numbers are written out as one long string:
123456789101112…
What is the 100th digit in the string?

Solutions start on page 153.

SET 3

OLYMPIAD 3

3A

3 MINUTES

56%

The digits of a four-digit number are 1, 3, 6, and 9, but not necessarily in that order. The thousands digit is prime. The hundreds digit is 3 more than the tens digit. What is the number?

3B

5 MINUTES

59%

Emma has 4 more quarters than nickels. The total value of her quarters and nickels is $3.10. In all, what is the number of nickels that Emma has?

3C

5 MINUTES

15%

The area of rectangle MATH is 30 sq cm and each side-length is a counting number of cm. H is the midpoint of $\overline{TO}$. The area of square ECHO is between 5 sq cm and 24 sq cm. Find the perimeter of the entire figure, in cm.

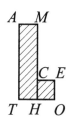

3D

6 MINUTES

43%

Sequence A counts down from 46 by 7: 46, 39, 32, and so on. Sequence B counts down from one number (not 46) by another number (not 7). In sequence B, the second number is 35, the sixth number is 23, and the sequence ends with the first single-digit number that it comes to. How many numbers are in sequence B?

3E

7 MINUTES

4%

Amy, Brett, and Cate each secretly write down Z, U, or T. What is the probability that Cate's letter is different from both Amy's letter and Brett's letter?

Solutions start on page 156.

4A
3 MINUTES
61%

January 1, 1990 was a Monday. What day of the week was February 1, 1990?

4B
4 MINUTES
52%

In an election, Ethan got 5 fewer votes than Christopher, who got 3 votes more than Olivia, who got 4 fewer votes than Ava. How many more votes did Ava get than Ethan?

4C
6 MINUTES
21%

Mrs. Allen spends $\frac{3}{5}$ of her money at the grocery store. Next she spends $\frac{3}{5}$ of her remaining money at the gas station. She then has $8.00 left. With what total number of dollars did Mrs. Allen start?

4D
7 MINUTES
22%

Jan and Nika ride their bikes. Jan rides at 5 miles per hour for 1 hour and then rides at 10 miles per hour for 30 minutes. Nika rides at a constant 8 miles per hour. The trips cover the same distance. For how many minutes does Nika ride?

4E
6 MINUTES
10%

In the multiplication shown, different letters represent different digits. What three-digit number does SAY represent?

$$\begin{array}{r} S\,A\,Y \\ \times\quad 3 \\ \hline B\,A\,B\,Y \end{array}$$

Solutions start on page 158.

SET 3

OLYMPIAD 5

5A
4 MINUTES
36%

A total of 20 marbles are placed into 5 cups. Each cup has a different number of marbles. No cup has exactly 4 marbles, and no cup is empty. What is the greatest number of marbles that any one cup can have?

5B
5 MINUTES
40%

Aidan writes the counting numbers in order. In Row 1, he writes the first number. In Row 2 he writes the next two numbers, and so on as shown. What is the thirteenth number in Row 16?

Row 1:   1
Row 2:   2   3
Row 3:   4   5   6
and so on ...

5C
6 MINUTES
14%

Joshua has more than 250 toy soldiers. When he tries to arrange them in rows of 3, there are 2 left over. When he tries to arrange them in rows of 5, there are 2 left over. When he tries to arrange them in rows of 7, there are 2 left over. What is the least number of toy soldiers Joshua may have?

5D
7 MINUTES
23%

The figure shows a regular hexagon: all 6 sides are congruent to each other and all 6 angles are congruent to each other. The area of the shaded rectangular region is 60 sq cm. What is the area of the hexagon, in sq cm?

5E
5 MINUTES
24%

In the sequence below, we add any two consecutive entries to get the very next entry. The last two entries are 37 and 60 in that order. The first entry is 4. How many entries are in this sequence in all?

$$\underline{4}, \ldots, \underline{}, \underline{37}, \underline{60}.$$

Solutions start on page 160.

Division E

SET 4

OLYMPIAD 1

1A
3 MINUTES
84%

What is the value of the following?
$$55 - 11 + 44 - 22 + 33 - 33 + 22 - 44 + 11 - 55$$

1B
5 MINUTES
38%

In all, how many two-digit prime numbers have 4 as one of their digits?

1C
5 MINUTES
21%

In the figure shown, two squares share corner A. The larger square has an area of 49 sq cm. The smaller square has an area of 25 sq cm. What is the perimeter of the shaded region, in cm?

A

1D
5 MINUTES
7%

Janine's number has three digits. One digit is a prime number. Another digit is a square number. The other digit is neither prime nor square. Her number is NOT divisible by 3. What is the greatest possible value of Janine's number?

1E
6 MINUTES
27%

In all, how many whole numbers between 400 and 600 are divisible by 9?

Solutions start on page 162.

SET 4
OLYMPIAD 2

2A
4 MINUTES
90%

Aaron, Becky, and Chris are wearing pink, yellow, and white shirts (though not necessarily in that order). Aaron is not wearing the yellow shirt. Becky says to Chris, "I like your white shirt." What color is Becky wearing?

2B
5 MINUTES
37%

If a three-digit number is divided by 5 or by 6, the remainder is 1 in each case. What is the least such three-digit number?

2C
5 MINUTES
13%

Abby lists four consecutive multiples of some number. The average of the first two multiples is 28 and the average of the last two is 44. What is the greatest multiple on Abby's list?

2D
6 MINUTES
18%.

As shown, the overlap of rectangles *ABCD* and *EFGH* is also a rectangle. The area of *ABCD* is 14 sq cm. The area of *EFGH* is 33 sq cm. *AD* = 7 cm and *EF* = 11 cm. Find the area of the entire figure, in sq cm.

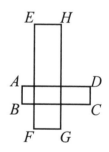

2E
6 MINUTES
11%

Three identical cubical boxes form a stack. It takes 350 sq cm of wrapping paper to completely wrap the whole stack with no overlap. Suppose each cube is wrapped separately and completely instead. What is the least amount of additional paper that is needed, in sq cm?

Solutions start on page 163.

Division E

3A
4 MINUTES
66%

The four-digit number 489A is divisible by 11.
What digit does A represent?

3B
5 MINUTES
70%

Emma has $1.85 in her pocket, all in quarters and nickels. Her father gives her another quarter. She now has the same number of quarters as nickels. How many nickels does Emma have in all?

3C
5 MINUTES
19%

Tony has an 8 cm by 12 cm paper rectangle. He folds it in half three times, each time making a smaller rectangle. What is the least possible perimeter of the rectangle after the third fold, in cm?

3D
5 MINUTES
40%

If 4 people can paint 2 fences in 5 hours, how many hours in all will it take for 8 people to paint 8 fences?

3E
7 MINUTES
13%

7^2 means 7×7 and its product is 49, which has a units (ones) digit of 9.
7^3 means $7 \times 7 \times 7$ and its product is 343, which has a units digit of 3.
7^4 means $7 \times 7 \times 7 \times 7$ and its product is 2401, which has a units digit of 1.
What is the units digit in the product of 7^{50}?

Solutions start on page 165.

SET 4

OLYMPIAD 4

4A
4 MINUTES
33%

A digital clock shows 2:35. This is the first time after midnight when all three digits are different prime numbers. What is the last time before noon when all three digits on the clock are prime numbers that are different from one another?

4B
5 MINUTES
13%

The only way that 10 can be written as the sum of 4 different counting numbers is $1 + 2 + 3 + 4$. In how many different ways can 15 be written as the sum of 4 different counting numbers? Assume that order does not matter.

4C
5 MINUTES
46%

The tower shown is made of congruent cubes stacked on top of each other. Some of the cubes are not visible. How many cubes in all are used to form the tower?

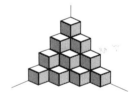

4D
6 MINUTES
4%

Hannah gives clues about her six-digit secret number:
  Clue 1: It is the same number if you read it from right to left.
  Clue 2: The number is a multiple of 9.
  Clue 3: Cross off the first and last digits. The only prime factor of the remaining four-digit number is 11.
What is Hannah's six-digit number?

4E
7 MINUTES
8%

Zach has 5 tiles. Each tile is formed from three 1-cm squares and is shaped like the one at the right. He moves the 5 tiles together to create a larger figure. What is the least possible perimeter of this larger figure, in cm?

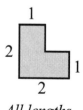

All lengths shown are in centimeters.

Solutions start on page 167.

5A
4 MINUTES

74%

Sara said, "If you divide my age by 3 and then add 8 years, the result is my age." How old is Sara, in years?

5B
5 MINUTES

59%

In the list of numbers 5, 8, 11, 14, ... , each number is 3 more than the number before it. What is the first number in the list that is greater than 100?

5C
7 MINUTES

22%

In the following, different letters represent different digits. What digit does the letter O represent?

$$\begin{array}{r} O\ N\ E \\ +\ F\ O\ U\ R \\ \hline F\ I\ V\ E \end{array} \qquad \begin{array}{r} O\ N\ E \\ \times\qquad 4 \\ \hline F\ O\ U\ R \end{array}$$

5D
7 MINUTES

16%

Each of 10 cards displays two different letters (A, B, C, D, or E), one on the front and the other on the back. The front of each card is shown. No two cards have the same pair of letters. What is the fewest cards you can turn over and be absolutely sure that an E will appear?

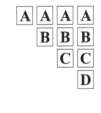

5E
5 MINUTES

36%

Suppose A and B represent any two numbers and the value of A ◎ B is given by the formula (A × A) – (B × B). What is the sum of (8 ◎ 5) and (5 ◎ 2)?

Solutions start on page 169.

SET 5

OLYMPIAD 1

1A

3 MINUTES

87%

What is the value of the following?

$$(8 \times 4) + (8 \times 3) + (8 \times 2) + (8 \times 1)$$

1B

5 MINUTES

38%

A bag contains 18 jelly beans. 4 are red, 6 are white and 8 are blue. Amanda takes them out one at a time without looking. What is the fewest jelly beans she must take out to be certain that at least 2 of the jelly beans she takes out are blue?

1C

5 MINUTES

40%

A prime number is a counting number with exactly two factors, the number itself and the number 1. In the sequence 2, 5, 11, 23, …, each number is obtained by doubling the previous number and adding 1. What is the first number in the sequence that is not a prime number?

1D

6 MINUTES

11%

A digital timer counts down from 5 minutes (5:00) to 0:00 one second at a time. For how many seconds does at least one of the three digits show a 2?

1E

6 MINUTES

9%

The top of a rectangular box is 15 cm by 20 cm and its height is 4 cm. An ant begins at one corner of the box and walks along the edges. It touches all eight corners. What is the shortest distance, in cm, that the ant may travel?

Solutions start on page 172.

Division E

SET 5
OLYMPIAD 2

2A
3 MINUTES
78%

What is the three-digit number CAT?

$$
\begin{array}{r}
3\ 4\ 5 \\
6\ 7\ 8 \\
+\ C\ A\ T \\
\hline
1\ 2\ 0\ 5
\end{array}
$$

2B
5 MINUTES
32%

Suppose a "twinner" is a number that is both 1 more than a prime number and 1 less than another prime number. For example, 30 is a twinner because 29 and 31 are both prime numbers. What is the sum of the three least twinners?

2C
5 MINUTES
8%

Five standard dice are rolled on a flat surface and the numbers on the top faces are totaled. How many different totals are possible?

(Standard dice have 6 faces, each showing a different number from 1 through 6.)

2D
5 MINUTES
34%.

The area of rectangle *ABCD* is 63 square centimeters. The area of rectangle *DCFE* is 35 sq cm. In each rectangle, the length of each side is a counting number of cm. Side *AB* is longer than side *DE*. How long is side *AE*, in cm?

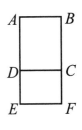

2E
7 MINUTES
8%

Ashley, Brenda, and Cate play a game with marbles. The winner of each round of the game gets from each of the other players as many marbles as the winner had at the start of that round. After Round 2, Ashley has 5 marbles, Brenda has 6, and Cate has 7. How many marbles did Ashley have at the start of the game?

Solutions start on page 174.

SET 5

OLYMPIAD 3

3A
4 MINUTES
79%

Joshua writes a four-digit number whose digits are 3, 5, 7, and 9, not necessarily in that order. The number is a multiple of 5. The first two digits and the last two digits have the same sum. The thousands digit is larger than the hundreds digit. What is Joshua's number?

3B
6 MINUTES
62%

One hat and two shirts cost $21. Two hats and one shirt cost $18. Megan has exactly enough money to buy one hat and one shirt. How much money does Megan have?

3C
6 MINUTES
43%

It takes 3 painters 4 hours to paint 1 classroom. How many hours does it take 1 painter to paint 2 classrooms of the same size as the first one? Assume all painters work at the same rate for the full time.

3D
5 MINUTES
42%

Mr. Wright wants to tile a 5 ft by 5 ft square floor. He has three kinds of square tiles: 1 ft by 1 ft, 2 ft by 2 ft, and 3 ft by 3 ft. Tiles may not overlap or be cut. What is the fewest tiles Mr. Wright may use to completely cover his floor?

3E
7 MINUTES
5%

111,111 is the product of 5 different prime numbers. What is the sum of those 5 prime numbers?

Solutions start on page 175.

SET 5

OLYMPIAD 4

4A
4 MINUTES
84%

Allie has half as much money as Ben. Ben has $3 more than Emma. Emma has 5 times as much money as Shauna. Shauna has $1. How much money do Allie and Ben have together?

4B
5 MINUTES
54%

Following only the paths shown, what is the number of different paths that go from A to B to C to D and touch each of those points exactly once?

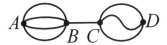

4C
5 MINUTES
67%

Sarah and Tyler ride their bikes. They start at the same time from the same point and ride in the same direction. Sarah travels 20 miles every hour, and Tyler travels 15 miles every hour. At the end of how many hours will Sarah be 30 miles ahead of Tyler?

4D
7 MINUTES
29%

Michael has some cards. If he puts them in 5 equal piles, there are 3 left over. If he puts them in 4 equal piles, there are 2 left over. If he puts them in 3 equal piles, there is 1 card left over. What is the fewest cards Michael may have?

4E
7 MINUTES
19%

The figure shown is made up of 6 congruent squares. The perimeter of the figure is 42 cm. It is folded along the dotted lines to form a box. How many 1-cm cubes can fit in the box?

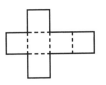

Solutions start on page 177.

SET 5
OLYMPIAD 5

5A
4 MINUTES
69%

In the figure below, what is the sum of the numbers in the shaded boxes?

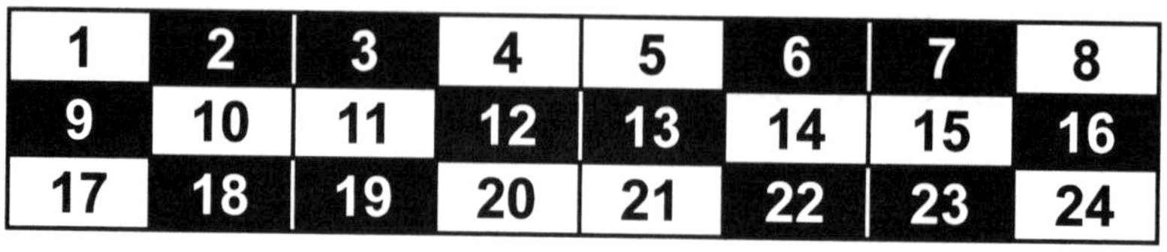

1	2	3	4	5	6	7	8
9	10	11	12	13	14	15	16
17	18	19	20	21	22	23	24

5B
5 MINUTES
24%

A toll bridge charges $4 for a car and $6 for a truck. One day 200 of these vehicles crossed the bridge and paid a total of $860 in tolls. How many of these vehicles were trucks?

5C
6 MINUTES
17%

Zach has 2 blue candies for every 1 red candy. After he eats 1 of the blues and 2 of the reds, Zach has 5 blue candies for every 2 red candies. How many candies does Zach start with?

5D
7 MINUTES
5%

A cubical box without a top is 5 cm on each edge. The box is filled with 125 identical 1-cm cubes that exactly fill the box. For how many 1-cm cubes does exactly one face touch the box?

5E
5 MINUTES
27%

The average of 6 consecutive odd numbers is 50. What is the least of these numbers?

Solutions start on page 179.

SET 6

OLYMPIAD 1

1A
3 MINUTES
38%

Suppose it is now 4:00 PM. What time will it be in 245 hours? Label your answer AM or PM.

1B
4 MINUTES
49%

Ashley's locker number is a three-digit multiple of 5. The tens digit is the sum of the hundreds digit and the ones digit. The sum of all three digits is 16. No two digits are the same. What is Ashley's locker number?

1C
5 MINUTES
27%

Ten friends have an average of 5 toy soldiers each. Lee joins them, and now the average is 6 toy soldiers each. How many toy soldiers does Lee have?

1D
6 MINUTES
25%

Tracy's Trophies charges by the letter for engraving. There is one fee for each vowel and a different fee for each consonant. CAROL costs $31 to engrave. GABRIEL costs $43 to engrave. How many dollars does BRIDGET cost to engrave?

1E
6 MINUTES
11%

As shown, the 5 × 5 "checkerboard" contains one shaded square. In this diagram, how many squares of any size do not include the shaded square?

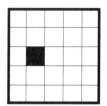

Solutions start on page 181.

SET 6
OLYMPIAD 2

2A
3 MINUTES
88%

What number does N represent?
$$10 + 20 + 30 + 40 + 50 + N = 220$$

2B
4 MINUTES
56%

What is the least multiple of 9 that is greater than 150?

2C
5 MINUTES
44%

There are 2 red cars and 3 blue cars. The 5 cars contain a total of 12 people. No car has more than 4 people. Every car has at least 1 person. The only cars with the same number of people are the red cars. How many people are in 1 red car?

2D
5 MINUTES
39%.

What number does G represent in the following?
A baseball team won $\frac{3}{4}$ of its first 24 games. Then the team lost its next G games. As a result, the team had now won exactly half of its games.

2E
7 MINUTES
26%

The first number on a list has two digits. The second number on the list is the first number plus the sum of its digits. The third number on the list, 44, equals the second number plus the sum of its (the second number's) digits. What is the first number?

Solutions start on page 183.

Division E

SET 6
OLYMPIAD 3

3A
3 MINUTES
76%

I am thinking of a number. If you subtract 3 from my number and then multiply by 4, the result is 28. What number am I thinking of?

3B
4 MINUTES
66%

What number between 104 and 140 is exactly divisible by 6 and exactly divisible by 15?

3C
6 MINUTES
27%

At the end of a power outage, a digital clock resets to 12:00 midnight. At 9:35 AM on the same day as the power outage occurred, the digital clock shows 3:50 AM. At what time did the power outage end?

(Label your answer AM or PM)

3D
6 MINUTES
28%

The figure shown is built from four 1×1 squares, four 2×2 squares, three 3×3 squares, and one 4×4 square (each measured in centimeters). What is the perimeter of the figure, in cm?

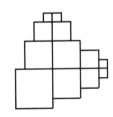

3E
6 MINUTES
46%

Two bugs walk from point *A* to point *D* along the sides of figure *ABCD*. They start and finish together. The first bug walks from *A* to *B* to *C* to *D* at an average speed of 3 cm per second. The second bug walks directly from *A* to *D*. What is the average speed of the second bug?

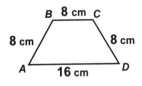

Solutions start on page 185.

4A

3 MINUTES

76%

Zach buys two hot dogs and three drinks for $14. Drinks cost $2 each. How much does one hot dog cost?

4B

5 MINUTES

57%

Michael has $5 less than Samantha. Samantha has $10 more than Rob. Rob has $15 less than Hailey. How many more dollars does Hailey have than Michael?

4C

5 MINUTES

26%

A list contains exactly 6 different counting numbers. No number in the list is a multiple of any other in the list. What is the least possible total of these 6 numbers?

4D

7 MINUTES

20%

Each of Mia's marbles show several colors. $\frac{2}{5}$ of the marbles show some red. $\frac{3}{4}$ of the marbles show some yellow. $\frac{6}{7}$ of the marbles show some blue. Mia has fewer than 250 marbles. How many of Mia's marbles show some blue?

4E

7 MINUTES

11%

Cheryl traces her name, CHERYL, by following the lines shown. She can change direction only at a letter. How many different paths can trace her name?

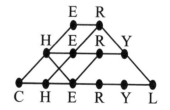

Solutions start on page 187.

SET 6

OLYMPIAD 5

5A
5 MINUTES
76%

How many digits are in the product of the following:
$$2 \times 3 \times 5 \times 2 \times 3 \times 5 \times 2 \times 3 \times 5?$$

5B
4 MINUTES
66%

Lisa has a secret 3-digit number. No digit is 0. She says:
   "The hundreds digit is a multiple of 4. The tens digit is a perfect square. The ones digit is a multiple of 3. The digits are in decreasing order."
What is Lisa's secret number?

5C
5 MINUTES
27%

The figure shown consists of 8 identical squares. The area of the figure is 8 square centimeters. What is the perimeter of the figure, in centimeters?

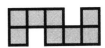

5D
7 MINUTES
28%

How many 3-digit numbers have exactly 2 digits that are the same?

5E
7 MINUTES
46%

A broken clover has 2 leaves, a normal clover has 3 leaves, and a lucky clover has 4 leaves. In a bunch of these clovers, there are twice as many normal clovers as broken clovers and 5 times as many normal clovers as lucky clovers. The bunch has a total of N leaves. N is greater than 200. What is the least value of N?

Solutions start on page 189.

SET 7
OLYMPIAD 1

1A
3 MINUTES
71%

Write the value of this expression as a whole number.
$$(20 + 40 + 60 + 80 + 100 + 120) - (10 + 30 + 50 + 70 + 90 + 110)$$

1B
5 MINUTES
41%

In a group of dogs and their owners, there are exactly 20 heads and 64 legs. How many dogs are in the group?

1C
5 MINUTES
66%

Three friends play a series of 8 games. For each game, the winner scores 8 points, the friend in second place scores 3 points, and the friend in last place scores 0 points. At the end of 8 games, Keri's score is 20 points. In how many of the games did Keri finish last?

1D
6 MINUTES
33%

How many four-sided figures can be traced, using only the lines in this picture?

1E
7 MINUTES
14%

Different letters represent different digits.
If ADD + ADD + ADD = SUMS and A is even,
what is the 4-digit number SUMS?

Solutions start on page 192.

Division E

SET 7
OLYMPIAD 2

2A
3 MINUTES

59%

The sum of the digits of the number 2010 is 3. What is the next larger number whose digits also add up to 3?

2B
4 MINUTES

69%

In the repeating pattern below, what will be the 78th letter written?
ABBCCD ABBCCD... (*and so on*)

2C
5 MINUTES

41%

If you triple Jen's age and subtract 16, the result will be the same as when you double her age and add 8. How old is Jen?

2D
6 MINUTES

16%

This figure consists of two squares. The length of each side is a whole number of centimeters. The combined areas of the squares is 100 sq cm. What is the perimeter of the entire figure?

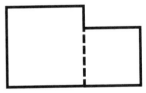

2E
7 MINUTES

14%

A pile of coins sits on a table. Sara takes half of the coins plus 4 more. Then Nick takes 2. Then Joe takes 2 more than half of what is left. Finally Selena takes 5. Four coins remain on the table. How many coins were on the table to start with?

Solutions start on page 194.

3A

3 MINUTES

47%

How many 2-digit numbers have one digit that is twice the other?

3B

4 MINUTES

71%

In a magic square, the sum of the numbers in each row and each column is the same. If exactly one number is changed in this picture, the result is a magic square. Which number must be changed?

22	1	16
9	13	19
10	25	4

3C

5 MINUTES

64%

Suppose the boxes are filled in with the digits from 0 through 6. Each digit is written exactly once. What three-digit number is the correct answer to the addition problem?

3D

7 MINUTES

10%

1 blue marble and 2 green marbles cost 16 cents.
1 red marble and 2 blue marbles also cost 16 cents.
1 green marble and 2 red marbles only cost 13 cents.
How much does 1 green marble cost?

3E

7 MINUTES

15%

The perimeter of rectangle $ABCD$ is 36 cm. Suppose side $\overline{AD}$ is folded up as shown so that D lies on the midpoint of side $\overline{AB}$ and $\overline{AE}$ is the crease. What is the area of figure $ABCE$?

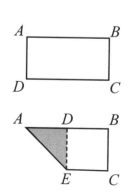

Solutions start on page 196.

SET 7
OLYMPIAD 4

4A
3 MINUTES
58%

What is the sum of the digits in the arrangement at the right?

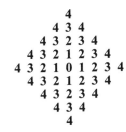

```
            4
          4 3 4
        4 3 2 3 4
      4 3 2 1 2 3 4
    4 3 2 1 0 1 2 3 4
      4 3 2 1 2 3 4
        4 3 2 3 4
          4 3 4
            4
```

4B
4 MINUTES
47%

Staci looks at the first and fourth pages of a chapter in her book. The sum of their page numbers is 47. On what page does the chapter begin?

4C
4 MINUTES
20%

The digits 1 through 9 are placed in the boxes shown, one per box. In each corner box is a prime number. In each box in the middle column is a square number. In the 3 boxes of the middle row is the least 3-digit number possible. What is that 3-digit number?

4D
7 MINUTES
28%

Different letters represent different digits. *AB* is an even 2-digit number. *EEE* is a 3-digit number. Find the 2-digit number *AB*.

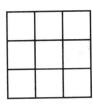

$$M \overline{)\, E\,E\,E}^{\,A\,B}$$

4E
6 MINUTES
14%

A rectangular solid that is 4 cm by 6 cm by 8 cm is painted on all six faces. Then the solid is cut into cubes that measure 2 cm on each side. How many of these cubes have only one face painted?

Solutions start on page 198.

SET 7
OLYMPIAD 5

5A
3 MINUTES
61%

If the 5-digit number 3367N is divisible by 15, what is the digit N?

5B
4 MINUTES
26%

Vera makes vegetable trays. Each tray uses $\frac{2}{3}$ of a pound of carrots. Vera needs to make 25 trays. She buys carrots only in 2-pound bags. How many bags of carrots must Vera buy to make the 25 trays?

5C
6 MINUTES
23%

At lunch, Hannah tells Dom, "If you give me 4 grapes, we will each have the same number of grapes." Dom tells Hannah, "If you give me 4 grapes, I will have five times as many grapes as you will have then." How many grapes does Hannah have?

5D
6 MINUTES
17%

The perimeter of a rectangular piece of paper is 50 cm. It is cut into 4 congruent rectangles as shown. What is the total of the perimeters of the four smaller rectangles?

5E
7 MINUTES
2%

AB, *CD*, *EF*, *GH*, and *JK* are five 2-digit numbers. Different letters represent different digits. Find the greatest possible value of the fraction below.

$$\frac{AB + CD + EF}{GH - JK}$$

Solutions start on page 200.

Division E

SET 8

OLYMPIAD 1

1A
3 MINUTES
77%

Find the value of $87 - 76 + 65 - 54 + 43 - 32 + 21 - 10$.

1B
5 MINUTES
38%

Grace chooses five different numbers from the list 1, 2, 3, 4, 5, 6, 7, 8, 9, 10. Two of those numbers are 4 and 5, and they are the only two numbers she picks that differ by 1. What is the greatest possible sum of the five numbers?

1C
5 MINUTES
48%

A 7×7 square is marked off into forty-nine 1×1 small squares. Each of the small squares along the edges of the large square is painted blue. How many small squares are painted blue?

1D
6 MINUTES
76%

The numbers 1, 2, 3, 4, 5, and 6 are placed in the diagram, one in each circle. The sum of the numbers along Side A is 13, along Side B is 13, and along Side C is 6. What number is in the circle at the top of the diagram?

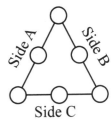

1E
6 MINUTES
15%

The region inside the circle can be cut into two parts by drawing 1 line through it, as shown. What is the greatest number of parts that can be formed by drawing 4 lines through the region?

Solutions start on page 202.

SET 8

OLYMPIAD 2

2A
3 MINUTES
74%

What is the value of $(47 \times 8) + (8 \times 27) + (26 \times 8)$?

2B
5 MINUTES
64%

Juan uses the digits 1, 2, 3, 4, 5, and 6 to make two three-digit numbers. Each digit is used once. The numbers are subtracted. What is the greatest possible difference?

2C
5 MINUTES
28%

Four volunteers can pack 12 boxes every 30 minutes. How many additional volunteers are needed to pack 72 boxes every hour? [Assume all volunteers work at the same rate.]

2D
6 MINUTES
19%

How many 3-digit numbers are multiples of 21?

2E
7 MINUTES
21%

All angles in the 8-sided figure shown are right angles. All lengths are given in centimeters. What is the area of the 8-sided figure?

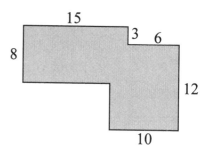

Solutions start on page 204.

SET 8

OLYMPIAD 3

3A
3 MINUTES
89%

What number does ◇ represent if ⬠ + ◇ = 20 and ⬠ + ⬠ = 24?

3B
4 MINUTES
17%

How many numbers between 10 and 99 have digits that differ by 3?

3C
5 MINUTES
25%

A large rectangle is cut into 6 smaller rectangles. How many rectangles of all sizes are in this diagram?

3D
6 MINUTES
41%

A teacher surveyed 24 students and discovered that
 • 18 of them like to play video games;
 • 15 of them like to go to the movies; and
 • 2 of them do not like either playing video games or going to the movies.
How many of the 24 students like both activities?

3E
7 MINUTES
56%

Every digit from 1 through 9 appears exactly once in the correct addition problem at the right. What three-digit number is the answer to the addition problem?

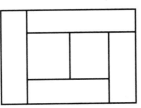

Solutions start on page 206.

SET 8
OLYMPIAD 4

4A
4 MINUTES
67%

Chloe divides the number *N* by 14 correctly and gets 5. Mia misreads the division sign as an addition sign and adds 14 to *N*. What sum does Mia get?

4B
4 MINUTES
48%

Kevin starts with the number 9 and counts by 7s. This results in the sequence 9, 16, 23, 30, 37, and so on. What is the twenty-fourth number in Kevin's sequence?

4C
5 MINUTES
18%

What is the least prime number that is the sum of 3 different prime numbers?

4D
6 MINUTES
31%

A standard checkerboard is 8 units by 8 units. To cover her checkerboard without any overlap, Jen uses three kinds of game pieces (shown at the right). Each game piece has an area of 5 sq units, What is the greatest number of pieces that Jen can place on the checkerboard?

4E
7 MINUTES
8%

Larry starts at the bottom of a long staircase. He climbs exactly $\frac{2}{3}$ of the stairs. Then, he goes back down exactly $\frac{1}{2}$ of the way to the bottom. From that spot, he climbs exactly $\frac{2}{3}$ of the way to the top. Finally, from there, he climbs 6 stairs to reach the top. How many stairs are in the staircase?

Solutions start on page 208.

SET 8

OLYMPIAD 5

5A
4 MINUTES
72%

What number is one-half of one-third of one-fourth of 240?

5B
5 MINUTES
57%

Each number from 1 through 16 is written one to a box. A path is formed by placing consecutive numbers in adjacent boxes horizontally or vertically, but not diagonally. Four numbers are shown. Find the sum of the numbers in the starred (*) boxes.

3			
	1		
5	*		*
		16	

5C
5 MINUTES
14%

Group A has 10 numbers with an average of 10. Group B has 20 numbers with an average of 20. Group C has 30 numbers with an average of 30. Group D has 40 numbers with an average of 40. The four groups are combined into a single group. What is the average of the combined group?

5D
5 MINUTES
14%

Judy has two more sisters than brothers. Her brother, Mark, has twice as many sisters as brothers. How many children are in their family?

5E
7 MINUTES
22%

Colored 1×1×1 blocks are to be placed in a 4×4×4 cardboard box. A red block is placed in one corner of the box. Next, the least number of green blocks are placed to completely hide the red block from view. Then, the least number of yellow blocks are placed to hide the green blocks from view. At this point, how many blocks have been placed in the box?

Solutions start on page 210.

OLYMPIAD PROBLEMS

DIVISION M
SETS 9-16

SET 9
OLYMPIAD 1

1A
4 MINUTES
50%

You are given five consecutive whole numbers. One of them is 17. What is the units (ones) digit of the product of the five numbers?

1B
5 MINUTES
32%

A train is exactly 12 miles from Smalltown at 7:00 PM. It travels toward Smalltown at a constant rate of 45 miles per hour. At what time does the train reach Smalltown?

1C
5 MINUTES
20%

Noelle collects autographs of famous mathematicians. Exactly one statement below is true:
- Noelle owns at least 77 autographs.
- Noelle owns at least 62 autographs.
- Noelle owns at least 45 autographs.

What is the greatest number of autographs Noelle can own?

1D
6 MINUTES
30%

$\frac{9}{37}$ is changed to a decimal. What digit lies in the 2005th place to the right of the decimal point?

1E
7 MINUTES
42%

In rectangle $ABCD$, all of $\overline{AC}$, $\overline{BD}$, and $\overline{FG}$ intersect at point E. $\overline{AD}$ is 12 cm long and $\overline{AB}$ is 18 cm long. What is the sum of the areas of the shaded regions, in sq cm?

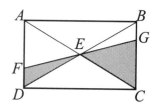

Solutions start on page 214.

SET 9
OLYMPIAD 2

2A
3 MINUTES

66%

In this correct addition of two 2-digit numbers, A and B represent different digits. Find the value of digit A.

$$\begin{array}{r} A\,B \\ +\,A\,A \\ \hline 1\,B\,2 \end{array}$$

2B
4 MINUTES

17%

Emily has 21 dimes. She places them in three piles, with an odd number of dimes in each pile. In how many different ways can she accomplish this?
[*Consider piles of 1, 1, and 19 dimes, for example, to be equivalent to piles of 1, 19, and 1 dimes.*]

2C
5 MINUTES

51%

Amy always tells the truth on Monday, Tuesday, Wednesday, and Thursday. Bill always tells the truth on Monday, Friday, Saturday, and Sunday. On the rest of the days, they may tell the truth or they may lie. One day last week, Amy and Bill both said, "I lied yesterday." On what day did they make those statements?

2D
6 MINUTES

17%.

Suppose $\frac{2}{N}$, $\frac{3}{N}$, and $\frac{5}{N}$ are three fractions in lowest terms. What are all the possible composite whole number values for N between 20 and 80?

2E
6 MINUTES

17%

The Mathematical Olympiads began in the prime year 1979. Find the product of the fractions below in simplest form:

$$(1 - \tfrac{1}{1980}) \times (1 - \tfrac{1}{1981}) \times (1 - \tfrac{1}{1982}) \times \ldots \times (1 - \tfrac{1}{2004}) \times (1 - \tfrac{1}{2005})$$

Solutions start on page 216.

SET 9
OLYMPIAD 3

3A
4 MINUTES
55%

A taxi ride costs $2 for the first $\frac{1}{5}$ mile and 40 cents for each additional $\frac{1}{5}$ mile. Dan has $9.60. What is the longest taxi ride he can afford, in miles? (Express your answer in simplest form.)

3B
4 MINUTES
49%

Sean correctly added the whole numbers from 1 through 12. Allie then added one of those same numbers to Sean's answer. Allie's answer was 3 more than a perfect square. Which whole number did Allie add to Sean's answer?

3C
5 MINUTES
35%

An integer is chosen at random from the set {41, 42, 43, ..., 67}. What is the probability that the chosen number is one more than a multiple of 4 or one more than a multiple of 5?

3D
6 MINUTES
23%

In this street map, all traffic enters at A and exits at either B or C. All traffic flows either south or east. At each intersection where there is a choice of direction, 70% of the traffic goes east and 30% goes south. What percent of the traffic exits at C?

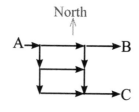

3E
6 MINUTES
24%

In circle O (shown) the diameters are perpendicular and $ABCD$ is a rectangle. $AM = 20$ cm. Using 3.14 to estimate π, find the circumference of the circle to the nearest centimeter.

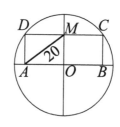

Solutions start on page 218.

SET 9

OLYMPIAD 4

4A

4 MINUTES

59%

David has 4 cages of hamsters. The second cage has $\frac{1}{2}$ as many hamsters as the first. The third cage has $\frac{1}{2}$ as many hamsters as the second. The fourth cage has $\frac{1}{2}$ as many hamsters as the third. What is the fewest hamsters David can have?

4B

4 MINUTES

40%

Let **X** represent the sum of the whole numbers less than x which are not factors of x. For example, **6** = 9 because 4 and 5 are the only whole numbers less than 6 which are not factors of 6, and 4 + 5 = 9. What is the value of **12** − **10** ?

4C

5 MINUTES

47%

The average (arithmetic mean) of P and Q is 18, while the average of R, S, and T is 43. What is the average of the five numbers P, Q, R, S, and T?

4D

6 MINUTES

21%

In circle O, radius $OA = 4$ cm and angle O measures 90°. Find the area of the shaded region to the nearest tenth of a square centimeter. Use the approximation $\pi \approx 3.14$.

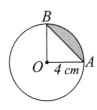

4E

7 MINUTES

15%

One hundred students were asked their opinion on three ice cream flavors. 65 said they liked strawberry, 75 said they liked chocolate, and 85 said they liked vanilla. What is the fewest students that could have said they liked all three flavors?

Solutions start on page 220.

SET 9

OLYMPIAD 5

5A
4 MINUTES
68%

Ten posts are placed 6 meters apart in a straight line. A fence runs from the first post to the last post. How long is the fence?
(Ignore the thickness of the posts.)

5B
5 MINUTES
37%

The product of three consecutive whole numbers is 15,600. What is the least of the three numbers?

5C
6 MINUTES
22%

72 more females than males are enrolled in Archimedes High School. 60% of the students are female. What is the number of male students that are enrolled?

5D
7 MINUTES
9%

Two semicircles are inscribed in a square with side 8 meters, as shown. Approximate the area of the shaded region to the nearest tenth of a square meter. Use the approximation 3.14 for π.

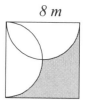

8 m

5E
5 MINUTES
47%

The value of a two-digit number is 10 more than 3 times the sum of its digits. The units digit is 1 more than twice the tens digit. What is the two-digit number?

Solutions start on page 222.

SET 10

OLYMPIAD 1

1A
3 MINUTES
81%

What is the value of the following?
$$40 - 36 + 32 - 28 + 24 - 20 + 16 - 12 + 8 - 4$$

1B
5 MINUTES
59%

When 18 is divided by the whole number N, the remainder is 4. This is true for how many different values of N?

1C
5 MINUTES
77%

Amy has four more quarters than dimes. The total value of all her quarters and dimes is $5.20. How many dimes does Amy have?

1D
6 MINUTES
33%

As shown, a square of area 100 sq cm is split into four separate smaller regions: A, B, C, and D. Regions B and C are squares. Find the sum of the perimeters of regions A, B, C, and D, in cm.

1E
6 MINUTES
24%

The denominators of two fractions are consecutive counting numbers. Both fractions are in lowest terms. Their sum is $\frac{51}{56}$. Find the greater of these two fractions.

Solutions start on page 224.

2A

3 MINUTES

69%

Maisie has three times as many CDs as Ken. Ken has twice as many CDs as Jo. Jo has more than 10 CDs. What is the least number of CDs that Maisie can have?

2B

5 MINUTES

40%

The cars of a circular Ferris wheel at an amusement park are equally spaced about the wheel's circumference. They are numbered consecutively beginning with 1. The cars numbered 14 and 30 lie on opposite ends of a diameter. How many cars are on the Ferris wheel?

2C

5 MINUTES

37%

Working as a team, 8 mathletes can solve 20 problems in 10 minutes. At this same rate, how many mathletes are needed in order to solve 30 problems in 5 minutes?

2D

6 MINUTES

16%.

As shown, points P, Q, and R lie on one line and points S, T, U, and V lie on another line. In all, how many different triangles can be formed using any three of the points P, Q, R, S, T, U, and V as vertices?

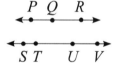

2E

6 MINUTES

47%

What is the greatest counting number that divides 17, 25, and 41 and leaves the same remainder in each case?

Solutions start on page 227.

SET 10
OLYMPIAD 3

3A
3 MINUTES
36%

Bill's five-day schedule continually repeats. It calls for him to work 4 days and then take the 5th day off. What is the greatest number of days off that Bill can take in any one month?

3B
4 MINUTES
54%

The digits 1, 3, 6, and 8 are arranged to form two 2-digit numbers. Each digit is used exactly once. The two 2-digit numbers are multiplied. What is the greatest product that can be obtained?

3C
5 MINUTES
26%

Miguel takes 5 tests. Each score is a whole number between 0 and 100, inclusive. The following statements are true:
    (I) The mean of his scores is 80,
    (II) the median is 81, and
    (III) there is just one mode and it is 88.
Find the least possible score Miguel could have received on any one test.

3D
5 MINUTES
30%

The price of a candy bar has increased 20%. How many candy bars can now be purchased for the amount of money that used to buy 42 candy bars?

3E
7 MINUTES
31%

Three adjacent squares rest on a horizontal line. Line *m* touches a corner of each square as shown. The lengths of the sides of the two smaller squares are 4 cm and 6 cm. Find the length of one side of the largest square.

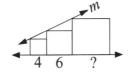

Solutions start on page 229.

SET 10
OLYMPIAD 4

4A
3 MINUTES
74%

Suppose $a \star b \oslash c$ means $a^b + c$.
Find the value of $(3 \star 2 \oslash 1) - (2 \star 1 \oslash 3)$.

4B
4 MINUTES
49%

When it is 7 AM in New York, it is noon in London. A plane leaves London at noon London time and arrives in New York at 11 AM New York time the same day. A second plane leaves New York at 12 noon New York time for London. What time in London is it when the second plane arrives?
Assume both planes fly for the same number of hours.

4C
5 MINUTES
47%

On a vacation trip, travel costs are 10¢ per mile for the first 75 miles and 18¢ per mile for the remaining 45 miles. Find the average cost per mile of the entire trip, in cents.

4D
5 MINUTES
26%

Bert has 40% more jelly beans than Vicki. What fractional part of Bert's jelly beans must be given to Vicki so that they each have the same number of jelly beans? Express your answer in lowest terms.

4E
7 MINUTES
22%

Two congruent circles and two parallel lines intersect in a total of five points as shown. The inner segment of each line is 6 centimeter long. Using $\pi \approx 3.14$, find the area of the shaded region to the nearest square centimeter.

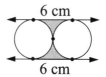

6 cm

6 cm

Solutions start on page 230.

Division M

SET 10

OLYMPIAD 5

5A
4 MINUTES
47%

A factory produces 10 widgets per second. How many hours does it take the factory to produce 90,000 widgets?

5B
5 MINUTES
43%

Find the least positive integer A so that the product of 45 and A is a perfect square number.

5C
6 MINUTES
39%

Lou eats 1 jelly bean on September 1st, 3 on September 2nd, 5 on September 3rd, and so on, through the 30 days of the month. Each day he eats 2 more than the day before. In all, how many jelly beans does Lou eat in September?

5D
7 MINUTES
16%

A square with an area of 18 square centimeters is inscribed in a circle as shown. Using the approximation $\pi \approx 3.14$, find the area of the shaded region to the nearest square centimeter.

5E
5 MINUTES
36%

What number exceeds 23 by 4 more than twice the amount by which 15 exceeds -3?

Solutions start on page 232.

SET 11

OLYMPIAD 1

1A
3 MINUTES

68%

What is the value of the following?

$$40 \times 30 \times 20 \times 10 \div 20 \div 40 \div 6$$

1B
5 MINUTES

35%

The map shows all the roads connecting the five towns shown. What is the number of different paths a traveler may take from Town A to Town E if she visits no town more than once?

(She doesn't have to visit every town.)

1C
5 MINUTES

35%

Rachel has 30 paper squares. Each square is 2 cm on a side. She arranges all of them, without overlapping, to form a rectangle. In cm, what is the smallest possible perimeter of the rectangle?

1D
5 MINUTES

4%

Mrs. Allen travels from home to work at 60 km per hour (kph). She returns along the same route. Her average speed for the round trip is 72 kph. What is her speed from work to home, in kph?

1E
6 MINUTES

31%

A, B, and C, in that order, are three consecutive whole numbers. Each is greater than 2000. A is a multiple of 4. B is a multiple of 5. C is a multiple of 6. What is the smallest possible value of A?

Solutions start on page 234.

SET 11
OLYMPIAD 2

2A
3 MINUTES
66%

Three dice, each with faces numbered 1 through 6, are arranged as shown. Seven faces are visible. Find the sum of the numbers on all the faces that are not visible.

2B
4 MINUTES
58%

Ava has $5 more than two-thirds of the amount Dan has. Ava has $23. What is the number of dollars that Dan has?

2C
5 MINUTES
10%

What is the total number of different ways that the blanks below can be filled in so that the resulting four-digit number is a multiple of 11?

__ 6 __ 8

2D
5 MINUTES
27%.

Rectangle *ABCD* is partitioned into five squares as shown. The length, in centimeters, of $\overline{AM}$ is a whole number. The area of rectangle *ABCD* is greater than 100 sq cm. Find the smallest possible area of rectangle *ABCD*, in sq cm.

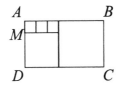

2E
7 MINUTES
3%

In an *up-and-down* counting number, the digits increase to a maximum digit and then decrease. This maximum is not the first or last digit. (Example: 2<u>5</u>6850 is an *up-and-down* number, but 2<u>55</u>876 is not.) How many different 4-digit *up-and-down* numbers have a maximum digit of 6?

Solutions start on page 236.

SET 11

OLYMPIAD 3

3A
3 MINUTES
77%

Together Jake and Emily have 20 CDs. Emily has 2 more CDs than Jake. What is the number of CDs that Jake has?

3B
5 MINUTES
38%

Austin and Taylor stand back-to-back. Each takes 10 steps away from the starting point in opposite directions and stops. Austin turns around and walks in a straight line path toward Taylor, and reaches her in 24 steps. What number of Austin's steps equal the length of five of Taylor's steps?

3C
5 MINUTES
21%

In how many ways can 50 be expressed as the sum of three different prime numbers?

(The same three numbers in a different order should not be considered a different answer.)

3D
6 MINUTES
20%

Triangle PQR is inscribed in rectangle $ABCD$, as shown. The length of $\overline{RQ}$ is $\frac{2}{5}$ of the length of $\overline{DC}$. The area of triangle PQR is 6.4 square centimeters. What is the area of rectangle $ABCD$ in sq cm?

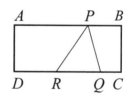

3E
7 MINUTES
9%

$1 + 3 + 5 + 7 + \cdots + 2003 + 2005 + 2007 = N^2$.
Find the whole number N.

Solutions start on page 238.

Division M

SET 11
OLYMPIAD 4

4A
3 MINUTES
64%

X, Y, and Z represent digits in the subtraction problem shown. Find the sum X + Y + Z.

$$\begin{array}{r} 8\,X\,4 \\ -\,3\,7\,Y \\ \hline Z\,7\,8 \end{array}$$

4B
4 MINUTES
44%

$1003^2 + N = 1005^2$. Find the whole number value of N.

4C
5 MINUTES
29%

On a trip, Liam agreed to drive $\frac{2}{3}$ of the total distance if Jessica drove the remaining distance. Upon completing his share of the driving, Liam fell asleep. When Liam awoke, Jessica still had 20% of her share left to drive. *In lowest terms*, for what fractional part of the whole trip was Liam asleep?

4D
5 MINUTES
13%

Marcia was absent on the day of a math test and took a makeup exam the next day. Marcia's grade of 87 raised the class average from exactly 73 to exactly 73.5. What number of students, including Marcia, took the test?

4E
7 MINUTES
21%

Each of the two squares touch the circle in exactly four points, as shown. The area of the outer square is 100 sq cm. Find the area of the inner square, in sq cm.

Solutions start on page 240.

5A

3 MINUTES

42%

Sara's number is the average of $\frac{1}{3}$ and $\frac{1}{2}$. Ali's number is the average of Sara's number and $\frac{1}{2}$. What is Ali's number?

5B

5 MINUTES

40%

The sum of the areas of three squares is 65 square centimeters. The length of a side of each square, in cm, is a counting number. Find the perimeter of the square that has the greatest area, in cm.

5C

5 MINUTES

7%

Team A and Team B play a series of games until one of them has won two games. No game ends in a tie. In any single game, the probability that Team A wins is 70%. What is the probability that they play exactly 2 games?

5D

7 MINUTES

25%

Starting at the same time on opposite shores of a lake, two boats cross back and forth for 35 minutes without stopping. One boat needs 5 minutes to cross the lake. The other boat needs 7 minutes. What is the number of times during the 35 minutes that the faster boat passes the slower boat going in the same or opposite direction?

5E

4 MINUTES

43%

The whole numbers 3, 4, 5, 6, 12, and 13 are arranged, without repetition, in a horizontal row so that the sum of any two numbers in adjoining positions is a perfect square. Find the sum of the middle two numbers.

Solutions start on page 242.

SET 12

OLYMPIAD 1

1A
4 MINUTES
74%

A horizontal line contains points *A*, *B*, *C*, and *D* in some order.
- ▶ *BD* is the greatest distance between any two of the points.
- ▶ *A* is the midpoint of $\overline{CD}$.
- ▶ Points *B* and *C* lie to the right of point *A*.

List the four points in order from left to right.

1B
5 MINUTES
49%

Sequence A lists all the prime numbers in increasing order: 2, 3, 5, 7, 11, 13, and so on. Sequence B lists the same numbers split into individual digits: 2, 3, 5, 7, 1, 1, 1, 3, 1, 7, 1, 9, and so on. What is the 24th digit in Sequence B?

1C
5 MINUTES
38%

The number 1008 is divisible by each of 3, 4, 6, and 8. What is the greatest number that is both less than 1100 and is also divisible by each of 3, 4, 6, and 8?

1D
6 MINUTES
34%

{1,2,7,15,17,18} is a set of six data values. Suppose each data value is multiplied by 3.6 and then 4 is added to each product. What is the mean of the new set of six data values?

1E
7 MINUTES
11%

How many triangles of all sizes are shown in the diagram?

Solutions start on page 244.

SET 12
OLYMPIAD 2

<table>
<tr><td>

2A

4 MINUTES

33%

</td><td>

The cube of a number N is equal to $12\frac{3}{4} - 2 \times 2.375$.
Find the value of N.

</td></tr>
</table>

<table>
<tr><td>

2B

5 MINUTES

41%

</td><td>

The dot plot shows the points scored and the grade
levels for each of 12 mathletes. To the nearest tenth
of a point, what is the mathletes' mean score?

</td><td>

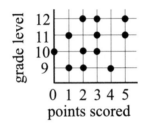

</td></tr>
</table>

<table>
<tr><td>

2C

5 MINUTES

37%

</td><td>

Simplify fully:
$$100 + 99 - 98 - 97 + 96 + 95 - 94 - 93 + \ldots + 4 + 3 - 2 - 1,$$
if the pattern of the sum of two consecutive integers followed by two
subtractions of consecutive integers is continued throughout.

</td></tr>
</table>

<table>
<tr><td>

2D

6 MINUTES

14%.

</td><td>

Rectangle $ABCD$ consists of six squares, each of area
1 sq cm. Using only the line segments shown, the
shortest paths from A to C are 5 cm long. One of these
5-cm paths from A to C is chosen at random. What is the
probability that the chosen path passes through point X?

</td><td>

</td></tr>
</table>

<table>
<tr><td>

2E

7 MINUTES

25%

</td><td>

A single piece of wire is folded to form a square with area 225 sq cm. The
wire is then straightened, cut into pieces of equal length, and those pieces
fastened together to form the frame of a cube. If no wire is wasted, find
the volume enclosed by the cube, in cubic centimeters.

</td></tr>
</table>

Solutions start on page 246.

Division M

3A
4 MINUTES
50%

How many positive integers are factors of both 36 and 60?

3B
5 MINUTES
47%

If $2^7 \times 5^3$ is multiplied out, what is the sum of the digits in the product?

3C
5 MINUTES
44%

Ali and Ben have a total of 36 CDs. After Ali gives Ben 40% of her CDs, Ben has twice as many as Ali. How many CDs did Ali have originally?

3D
6 MINUTES
24%

When $N = \frac{1}{101}$, what is the value of the following expression in simplest form?

$$11\left(\frac{1}{N} - 1\right) + \frac{9}{N}$$

3E
6 MINUTES
11%

Three cubes with edges of length 1, 2, and 3 cm, respectively, are glued together to form a solid figure. Find the least possible surface area of the resulting 3-dimensional figure, in sq cm.

Solutions start on page 248.

SET 12

OLYMPIAD 4

4A

3 MINUTES

36%

Find the sum of the integers from −2007 through +2009, inclusive.

4B

5 MINUTES

52%

The sum of the lengths of three sides of a rectangle is 55 cm. Each side is a whole number of cm in length. The length is 8 cm more than the width. Find the perimeter of the rectangle, in cm.

4C

4 MINUTES

40%

Jen travels from home on a straight road. After a rest she returns along the same route. The graph shows her distance from home at any given time. What was her average speed for the entire 4-hour trip, in miles per hour?

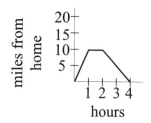

4D

6 MINUTES

20%

The pages of a book are consecutively numbered from 1 through 384. How many times does the digit 8 appear in this numbering?

4E

6 MINUTES

11%

The product of 180 and the positive integer N is a perfect cubic number. What is the least possible value of N?

Solutions start on page 249.

SET 12

OLYMPIAD 5

5A
4 MINUTES

41%

2 pens and 3 erasers together cost 40 cents. 2 erasers and 3 pens together cost 55 cents. What is the total cost of 1 pen and 1 eraser, in cents?

5B
6 MINUTES

14%

How many positive integers less than 100 can be expressed as the product of two different odd prime numbers?

5C
6 MINUTES

31%

Line segment $\overline{AB}$ joins points $A(4,15)$ and $B(10,6)$. Point T lies on segment $\overline{AB}$ and is one-third of the way from A to B. Find the coordinates of point T in simplest terms.

5D
7 MINUTES

27%

Some pennies are arranged in rows. The number of pennies in each row is the same as the number of rows. After 10 pennies are removed, the remaining pennies can be arranged into 2 fewer rows, but with 1 additional penny in each row. How many pennies were there originally?

5E
5 MINUTES

41%

The even integers from 2 through 18 are placed in the grid shown so that the sum of the numbers in each row, column, and diagonal is the same. What number does x represent?

	2	x
6		
	18	

Solutions start on page 251.

SET 13

OLYMPIAD 1

1A
3 MINUTES
61%

Express as a single number:
$$125 \times 25 \times 5 \times 2 \times 4 \times 8$$

1B
3 MINUTES
60%

Find the least whole number N so that $123 + N$ is a perfect square.

1C
5 MINUTES
36%

How many numbers between 19 and 79 are the product of two even numbers?

1D
6 MINUTES
21%

Points A, B, C, and D lie on a straight line in the given order. $AC = 25$ cm and $BD = 46$ cm. The ratio of length CD to length AB is 5:2. Find the length of line segment BC in cm.

1E
7 MINUTES
23%

A bookseller has 15 different novels: 4 are in German, 5 are in Spanish, and 6 are in French. Emma buys two novels. They are written in two different languages. In how many different ways can this be done? Ignore the order in which she buys them.

Solutions start on page 254.

SET 13

OLYMPIAD 2

2A
3 MINUTES
47%

As shown, $\overleftrightarrow{AOB}$ is a straight line; $\overrightarrow{OC}$, $\overrightarrow{OD}$, and $\overrightarrow{OE}$ are rays. $\angle COE$ and $\angle DOB$ each contain 90°. $\angle COB$ contains 130°. Find the number of degrees in $\angle DOE$.

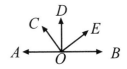

2B
5 MINUTES
39%

Find the value of the following:

$$\frac{2.3 \times 2.01 + 3.7 \times 2.01}{0.3 \times 4.02}$$

2C
6 MINUTES
25%

Mr. Alvarez gives each of his students 4 sheets of paper and 16 sheets are left over. But if two students were absent, each of the remaining students would receive 5 sheets, with only 3 sheets left over. How many sheets of paper does Mr. Alvarez have?

2D
5 MINUTES
43%.

The sum $1 + 3 + 5 + \cdots + 21 + 23 + 25$ is 169.
Find the sum $1 + 5 + 9 + \cdots + 41 + 45 + 49$, in which each successive term after the first is 4 greater than the previous term.

2E
5 MINUTES
31%

Jess runs an outdoor stand at City Stadium. When it rains, Jess earns $1500 selling umbrellas. But when it doesn't rain, she earns $400 selling sunglasses. On any given day, the chance of rain is 40%. On the average, how much can Jess expect to earn daily?

Solutions start on page 256.

SET 13
OLYMPIAD 3

3A
3 MINUTES
50%

Find the number of digits to the left of the decimal point when 500 million is divided by one hundred seventy thousand.

3B
5 MINUTES
37%

Kim multiplies all the counting numbers from 30 through 2 inclusive:
$$30 \times 29 \times 28 \times 27 \times \ldots \times 4 \times 3 \times 2.$$
If this expression is rewritten as the product of prime numbers, how many times will 7 be used as a factor?

3C
4 MINUTES
16%

Chloe and Jack play 3 games. The probability that Chloe wins any game is $\frac{3}{5}$. What is the probability that Chloe wins for the first time in the third game?

3D
5 MINUTES
42%

A semicircle rests atop a 12 cm by 6 cm rectangle. Two quarter-circles, each of radius 6 cm are removed from the bottom corners of the rectangle. Find the number of square cm in the area of the shaded region thus formed.

3E
7 MINUTES
16%

Find whole numbers a, b, and c so that

$$a + \frac{1}{b + \frac{1}{c}} = \frac{45}{7}$$

Solutions start on page 258.

SET 13
OLYMPIAD 4

4A
3 MINUTES
69%

Suppose $52 \times 50 \times N = 40 \times 13 \times 35$.
Find the whole number N.

4B
5 MINUTES
63%

Two consecutive positive integers are each less than 100. One integer is divisible by 17 and the other integer is divisible by 21. Find the greater of the two integers.

4C
5 MINUTES
40%

Three circles are externally tangent as shown. Their areas are 9π, 25π, and 100π square centimeters. A triangle is formed by connecting the centers of the three circles. Find the perimeter of the triangle, in cm.

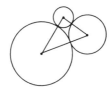

4D
6 MINUTES
57%

The four-digit whole number 3■11 is exactly divisible by 13. Find the missing digit ■.

4E
7 MINUTES
22%

A square is positioned in quadrant I on graph paper so that two vertices lie on the axes, while a third vertex lies at the point (7,4). Find the area of the square.

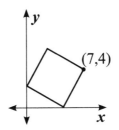

Solutions start on page 260.

SET 13
OLYMPIAD 5

5A
3 MINUTES
59%

For any two numbers a and b, define the value of $a ✴ b$ as $a + 3 × b$. For example, $4 ✴ 5$ means $4 + 3 × 5 = 19$. If $2 ✴ 6$ and $N ✴ 4$ represent the same number, what is the value of N?

5B
5 MINUTES
45%

Express the product as a fraction in simplest terms.

$$\frac{1}{3} × \frac{2}{4} × \frac{3}{5} × \frac{4}{6} × \frac{5}{7} × \frac{6}{8} × \frac{7}{9} × \frac{8}{10}$$

5C
5 MINUTES
46%

The sum of the integers from -10 through N, inclusive, equals 50. Find N.

5D
5 MINUTES
13%

The Pumas lost 7 of their first 9 games. By winning 75% of their remaining games, they ended with victories in exactly $\frac{2}{3}$ of all their games. In all, how many games did they win?

5E
7 MINUTES
26%

The rectangular top of an in-ground swimming pool is 20 m by 6 m. The pool is 4 m deep at one end and 1 m deep at the other. How many cubic meters of water can the pool hold?

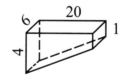

Not drawn to scale.
All measures in meters.

Solutions start on page 262.

SET 14

OLYMPIAD 1

1A
3 MINUTES
60%

25 digits are shown. Find the sum of the digits.

$$
\begin{array}{cccc}
2 & 2 & 2 & 2 \\
2 & 2 & 6 & 2 \\
2 & 6 & 6 & 2 \\
6 & 6 & 6 & 2 \\
4 & 4 & 4 & \\
4 & 4 & 4 & 4
\end{array}
$$

1B
4 MINUTES
51%

How many quarters (worth 25 cents each) must be added to 12 nickels (worth 5 cents each), so that the average value of a coin in the new enlarged collection is 10 cents?

1C
5 MINUTES
8%

How many different sums can be obtained by adding two <u>different</u> integers chosen from the set below?

$$\{-12, -11, -10, \ldots, +6, +7, +8\}$$

1D
5 MINUTES
9%

561 is the product of 3 different prime numbers. How many factors of 561 are not prime?

1E
7 MINUTES
15%

In rectangle $ABCD$, P is the midpoint of side $\overline{BC}$ and Q is the midpoint of $\overline{CD}$. The area of $\triangle APQ$ is what fractional part of the area of rectangle $ABCD$?

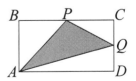

Solutions start on page 264.

SET 14

OLYMPIAD 2

2A
3 MINUTES
50%

Write as a single decimal:

$$1 - \frac{2}{10} + \frac{3}{100} - \frac{4}{1000}$$

2B
4 MINUTES
74%

Amy picks a whole number, squares it and then subtracts 1. She gives her final number to Brian. Brian adds 3 to the number Amy gave him and then doubles that result. Brian's final result is 54. With what number did Amy start?

2C
6 MINUTES
45%

Alex, Bruno, and Charles each add the lengths of two sides of the same triangle correctly. They get 27 cm, 35 cm, and 32 cm, respectively. Find the perimeter of the triangle, in cm.

2D
6 MINUTES
37%.

The first three terms in a sequence are: 1, 2, 3. Each term after that is the opposite of the sum of the three <u>previous</u> terms. For example, the 4th term is ⁻6 (the opposite of $1 + 2 + 3$), and the 5th term is 1. What is the 99th term?

2E
7 MINUTES
40%

Find the whole number value of

$$\sqrt{1 + 3 + 5 + \ldots + 45 + 47 + 49}$$

Solutions start on page 266.

SET 14
OLYMPIAD 3

3A
4 MINUTES
60%

When Isaac opens a book, the product of the page numbers on the open pages is 420. Find the sum of the two page numbers.

3B
5 MINUTES
45%

A squirrel buries a total of 80 acorns in N holes. Find the greatest possible value of N, provided:
(1) No hole is empty, and
(2) No two holes contain the same number of acorns.

3C
5 MINUTES
27%

The sum of a proper fraction in lowest terms and its reciprocal equals $2\frac{4}{15}$. Find the original proper fraction.

3D
7 MINUTES
21%

The picture shows a "spiral" that begins at the origin **(0,0)** and passes through every lattice point in the plane. Each small arrow is 1 unit in length. Following the "spiral", what is the length of the path from the origin to the point (5,3)?

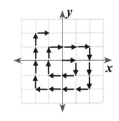

3E
7 MINUTES
15%

How many degrees are in the angle formed by the hands of a clock at 8:24?

Solutions start on page 268

SET 14

OLYMPIAD 4

4A
4 MINUTES
43%

Some students are in a line. Abby is in the center of the line. Sara is 3 places in front of her, Eli is 4 places behind Sara, and Kayla is 2 places in front of Eli. Kayla is the third person in line. How many students are in the line?

4B
4 MINUTES
35%

Given the data: 3, 6, 6, 8, 10, 12. Express in lowest terms:

$$\frac{3 \times \text{median} - \text{mode}}{6 \times \text{mean}}$$

4C
4 MINUTES
50%

Find the integer that exceeds $^-5$ by the same amount that $^+13$ exceeds $^-1$.

4D
6 MINUTES
13%

A circle with radius 5 centimeters intersects a circle with radius 3 cm as shown. The area of the shaded region is $\frac{7\pi}{2}$ square centimeters. Find the total combined area <u>inside</u> the circles, but <u>outside</u> the shaded region. Leave your answer in terms of π.

4E
7 MINUTES
6%

How many different triangles can be formed whose 3 vertices are chosen from the rectangular array of 8 points shown?

$\bullet \quad \bullet \quad \bullet \quad \bullet$

$\bullet \quad \bullet \quad \bullet \quad \bullet$

Solutions start on page 270.

SET 14

OLYMPIAD 5

5A
4 MINUTES
60%

How many 2-digit numbers are there in which the ones digit is greater than the tens digit?

5B
5 MINUTES
45%

A bank has two plans for checking accounts. In plan A, the charge is $7.50 a month with no fee for each check. In plan B, the charge is $3 a month plus an additional 20 cents for each check written. What is the <u>least</u> number of checks a customer must write each month so that plan A costs less than plan B?

5C
5 MINUTES
27%

Suppose the base of a triangle is increased by 20%, and its height is increased by 30%. By what percent is the area of the triangle increased?

5D
6 MINUTES
21%

Starting with 1, Sara lists the counting numbers in order but omits all those that use the digit 9. What is the 300th number on her list?

5E
7 MINUTES
15%

Line segments form a path that starts at (0,0), is drawn to (1,0), and then to (1,2). Each new segment forms a right angle with the previous segment and is 1 unit longer than that segment. The path ends at (0,0). How many segments are in the shortest possible path?
(*Hint: Consider horizontal and vertical segments separately.*)

Solutions start on page 272.

1A

3 MINUTES

76%

Find the whole number N if:
$$2 \times 6 \times 10 \times 14 = 1 \times 3 \times 5 \times 7 \times N$$

1B

4 MINUTES

66%

In a hotel, 40 people occupy exactly 26 rooms. Each room is occupied by either one or two people. How many rooms are occupied by exactly one person?

1C

5 MINUTES

40%

Rectangle $ABCD$ is divided into five congruent smaller rectangles, as shown. The lengths BC and CD differ by 6 millimeters. What is the area of $ABCD$?

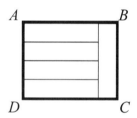

1D

6 MINUTES

25%

Three roommates share the cost of a $300 television. The first pays one-half the total amount paid by the second and third roommates. The second roommate pays one-third the total amount paid by the first and third roommates. How much does the third roommate pay toward the television?

1E

6 MINUTES

12%

Six girls of differing heights are arranged in 2 rows of 3 each. Each girl is taller than the girl in front of her and also taller than the girl to her right. How many arrangements of the six girls are possible?

Solutions start on page 274.

SET 15

OLYMPIAD 2

2A
3 MINUTES
51%

$PQ \times QP = 2701$, where P and Q represent 2 different digits. Find both 2-digit numbers, PQ and QP.

2B
4 MINUTES
37%

Suppose $\frac{A}{6} + \frac{B}{12} = \frac{3}{4}$, in which A and B are positive integers and each fraction is in lowest terms. Find the sum A + B.

2C
5 MINUTES
41%

The consecutive odd numbers are arranged in rows as shown. Each row has one more number than the previous row. Find the sum of all ten numbers in the tenth row.

```
1
3   5
7   9   11
13  15  17  19
```
and so on ...

2D
5 MINUTES
8%

480 congruent cubes are placed in the corner of a room and arranged into a rectangular solid that is 6 cubes by 8 cubes by 10 cubes. How many of those cubes have at least one face visible to an observer in the room?

2E
7 MINUTES
7%

How many fractions from the list below have decimal representations that terminate?

$$\frac{1}{2}, \frac{1}{3}, \frac{1}{4}, \cdots, \frac{1}{48}, \frac{1}{49}, \frac{1}{50}$$

Solutions start on page 276.

3A

3 MINUTES

67%

Let p, q, and r represent the missing digits in the subtraction shown. Find the sum p + q + r.

$$\begin{array}{r} 8\ 4\ p \\ -\ q\ 6\ 8 \\ \hline 4\ r\ 3 \end{array}$$

3B

5 MINUTES

39%

For how many positive integer values of x is the expression $\sqrt{50-x}$ also a positive integer?

3C

6 MINUTES

25%

Both P and $(98 - P)$ are prime numbers. What is the least possible value of P?

3D

5 MINUTES

29%

Line segment $\overline{AB}$ has endpoints $A(-5,4)$ and $B(7,13)$. Point C lies on $\overline{AB}$ and is two-thirds of the way from point A to point B. Find the coordinates (x,y) of point C.

3E

6 MINUTES

21%

The symbol 3! means $3 \times 2 \times 1$, which equals 6. Similarly, 4! means $4 \times 3 \times 2 \times 1$, which equals 24. Find the greatest prime factor of the sum $5! + 7!$

Solutions start on page 278.

SET 15
OLYMPIAD 4

4A
3 MINUTES
81%

In the 4 × 4 grid shown, the numbers 1, 2, 3, and 4 can appear exactly once in each row, each column, and each separate 2 × 2 grid. Five entries are given. What number should replace X?

	4	1	
			2
3			X
		3	

4B
4 MINUTES
44%

Express in lowest terms:
$$\frac{5 - 10 + 15 - 20 + \cdots - 490 + 495 - 500}{7 - 14 + 21 - 28 + \cdots - 686 + 693 - 700}$$

4C
5 MINUTES
53%

The sum of three whole numbers, A, B, and C, is 32. C is 10 more than A. B differs from one of the other numbers by 3 and the other by 7. Find B.

4D
6 MINUTES
16%

In the tin can shown, the height is 8 cm and the circumference is 12 cm. Points A and B lie "opposite" each other on the two rims. Find the shortest distance along the surface of the can from A to B.

4E
7 MINUTES
20%

Two different primes are randomly selected from the first nine prime numbers. What is the probability that their sum is 30?
(Answer must be expressed in fraction form.)

Solutions start on page 280.

SET 15

OLYMPIAD 5

5A
3 MINUTES
39%

What is the greatest 4-digit number ABCD such that
A = B × C and B = C × D?
(The digits A, B, C, and D are not necessarily different.)

5B
4 MINUTES
68%

Find the mean of x and y, if $23 - x = y - 71$.

5C
5 MINUTES
50%

If $2^{15} + 3^{10}$ is evaluated, what is the ones digit in the final result?

5D
6 MINUTES
44%

A sailboat changes course at a rate of 3° [3 degrees] per second. What is the least number of seconds the sailboat needs to change from a heading (direction) of 41° East of North (shown) to a new heading of 59° West of South?

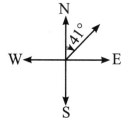

5E
7 MINUTES
30%

Three circles with areas 4π, 9π, and 16π intersect as shown. The largest circle is partitioned into shaded region A and unshaded regions B and C. If the total area of the shaded regions is 17π, find the area of region A in terms of π.

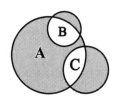

Not drawn to scale.

Solutions start on page 282.

1A
3 MINUTES
76%

2013 is multiplied by 10,001. Find the sum of the digits in the product.

1B
3 MINUTES
47%

Six consecutive whole numbers are each divided by 6. Find the sum of the resulting six remainders.

1C
5 MINUTES
24%

On a number line, two different integers are each twice as far from +7 as from −2. Find both of these integers.

1D
6 MINUTES
16%

The arithmetic mean (average) of five positive integers is 30. What is the greatest possible value of their median?

1E
7 MINUTES
9%

A $10 \times 10 \times 10$ cube is painted red on all faces and then cut into ten $10 \times 10 \times 1$ slices. Each slice is then cut into twenty-five $2 \times 2 \times 1$ blocks. How many of the 250 blocks have exactly one face painted red?

Solutions start on page 283.

2A

4 MINUTES

43%

October 25, 2018 will be a Thursday. What day of the week will August 1, 2018 be?

[*August has 31 days, while September has 30 days.*]

2B

5 MINUTES

53%

In rectangle *ABCD*, *E* and *F* are the midpoints of sides $\overline{AB}$ and $\overline{DC}$ as shown. $\overline{AF}$, $\overline{FB}$, $\overline{DE}$, and $\overline{EC}$ are line segments. If *AB* = 16 centimeters and *BC* = 8 centimeters, find the area of the shaded region.

2C

5 MINUTES

47%

Find the whole number *P* such that each of the following conditions is satisfied:

- *P* is a two-digit prime,
- *P* + 3 is a perfect square,
- *P* + 6 is the next greater two-digit prime.

2D

6 MINUTES

25%

A train is $\frac{1}{4}$ mile long and travels at a constant speed of 8 miles per hour. A boy on a bicycle, traveling at a constant speed of 11 miles per hour, rides on a road next to the track. From the moment he passes the rear of the train, it takes him *M* minutes to reach the front. Find *M*.

2E

7 MINUTES

15%

Find the least value of the fraction $\frac{a}{b}$, such that $\frac{a}{b}$ is an improper fraction in lowest terms; and if $\frac{a}{b}$ is divided by either $\frac{6}{25}$ or $\frac{8}{15}$, the quotient is a whole number.

Solutions start on page 285.

SET 16

OLYMPIAD 3

3A
3 MINUTES
53%

The integers from 1 through 10 inclusive are placed in the 10 circles shown, one integer in each circle. Each number in the lower 3 rows is the positive difference between the numbers in the 2 circles immediately above it. Find the values of X and Y.

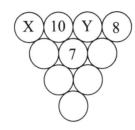

3B
4 MINUTES
75%

A, B, and C represent weights in the three balance scales shown. Find C.

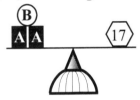 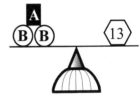 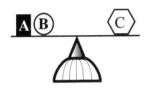

3C
5 MINUTES
13%

Two boys and six girls are seated randomly in 8 chairs around a circular table. Express as a fraction, in lowest terms, the probability that the two boys are seated next to each other.

3D
6 MINUTES
32%

One year, a farmer planted 1 tree. Each year thereafter, he planted a group of trees in the pattern "⌐⌐" as shown. The diagram shows the result at the end of Years 1, 2, and 3. By the end of Year 9, how many trees had he planted in all?

3	3	3	3	3
3	2	2	2	3
3	2	1	2	3

(Each number in the diagram indicates the year that tree was planted.)

3E
7 MINUTES
7%

The coordinates of the vertices of a rectangle are $A(-5, 4)$, $B(3,4)$, $C(3,-2)$, and $D(-5,-2)$. The length of $\overline{AC}$ is 10. Point E is on $\overline{AC}$ such that $\overline{BE}$ is perpendicular to $\overline{AC}$. What is the length of $\overline{BE}$?

Solutions start on page 287.

4A
3 MINUTES
29%

On graph paper, Maya draws a path from point $A(-1,0)$ to point $B(3,5)$, and then to point $C(7,-3)$. The path follows the lines of the paper, always moving right, left, up or down. How long is the shortest path Maya can draw?

4B
4 MINUTES
51%

Five rays share a common vertex, as shown. The measure of angle ABC is less than 90°. In all, how many acute angles are in the diagram?

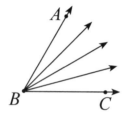

4C
5 MINUTES
17%

A sports arena has a total capacity of 20,000 fans and ushers. One usher is required for every 30 fans. What is the greatest number of fans that can be in attendance?

4D
5 MINUTES
47%

Lines l and m are parallel. Point A is on line l and point C is on line m. Point B is in the interior of the two parallel lines. The angle measures are shown at the right. Find the number of degrees in the acute angle ABC.

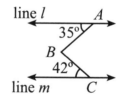

4E
7 MINUTES
6%

How many fractions, in lowest terms, between $\frac{1}{4}$ and $\frac{3}{8}$ *inclusive*, are exactly equivalent to a decimal that is written using three decimal places?

Solutions start on page 289.

SET 16

OLYMPIAD 5

5A
4 MINUTES
61%

The faulty odometer of a used car registers 4.6 miles for every 5 miles actually driven. When travelling from Acton to Bywater, the faulty odometer registers 92 miles. How far apart are Acton and Bywater?

5B
4 MINUTES
47%

The first four terms of the sequence 2, –3, –2, 3, 2, –3, –2, 3, … repeat endlessly. Find the sum of the first 2013 terms.

5C
5 MINUTES
42%

Suppose $5x - 2y = 30$. Find the integer value of $y - \frac{5}{2}x$.

5D
6 MINUTES
26%

This year, 1 out of every 55 adults started a new business. This rate represented an increase of 20% over last year's rate of 1 new business start-up out of every N adults. Find N.

5E
7 MINUTES
18%

The floor plan of an enclosed area consists entirely of straight walls meeting at right angles. The room partly shown has "inside" corners at A, C, D, and F and "outside" corners at B and E. The complete room has 23 inside corners and P outside corners. Find P.

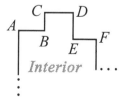

Solutions start on page 291.

HINTS

DIVISION E
DIVISION M

1A. Multiply and then subtract.

1B. Examine A in the hundreds place. What addition produces the 2-digit sum CD?

1C. Split the rectangle into four smaller rectangles.

1D. Build an organized table of the pairs of factors of 60.

1E. How many pieces can you take before you are forced to take a 15th piece of any one color?

2A. What could the tens digit be?

2B. How many 8-second periods are there in 2 minutes?

2C. What is the sum of the three numbers in each row, column, and diagonal?

2D. Think about each small square. What is its area? the length of each side?

2E. Count the number of 7s in an organized way.

3A. How many weeks are there in 45 days?

3B. What is the sum of the five numbers?

3C. For every additional black square, how many more white squares are there?

3D. How is the area of the border related to the areas of the picture and the total area?

3E. Construct a chart of all possible outcomes. This is called a *sample space*.

4A. What other numbers are said by the student who says, "1"?

4B. What is the least common denominator?

4C. Can the sums be equal if Mr. Sullivan lives in house number 2? 3? 4? 5?

4D. How many faces of each cube are painted?

4E. What is the least common multiple of 2, 3, 4, and 5? the next least common multiple?

5A. Make a 4 by 4 table that compares each shirt color to each name.

5B. To minimize the fraction, how large should the numerator be? the denominator?

5C. What was the area of the paper before the rectangles were cut out?

5D. What is the fewest number of small slices possible?

5E. In how many ways can you find three different counting numbers whose sum is 8?

HINTS ⬡ SET 2

1A. Follow the directions carefully.
1B. What is the sum of the two smaller numbers?
1C. Determine the order of the cups by using one statement at a time.
1D. Express each distance in the same unit of measure.
1E. What is the value of the extra stamps if you pair each 30¢ stamp with a 40¢ stamp?

2A. What is the 6th point touched by the ant? the 11th? the 16th?
2B. Using one condition at a time, sketch and change a diagram to put the people in order.
2C. Make a chart that shows both their ages year by year.
2D. What is the length and width of each small rectangle?
2E. Build two tables, one for before the transaction and the other for after.

3A. How does dividing the greater number by 4 change the product and the question?
3B. Last year her age was a multiple of both 4 and 9.
3C. Which tiles are counted twice when computing the perimeter?
3D. How many cars are in each category?
3E. Is the product of two odd numbers odd or even? the sum?

4A. How many Fridays are in the next 7 days? 14? 21?
4B. What values for H are possible?
4C. How many rooms are there?
4D. In how many points can the circle intersect the triangle?
4E. How many pages require 1 digit? 2?

5A. What is the average of the two pages?
5B. What is the sum of the heights of the four adults?
5C. Make an organized list of all three-digit numbers whose digits add up to 19.
5D. Find the common difference between any two consecutive terms.
5E. What entry is below "1"?

HINTS ⊕ SET 3

1A. Pair the numbers for easier addition.
1B. How many people remain if the "extra" 12 women leave?
1C. What is the number of rectangles that contain one box? two? three?
1D. What are the six numbers whose sum is 21?
1E. In an organized table assign different current ages to Rebekah.

2A. How many 22s are there on the left side of the equation?
2B. If Abby sits in a specific unnumbered chair, where could each of the others sit?
2C. Suppose the repeated factor is 2. What primes could the third factor be?
2D. Can you split the given figure into smaller rectangles?
2E. How many digits are there in the first nine numbers? the next ten? the ten after that?

3A. Which of the choices can be in the thousands place?
3B. How could you pair each nickel with a quarter?
3C. What could be the length of $\overline{HO}$?
3D. If you can diagram A as <u>46</u>, <u>39</u>, <u>32</u>, __, __, __, ..., how can you diagram B?
3E. List all possibilities. Circle those in which Cate's letter is different.

4A. What were the dates for each Monday?
4B. Suppose Ava got 10 votes. How many votes did each of the others get?
4C. Work backwards.
4D. How far did Jan ride?
4E. Since SAY has 3 digits, what are the possible values for B?

5A. To maximize the contents of one cup, minimize the contents of each of the others.
5B. What is the last entry in each row? What set of numbers is this?
5C. What are the first few common multiples of 3, 5, and 7?
5D. Split the hexagon into congruent triangles and rearrange the shaded regions.
5E. What entry immediately precedes 37?

HINTS ⊕ SET 4

1A. Simplify the arithmetic by pairing like numbers.
1B. Can 4 be a ones digit?
1C. What is the length of the shortest line segment?
1D. Consider each digit separately.
1E. How many multiples of 9 are less than 600? 400?

2A. What color is Aaron wearing?
2B. List the first few common multiples of 5 and 6.
2C. What pairs of numbers have an average of 28? 44?
2D. Find the lengths of all the segments, starting with $\overline{AB}$ and $\overline{EH}$.
2E. What is the area of one face of each cube?

3A. Divide by 11.
3B. What is the maximum number of quarters? the minimum?
3C. Make a table, listing all the possibilities.
3D. How long does it take 4 people to paint all 8 fences?
3E. To get the units digit of a power of 7, multiply only the units digit of the previous powers of 7.

4A. Arrange the single-digit primes from greatest to least.
4B. Make an organized list, starting with the greatest number possible.
4C. How many cubes are in the tallest stack?
4D. Start with Clue 3.
4E. Of all rectangles with a given area, the square has the least perimeter.

5A. Represent Sara's age by a rectangle and then split it into thirds.
5B. Each number on the list is 2 more than a multiple of 3.
5C. Eliminate all but one value for the letter O.
5D. List all possible pairings, avoiding any duplications.
5E. Evaluate each expression separately.

HINTS ⊕ SET 5

1A. What is the total number of 8s?
1B. How many jelly beans can she take before she is forced to take a second blue one?
1C. Use tests of divisibility on each number in the sequence.
1D. How many seconds in each minute contain at least one 2?
1E. Along which edge should the ant travel the least number of times?

2A. What digits do T, A, and C represent, in that order?
2B. List the first several prime numbers and then circle the twinners.
2C. What is the least possible sum? the greatest?
2D. What are the lengths of $\overline{AD}$ and $\overline{DE}$?
2E. After each round the winner has *tripled* what she had before the round.

3A. Consider one condition at a time.
3B. What is the cost of 3 hats and 3 shirts?
3C. How many hours does 1 painter need to paint 1 classroom?
3D. Start by placing the largest tile first.
3E. In ascending order, divide out the prime factors until all five primes are found.

4A. How much money does Shauna have? Emma? Ben? Allie?
4B. Make an organized list, using additional letters to name each path.
4C. How many miles is Sarah ahead of Tyler each hour?
4D. If Michael has 2 more cards, how many would be left over when he puts them in piles?
4E. How long is each edge of the box?

5A. How can you pair the numbers so that each pair has the same sum?
5B. If half the vehicles were cars, what would be the total of all the tolls?
5C. Make "before" and "after" tables that test the possible numbers of candies.
5D. Sketch it. How many cubes touch the front of the box with only one face?
5E. What odd numbers are closest to the given average?

HINTS ⬡ SET 6

1A. What time will it be in 24 hours? 48? 72?
1B. What are the two possibilities for the ones digit?
1C. What is the total number of toy soldiers before Lee joins? After?
1D. How many more consonants, vowels and dollars exist for GABRIEL than for CAROL?
1E. In an organized way, count the number of 1×1, 2×2, 3×3, and 4×4 squares.

2A. Combine all the numbers on the left.
2B. Divide 150 by 9 to get close.
2C. If no two cars had the same number of people, what is the fewest number of people?
2D. What was the team's won-lost record for its first 24 games?
2E. Form lists that follow the rule, starting with 10, 11, 12, …

3A. Work backwards.
3B. Which appropriate multiples of 15 are also divisible by 6?
3C. For how many hours did the power outage last?
3D. Find the length of each outer segment beginning with the smallest square.
3E. How long does the bug take to walk from *A* to *D*?

4A. What do three drinks cost?
4B. Assign any convenient amount to Michael.
4C. Count up from 2, omitting all multiples of numbers already on the list.
4D. The total number of marbles must be divisible by each denominator.
4E. Use a tree diagram, making duplicate letters look different.

5A. Simplify the arithmetic by grouping the numbers.
5B. What possibilities exist for each digit?
5C. How long is one side of a small square?
5D. The 3-digit numbers will look like *ABB*, *BAB*, or *BBA*. Consider each case separately.
5E. The number of normal clovers must be a multiple of what whole number?

HINTS ⊕ SET 7

1A. Evaluate each set of parentheses separately.
1B. If all the heads belonged to owners, how many legs would there be?
1C. How many games could Keri have won? How many second places?
1D. How many four-sided figures consist of 1 triangle? 2? 3?
1E. Since the S on the left must equal 1 or 2, what values could D be?

2A. The thousands digit must be 2.
2B. How many letters are in the repeating pattern?
2C. If you place 0 and J (for Jen's age) on a number line, where would you place 2J and 3J?
2D. The sum of what two square numbers is 100?
2E. Work backwards.

3A. What are the two lists you could make?
3B. What is the sum of each row? column?
3C. What is the hundreds digit in the sum?
3D. Assign some convenient costs to 1 green marble and find the costs of the other marbles.
3E. Compare the lengths of $\overline{AB}$ and $\overline{BC}$.

4A. How many times does each of the digits appear?
4B. What is added to the first page to get to the fourth page?
4C. Place all four prime numbers into each corner box.
4D. EEE represents 111 or 222 or 333, and so on. What numbers divide each of them?
4E. Sketch the figure and mark every cube that has just one painted face.

5A. Simply divide.
5B. How many pounds of carrots do 25 trays require?
5C. When one person gains 4 grapes, how many does the other person lose?
5D. When you draw the diagram, separate the four smaller rectangles.
5E. To maximize a fraction, maximize the numerator and minimize the denominator.

HINTS ⊕ SET 8

1A. Pair the numbers for easier addition.
1B. Work your way down from the greatest choice.
1C. Draw the picture and count.
1D. What number is common to each set whose sum is 13?
1E. Draw new lines, one at a time.

2A. What is the product within each set of parentheses?
2B. What are the greatest and least three-digit numbers?
2C. How many boxes can 4 volunteers pack in one hour?
2D. How many multiples of 21 are less than 100? 1000?
2E. What is the area of each overlapping rectangle?

3A. What number does ⌂ represent?
3B. Is 14 one of the numbers? 41?
3C. How many different sized rectangles are there? How many of each size are there?
3D. How many students liked video games but not movies? movies but not video games?
3E. Where *can't* you place the 8 or the 9?

4A. What number is N?
4B. How many 7s are added to the starting number?
4C. Try some small prime numbers.
4D. Compare the area of a game piece to the area of the checkerboard by division.
4E. Draw a diagram to show each action taken.

5A. Work from right to left.
5B. After placing 2 and 4, there are two possibilities for 6. Examine the results of each.
5C. Add all 100 numbers.
5D. Make two tables of possibilities, one from Judy's perspective and one from Mark's.
5E. Make three sketches, one for the red, one for the orange and one for the yellow.

1A. Examine a few different sets that each contain 17.

1B. Traveling 45 miles per hour is equivalent to traveling how far each minute?

1C. The three statements partition the whole numbers into four sets. Test one number in each set against all three statements.

1D. If the fraction is converted to decimal form, what pattern of the digits emerges?

1E. What happens if you rotate $\triangle EGC$ a half-turn about point E?

2A. In the tens column, what are the possible values of A?

2B. Make an organized list, starting with $1 + 1 + 19$.

2C. On what days did at least one person *not* make the statement?

2D. What values of N between 20 and 80 are not multiples of 2, 3, or 5?

2E. Change each expression in parentheses into a proper fraction.

3A. What is the total cost of the ride *after* the first $\frac{1}{5}$ mile?

3B. What is the sum of all the whole numbers up to and including 12?

3C. List the multiples of 4 and of 5 in the interval $\{40, 41, 42, \ldots, 66\}$.

3D. What percent of the traffic exits at B?

3E. What is the length of $\overline{DO}$?

4A. Assume the least number for the fourth cage and then work backwards.

4B. What is the value of **12**? **10**?

4C. Find the sum of P, Q, R, S, and T.

4D. What is the area of the quarter-circle?

4E. How many students could have liked both strawberry and chocolate?

5A. How many sections of fence are there?

5B. Because 15,600 ends in two zeros, what could be the units digit of one of the three numbers?

5C. By what percent does the percent of females exceed the percent of males?

5D. Draw two lines to divide the square into four small squares.

5E. Which two-digit numbers satisfy the second sentence?

HINTS ⊕ SET 10

1A. How much is 40 – 36? 32 – 28? 24 – 20?
1B. Is every factor of 14 a value of N?
1C. If every dime is paired with a quarter and the other coins discarded, what would the total value be?
1D. Opposite sides of a rectangle are congruent to each other.
1E. How are the two denominators related to 56?

2A. What is the fewest CDs that Jo could have?
2B. Which car is opposite car 1? car "0"?
2C. How much time does one mathlete working alone need to solve all 20 problems?
2D. Does it matter which line has two of the three points?
2E. Try the same problem using 3, 5, and 9. Then try 4, 7, and 19. How do your answers relate to the given numbers?

3A. Should you start the month with a day of work or a day off?
3B. Which digits should occupy the tens places?
3C. What is the sum of the five numbers?
3D. Suppose each candy bar cost $1 originally.
3E. How much does the line rise for each centimeter that it moves to the right?

4A. Evaluate each expression in parentheses separately.
4B. How many hours is London ahead of New York?
4C. The total cost is the product of the average cost and the distance.
4D. Suppose Vicki has 100 jelly beans.
4E. Draw three convenient vertical lines and then rearrange the rectangles.

5A. How many widgets does the factory produce each hour?
5B. Factor each of 4, 9, 16, and 36 into primes. What is true of the number of factors?
5C. How many jelly beans has Lou eaten by the end of day 2? 3? 4?
5D. Draw the diagonals of the square and examine the legs of one right triangle.
5E. Work backwards, starting from the end of the given sentence.

HINTS ⬡ SET 11

1A. How can you minimize the arithmetic by rearranging the numbers?
1B. A tree diagram may help.
1C. What dimensions might Rachel's rectangle have?
1D. How long would she travel each way if the round trip were assumed to be 360 km?
1E. Find the units digits of B, A, and C in that order.

2A. What is the sum of the numbers on *all* the faces?
2B. Use two related line segments to represent Ava's and Dan's amounts.
2C. What is the divisibility rule for 11?
2D. Assign a convenient length to $\overline{AM}$. How would you adjust the area of $ABCD$ that you found?
2E. The maximum digit could occupy which places?

3A. How does it simplify the problem if you remove Emily's 2 "extra" CDs?
3B. How many steps does Austin make after returning to the starting point?
3C. What must be true for the sum of 3 prime numbers to be even?
3D. The heights of the triangle and the rectangle are equal.
3E. What is the sum of the first 2 terms? 3 terms? 4?

4A. Rewrite the subtraction problem as an addition problem.
4B. Place a square 1003×1003 conveniently into another square 1005×1005.
4C. Represent the trip by a number line segment divided into fifteenths.
4D. Marcia's score was how many points above the class average?
4E. Rotate the inner square 45 °.

5A. What is Sara's number?
5B. Search in an organized way for three squares numbers whose sum is 65.
5C. What is the probability that Team B wins both games? Team A?
5D. Use a diagram to show their elapsed times, not their paths.
5E. Pick any number from the list and see what other numbers belong next to it.

HINTS (MATH OLYMPIADS) SET 12

1A. Consider one condition at a time.
1B. Make an organized list of Sequence A.
1C. What multiples of 8, starting with 1008, are also divisible by 6?
1D. Do the indicated computations with each number, checking against careless errors.
1E. How many triangles consist of one region? Two? Three?

2A. Work entirely with either decimals or fractions.
2B. What is the total number of points scored?
2C. What is the value of $(100 - 98)$? $(99 - 97)$? $(96 - 94)$? $(95 - 93)$?
2D. In an organized way, trace every path. Separate those that include X from the others.
2E. How long is the wire?

3A. Every common factor of two integers is a factor of their greatest common factor.
3B. How does the fact that $2 \times 5 = 10$ simplify the problem?
3C. Work backwards.
3D. The reciprocal of N is $\frac{1}{N}$.
3E. To minimize the surface area, glue each cube to both of the others.

4A. What is the sum of any negative number and its opposite?
4B. Draw and examine each of the possible diagrams.
4C. The vertical axis shows how far from home she is, not how far she traveled.
4D. How many 8s are in the ones place? the tens place?
4E. In a cubic number, each prime factor appears in trios.

5A. What is the cost of 5 pens and 5 erasers?
5B. Make an organized list of pairs of primes, starting with 3×5.
5C. Consider separately the horizontal and vertical distances from A to B.
5D. Make a table of square numbers. Then adjust the two equal factors of each number as indicated by the problem.
5E. What is the sum of the numbers in each row, column, and diagonal?

HINTS SET 13

1A. Rearrange the numbers.
1B. What is the next square number after 121?
1C. Test several pairs of even numbers. What seems to be true of each product?
1D. Sketch line segment *ABCD*.
1E. Make an organized list of all 15 novels, showing all the pairings.

2A. How many degrees does angle *COD* contain?
2B. Did you notice that 2.01 is a factor of each of the three terms?
2C. With two students absent and the others getting 4 sheets each, how many sheets would be left over?
2D. How would the result of doubling each term of the 1st series compare to the 2nd series?
2E. On average, what is Jess' total earnings for every 5 days she works?

3A. Write in fraction form and simplify first.
3B. Which of the given counting numbers are multiples of 7?
3C. What is the probability that Jack wins both the first and second games?
3D. How will moving the semicircle simplify the problem?
3E. Write $\frac{45}{7}$ as a mixed number to find a.

4A. Can you divide both sides of the equation by any factors common to both sides?
4B. The problem does not say which multiple is greater.
4C. What is the radius of each circle?
4D. Divide by 13: 3011, 3111, 3211, …, 3911.
4E. Use the axes, a horizontal line and a vertical line to box in the given square.

5A. Evaluate 2 ✲ 6 and N ✲ 4, and then set them equal.
5B. Is there any limit to the number of cancellations within a single problem?
5C. Eliminate each negative number by pairing it with its opposite.
5D. The Pumas won 2 of 9, then 5 of 13, then 8 of 16, and so on.
5E. What two common shapes do you get if you split the pool horizontally?

HINTS ⊕ SET 14

1A. How many 2s are there? 4s? 6s?
1B. How many nickels must be grouped with each quarter so as to average 10¢ per coin?
1C. What is the least sum possible? the greatest?
1D. Divide 561 by each prime. What other factors are there?
1E. Suppose *ABCD* is 6 units by 4 units.

2A. Convert each fraction to decimal form.
2B. Work backwards.
2C. Assume a convenient length for one side and then adjust as you find the other sides.
2D. What pattern appears when you find the first several terms?
2E. What is the square root of 1? 1 + 3? 1 + 3 + 5?

3A. What units digit is likely for one of the factors of 420?
3B. "Fill" the holes one at a time.
3C. What denominators are possible if the denominator of their sum is 15?
3D. In each rotation, how many units are needed to reach the top right corner?
3E. Through how many degrees does each hand move between 8:00 and 8:24?

4A. Sketch the line and place each student on it.
4B. What is the mean? mode? median?
4C. By what amount is ⁺13 greater than ⁻1?
4D. Find the area of the unshaded region of each circle separately.
4E. The base of the triangle could be either in the upper or lower set of points.

5A. In an organized way, list the tens digit for each ones digit.
5B. Make a table comparing costs for different numbers of checks.
5C. In ratio problems, assigning a convenient number usually does not affect the answer.
5D. How many of the first 300 counting numbers must be replaced?
5E. Draw several paths to become familiar with the patterns.

HINTS ⊛ SET 15

1A. Simplify each side of the equation.
1B. If every room has just 1 student, how many other students must become roommates?
1C. Which segments are 6 mm long?
1D. How much does the first roommate pay?
1E. Sketch the girls' positions. Start by placing the shortest and tallest girls.

2A. What values of P and Q allow the units digit of the product to be 1?
2B. What values of A allow $\frac{A}{6}$ to be in lowest terms?
2C. How does the sum of the entries in each row compare to the row number?
2D. Sketch the 3 visible faces of the solid. Mark the cubes that display 2 faces. 3 faces.
2E. Only denominators that are factors of a power of 10 produce terminating decimals.

3A. Rewrite the problem as an addition and work right to left.
3B. List the square whole numbers less than 50.
3C. Let $P = 2, 3, 5, \ldots$, then test the values of $98 - P$ to see which is prime.
3D. Sketch $\overline{ACB}$ and count the boxes horizontally from A to B.
3E. Factor 7! into $7 \times 6 \times (5!)$.

4A. What entries belong in the two boxes below the "1"?
4B. What is the result of factoring the numerator? denominator?
4C. What are the two possibilities for B?
4D. Cut the label of the can vertically and flatten it on a table.
4E. List all nine primes. Then add pairs of them in an organized way.

5A. What is the greatest value A can be? Given A, what is the greatest value B can be?
5B. Assign three different values for x and compute y. What is true of their average?
5C. What pattern emerges for the successive powers of 2?
5D. Copy the diagram, showing the number of degrees that the boat turns.
5E. What is the sum of the areas of regions B and C?

HINTS ⊗ SET 16

1A. Simply multiply.
1B. Can you find 6 convenient consecutive whole numbers to test?
1C. +7 and –2 separate the number line into how many parts?
1D. What is the total of the five positive integers?
1E. If you sketch the cube, how many of the required blocks can you see?

2A. What are the dates of the Thursdays from August 1, 2018 to October 25?
2B. Draw $\overline{EF}$.
2C. It is easier to start by listing the perfect squares than the primes.
2D. If the train were still, how fast would the boy ride to take the same M minutes?
2E. Write each division as a multiplication.

3A. What number should be in the circle between 10 and 8?
3B. What would be the result of combining the first two balanced scales?
3C. Does the problem change if you do not seat the girls at all?
3D. How many more trees were planted each year than in the preceding year?
3E. How many different ways can the area of $\triangle ABC$ be found?

4A. Sketch it.
4B. Label each ray and list the angles.
4C. Are the ushers included in the 20,000 people?
4D. If drawing a useful line doesn't simplify the problem, try a different line.
4E. How many three-digit decimals are there between the two given values?

5A. How many miles does the faulty odometer register when the car travels 10 miles?
5B. What is the sum of the first 4 terms? 8 terms? 12 terms? 24? 100?
5C. What is the corresponding value of x if $y = 0$? What then is the value of $y - \frac{5}{2}x$?
5D. If a set of 100 people is increased by 20%, how many people would there be?
5E. How many outies would there be if there were 4 innies? 5? 6? 7?

ANSWERS

DIVISION E
DIVISION M

ANSWERS: DIVISION E

SET #1

Olympiad 1	Olympiad 2	Olympiad 3	Olympiad 4	Olympiad 5
1A. 43	2A. 45, 54	3A. 7	4A. Diego	5A. Mr. Red
1B. 1065	2B. 90	3B. 11	4B. 5	5B. $\frac{3}{16}$
1C. 48	2C. 7	3C. 106	4C. 8	5C. 11
1D. 12	2D. 144	3D. 400	4D. 288	5D. 50
1E. 51	2E. 156	3E. $\frac{20}{36}$ or $\frac{5}{9}$	4E. 301	5E. 230 grams

SET #2

Olympiad 1	Olympiad 2	Olympiad 3	Olympiad 4	Olympiad 5
1A. 16	2A. C	3A. 15	4A. 8	5A. 124
1B. 9	2B. Jennie	3B. 73 years	4B. 19	5B. 195
1C. Red	2C. 2003	3C. 24	4C. $\frac{5}{25}$ or $\frac{1}{5}$	5C. 964
1D. 2100	2D. 184	3D. 16	4D. 20	5D. 4
1E. 37	2E. 25	3E. 2	4E. 122	5E. 4

SET #3

Olympiad 1	Olympiad 2	Olympiad 3	Olympiad 4	Olympiad 5
1A. 400	2A. 9	3A. 3961	4A. Thursday	5A. 9
1B. 56	2B. Dalia	3B. 7	4B. 6	5B. 133
1C. 24	2C. 4	3C. 32	4C. 50	5C. 317
1D. 9	2D. 119	3D. 11	4D. 75	5D. 90
1E. 12	2E. 5	3E. $\frac{12}{27}$ or $\frac{4}{9}$	4E. 570	5E. 7

SET #4

Olympiad 1	Olympiad 2	Olympiad 3	Olympiad 4	Olympiad 5
1A. 0	2A. Yellow	3A. 5	4A. 7:53	5A. 12
1B. 3	2B. 121	3B. 7	4B. 6	5B. 101
1C. 28	2C. 48	3C. 14	4C. 20	5C. 3
1D. 985	2D. 41	3D. 10	4D. 513 315	5D. 1
1E. 22	2E. 100	3E. 9	4E. 16	5E. 60

ANSWERS: DIVISION E

SET #5

Olympiad 1	Olympiad 2	Olympiad 3	Olympiad 4	Olympiad 5
1A. 80	2A. 182	3A. 9375	4A. $12	5A. 150
1B. 12	2B. 22	3B. $13	4B. 12	5B. 30
1C. 95	2C. 26	3C. 24	4C. 6	5C. 24
1D. 120	2D. 14	3D. 8	4D. 58	5D. 57
1E. 66	2E. 10	3E. 71	4E. 27	5E. 45

SET #6

Olympiad 1	Olympiad 2	Olympiad 3	Olympiad 4	Olympiad 5
1A. 9 PM	2A. 70	3A. 10	4A. $4	5A. 5
1B. 385	2B. 153	3B. 120	4B. 10	5B. 843
1C. 16	2C. 2	3C. 5:45 AM	4C. 41	5C. 18
1D. 45	2D. 12	3D. 40	4D. 120	5D. 243
1E. 39	2E. 29	3E. 2 cm/sec	4E. 9	5E. 240

SET #7

Olympiad 1	Olympiad 2	Olympiad 3	Olympiad 4	Olympiad 5
1A. 60	2A. 2100	3A. 8	4A. 120	5A. 5
1B. 12	2B. D	3B. 9	4B. 22	5B. 9
1C. 3	2C. 24	3C. 105	4C. 618	5C. 8
1D. 6	2D. 44 cm	3D. 5¢	4D. 74	5D. 100 cm
1E. 2532	2E. 56	3E. 54 sq cm	4E. 4	5E. 222

SET #8

Olympiad 1	Olympiad 2	Olympiad 3	Olympiad 4	Olympiad 5
1A. 44	2A. 800	3A. 8	4A. 84	5A. 10
1B. 29	2B. 531	3B. 13	4B. 170	5B. 22
1C. 24	2C. 8	3C. 11	4C. 19	5C. 30
1D. 6	2D. 43	3D. 11	4D. 12	5D. 13
1E. 11	2E. 220 sq cm	3E. 891	4E. 27	5E. 10

ANSWERS: DIVISION M

SET #9

Olympiad 1	Olympiad 2	Olympiad 3	Olympiad 4	Olympiad 5
1A. 0	2A. 7	3A. 4	4A. 15	5A. 54 m
1B. 7:16 pm	2B. 12	3B. 6	4B. 13	5B. 24
1C. 61	2C. Friday	3C. $\frac{11}{27}$	4C. 33	5C. 144
1D. 2	2D. 49, 77	3D. 51	4D. 4.6	5D. 22.9
1E. 54	2E. $\frac{1979}{2005}$	3E. 126	4E. 25	5E. 49

SET #10

Olympiad 1	Olympiad 2	Olympiad 3	Olympiad 4	Olympiad 5
1A. 20	2A. 66	3A. 7	4A. 5	5A. $2\frac{1}{2}$
1B. 2	2B. 32	3B. 5103	4B. 9 pm	5B. 5
1C. 12	2C. 24	3C. 63	4C. 13	5C. 900
1D. 80	2D. 30	3D. 35	4D. $\frac{1}{7}$	5D. 10
1E. $\frac{5}{8}$	2E. 8	3E. 9 cm	4E. 8	5E. 63

SET #11

Olympiad 1	Olympiad 2	Olympiad 3	Olympiad 4	Olympiad 5
1A. 50	2A. 37	3A. 9	4A. 15	5A. $\frac{11}{24}$
1B. 7	2B. 27	3B. 7	4B. 4016	5B. 24
1C. 44	2C. 8	3C. 5	4C. $\frac{4}{15}$	5C. 58%
1D. 90	2D. 112	3D. 32	4D. 28	5D. 7
1E. 2044	2E. 135	3E. 1004	4E. 50	5E. 25

SET #12

Olympiad 1	Olympiad 2	Olympiad 3	Olympiad 4	Olympiad 5
1A. D, A, C, B	2A. 2	3A. 6	4A. 4017	5A. 19
1B. 3	2B. 2.6	3B. 7	4B. 68	5B. 16
1C. 1080	2C. 100	3C. 20	4C. 5	5C. (6,12)
1D. 40	2D. 0.6	3D. 2009	4D. 73	5D. 64
1E. 35	2E. 125	3E. 72	4E. 150	5E. 12

SET #13

Olympiad 1	Olympiad 2	Olympiad 3	Olympiad 4	Olympiad 5
1A. 1,000,000	2A. 50	3A. 4	4A. 7	5A. 8
1B. 21	2B. 10	3B. 4	4B. 85	5B. $\frac{1}{45}$
1C. 15	2C. 108	3C. $\frac{12}{125}$	4C. 36	5C. 14
1D. 11	2D. 325	3D. 72	4D. 2	5D. 38
1E. 74	2E. $840	3E. $a=6, b=2, c=3$	4E. 25 sq units	5E. 300

SET #14

Olympiad 1	Olympiad 2	Olympiad 3	Olympiad 4	Olympiad 5
1A. 92	2A. .826	3A. 41	4A. 7	5A. 36
1B. 4	2B. 5	3B. 12	4B. $\frac{1}{3}$	5B. 23
1C. 39 sq mm	2C. 47	3C. $\frac{3}{5}$	4C. 9	5C. 56
1D. 5	2D. 3	3D. 82 units	4D. 27π sq cm	5D. 363
1E. $\frac{3}{8}$	2E. 25	3E. 108	4E. 48	5E. 7

SET #15

Olympiad 1	Olympiad 2	Olympiad 3	Olympiad 4	Olympiad 5
1A. 16	2A. 37, 73	3A. 11	4A. 4	5A. 9919
1B. 12	2B. 8	3B. 7	4B. $\frac{5}{7}$	5B. 47
1C. 720 sq mm	2C. 1000	3C. 19	4C. 12	5C. 7
1D. $125	2D. 165	3D. (3,10)	4D. 10 cm	5D. 54
1E. 5	2E. 11	3E. 43	4E. $\frac{3}{36}$	5E. 10π

SET #16

Olympiad 1	Olympiad 2	Olympiad 3	Olympiad 4	Olympiad 5
1A. 12	2A. Wednesday	3A. $X=9, Y=3$	4A. 21	5A. 100 miles
1B. 15	2B. 32 sq cm	3B. 10	4B. 10	5B. 2
1C. 1 & –11	2C. 61	3C. $\frac{2}{7}$	4C. 19,354	5C. –15
1D. 49	2D. 5	3D. 153	4D. 77	5D. 66
1E. 114	2E. $\frac{24}{5}$	3E. 4.8	4E. 126	5E. 19

SOLUTIONS, STRATEGIES, & FOLLOW-UPS

DIVISION E
SETS 1-8

Set 1 — Olympiad 1

1A *Strategy: First evaluate the left side of the equation.*
$5 \times 11 = 55$, so $55 = \square + 12$.
Then $\square = 55 - 12 = 43$.
To make the statement true, replace the square by 43.

> ***FOLLOW-UP****: Given $15 \times \square = \square + 84$. What one number can replace both squares to make the statement true?* [6]

1B *Strategy: Work left to right.*
The sum of a three-digit number and a two-digit number is less than 1100. The sum is 1000 or more only if the three-digit number is greater than 900. So C = 1, A = 9 and D = 0. The problem now is

$$\begin{array}{r} A\,A\,A \\ +\ \ B\,B \\ \hline C\,D\,6\,E \end{array} \qquad \Longrightarrow \qquad \begin{array}{r} 9\,9\,9 \\ +\ \ B\,B \\ \hline 1\,0\,6\,E \end{array}$$

The sum of 9 and B results in a "carry" into the tens column. Thus, in the tens' column, the sum of 10 and B ends in 6, so that B = 6. This makes the addition $999 + 66 = 1065$. **The four-digit number is 1065.**

1C *Strategy: Split the region into simpler figures.*
Draw line segments as shown to split the given rectangle into four smaller rectangles. Each small rectangle is cut in half by its diagonal. Half of each small rectangle is shaded. Therefore half of the whole original rectangle is shaded. The area of the original rectangle is $16 \times 6 = 96$ sq m, so **the area of the shaded part of the rectangle is 48 sq m.**

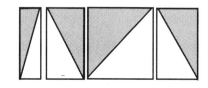

1D *Strategy: Make an organized table of factor pairs of 60.*
For $\frac{60}{N}$ to be a whole number, N must be a factor of 60. The factor pairs for 60 are listed in the table at the right. If N is any of these twelve factors, $\frac{60}{N}$ represents a whole number.
N can be any of 12 different values.

Factor Pairs		
1	×	60
2	×	30
3	×	20
4	×	15
5	×	12
6	×	10

FOLLOW-UPS: *(1) How many factors (divisors) does each of the following have: 120? 180? 300? (Note that these are 60 × 2, 60 × 3, and 60 × 5.)* [16 factors; 18 factors; 18 factors]   *(2) (EXPLORATION) Find the 3 least numbers that have exactly three factors. What property do they share?* [4, 9, 25; They are squares of prime numbers.] *Repeat for numbers that have exactly five factors.* [16, 81, 625; they are fourth powers of primes.]

1E <u>Strategy</u>: *Consider the worst case.*
Determine the largest number of pieces you could take and still not have 15 of the same color. You could take all 12 yellow, all 10 blue, 14 of the green, and 14 of the red pieces and still not have 15 of the same color; so far you have a total of 50 pieces. The next piece you take, whether green or red, gives you 15 matching pieces. **The least number of pieces you must take to be sure that you have 15 pieces of the same color is 51.**

FOLLOW-UP: *Ana has 8 pennies, 3 quarters, 6 nickels, and 5 dimes in her piggy bank. She needs a dollar to buy a card. What is the greatest number of coins Ana can take out of the bank and still not have enough for the card?* [19]   *What is the fewest number of coins that will get her the card?* [6]

Olympiad 2

2A <u>Strategy</u>: *Consider the tens digits first.*
The numbers are between 40 and 60, so the tens digit is 4 or 5. Because the numbers are palimages, 5 and 4 are the only possible units digits. The numbers are different, so **the numbers are 45 and 54.**

FOLLOW–UP: *A number is called a* **PALINDROME** *if it reads the same when written left-to-right and right-to-left. For example 13831 is a palindrome. How many palindromes are there between 1000 and 2000?* [10] *Between 30,000 and 50,000?* [200]

2B **METHOD 1:** <u>Strategy</u>: *Find the number of 8-second periods in the interval.*
Two minutes contain 120 seconds. Because 120 ÷ 8 = 15, a two-minute interval has 15 periods of 8 seconds each. Because the cricket chirps 6 times in each period, **the cricket chirps 15 × 6 = 90 times in two minutes.**

METHOD 2: _Strategy: Set up a proportion using chirps per second._
Let N = the number of chirps in 120 seconds.

Then $\frac{chirps}{sec.}$ is equal to $\frac{6}{8} = \frac{N}{120}$.

Since $120 \div 8 = 15$, $\frac{6}{8} = \frac{6 \times 15}{8 \times 15} = \frac{90}{120}$. Then $N = 90$.

The cricket chirps 90 times in two minutes.

> **FOLLOW–UP:** _Jim can cut a log into 5 pieces in 6 minutes. At that rate, how long will it take him to cut a log of the same thickness into 25 pieces? [36 minutes (Hint: how many cuts are made?)]_ _Why is this problem different from 2B?_

2C **METHOD 1:** _Strategy: Find the "magic sum."_
To find the sum of the numbers in each row ("the magic sum"), divide the sum of all the numbers by the number of rows. $1 + 3 + 5 + \ldots + 17 = 81$, so the magic sum is $81 \div 3 = 27$.

Since $5 + A + 13 = 27$, square A contains 9. Then $1 + 9 + B = 27$, so square B contains 17. Finally, $X + 17 + 3 = 27$, so **7 goes in the square marked "X".**

METHOD 2: _Strategy: Find the number in the middle square._
The mean of the odd numbers 1 through 17 is 9. Therefore, 9 is the value in the middle box of this 3×3 magic square. The sum of the numbers in the middle row then is 27, which is the magic sum. Proceed as in Method 1 to find that the square marked "X" contains 7.

> **FOLLOW–UPS:** _(1) Complete the magic square at the right using the first nine even numbers._ _[The rows, from left to right, are 12, 14, 4; 2, 10, 18; 16, 6, 8]_ _(2)_ **EXPLORATION:** _Note that the sum of the first nine odd numbers is 81. What is the sum of the first ten odd numbers? [100] The first eleven? [121]_ _What is the sum of the odd numbers from 1 through 27? [196] From 1 through 99? [2500]_

2D _Strategy: Determine the length of the side of a small square._
The figure consists of 20 small congruent squares. The area of each small square is $\frac{1}{20}$ of the total area of 320 sq cm, which is 16 sq cm. Then the length of a side of each small square is 4 cm. **The perimeter of the entire figure** consists of 36 sides, so it **is** $36 \times 4 = $ **144 cm.**

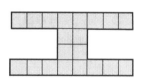

2E *Strategy: Count the number of 7s in an organized way.*

METHOD 1: From pages 1 through 100, the digit seven appears 10 times as a units digit and 10 times as a tens digit (the 70s) for a total of 20 times. The remaining 5 sevens are used to number pages 107, 117, 127, 137, and 147. A 26th seven would be required to number page 157. Therefore, **the largest number of pages the book can have is 156.**

METHOD 2: This table separates the numbers in which 7 appears in the tens place from the rest of the numbers. Adjust the cumulative total once it passes 25 sevens.

pages	Number of Sevens			
	units place	tens place	subtotals	cum.
1 to 69	7	0	7	7
70 to 79	1	10	11	18
80 to 169	9	0	9	27

Numbering up to page 169 requires 27 sevens. This is two more than are available. The two pages less than 169 that should not be numbered are pages 167 and 157. The largest number of pages the book can have is 156.

Olympiad 3

3A **METHOD 1:** *Strategy: Use the definition of a week.*
In 45 consecutive days there are 6 weeks and 3 days. Each of the 6 weeks contains one Monday. In order to have the greatest number of Mondays, one of the 3 days left must also be a Monday. **The greatest number of Mondays that can occur in 45 consecutive days is 7.**

METHOD 2: *Strategy: Start at 1 and count by sevens.*
Suppose day 1 is a Monday. Mondays will occur on days 1, 8, 15, 22, 29, 36, 43. The next Monday would be after day 45. The greatest number of Mondays in 45 consecutive days is 7.

> *FOLLOW-UP: Today is Tuesday. What day is it 100 days from now? 1000?* [Thursday; Monday]

3B *Strategy: Find the sum of the five numbers.*
Because the average of the five numbers is 8, the sum of those five numbers is $5 \times 8 = 40$. The sum of the other three numbers is $40 - 2 - 5 = 33$. Then **the value of any one of the three equal numbers is** $33 \div 3 = $ **11.**

> *FOLLOW-UPS: The average of five different counting numbers is 8. Consider the greatest of these numbers. (1) What is its greatest possible value?* [30]   *(2) What is its least possible value?* [10]

3C   **METHOD 1:** _Strategy_: _Find a pattern from a table of simpler cases._

Number of black squares	1	2	3	4	5	...	50
Number of white squares	8	10	12	14	16	...	?

According to the table, for every black square added, two white squares are added. To jump from 5 to 50 black squares, add 45 black squares. So to jump from 16 white squares, add $2 \times 45 = 90$ white squares to get **106 white squares** that **surround one row of 50 black squares**.

METHOD 2: _Strategy_: _Cut the ends off the figures; look for a pattern._
There are 6 white squares at the ends of each figure, 3 at each end. Each end square is checked. The center section contains 2 white squares for every black square. Therefore, the number of white squares is 6 more than twice the number of black squares. (Algebraically, this is written $W = 2 \times B + 6$) Thus, 106 white squares will surround one row of 50 black squares.

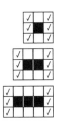

> **FOLLOW-UP:** _Suppose, instead of a single row of black squares, the white squares surround a square of black squares. How many white squares surround a square block of 2500 black squares?_ [204]

3D   **METHOD 1:** _Strategy_: _Find the areas of the two rectangles and subtract._
The area of the whole 20×30 framed rectangle is 600 sq cm. To find the dimensions of the picture itself, subtract 10 cm (5 cm from each end) from the dimensions of the whole rectangle. The picture is 10 cm by 20 cm. Its area is 200 sq cm. **The area of the shaded border is** $600 - 200 = $ **400 sq cm.**

METHOD 2: _Strategy_: _Split the desired region into more familiar figures._
The diagram at the right shows one of several ways to partition the shaded region. The area of each region **A** is $5 \times 5 = 25$ sq cm, of each region **B** is $5 \times 20 = 100$ sq cm, and of each region **C** is $5 \times 10 = 50$ sq cm. The area of the shaded border is then $(4 \times 25) + (2 \times 100) + (2 \times 50) = 400$ sq cm.

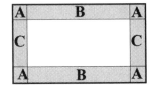

3E   **METHOD 1:** _Strategy_: _Count in an organized way._
The product is divisible by 3 if either number is 3 or 6. The chart shows all possible outcomes when two dice are rolled. An "**x**" marks each outcome in which the product is divisible by 3.

There are 36 possible outcomes when two dice are rolled. In 20 of them the product of the two top numbers is divisible by 3. **The probability that the product of the two top numbers is divisible by 3 is $\frac{20}{36}$ or $\frac{5}{9}$.**

METHOD 2: _Strategy: Examine each die separately and subtract duplications._

As shown above, there are $6 \times 6 = 36$ possible outcomes. The rows (across) show the 12 times when the red die displays either 3 or 6. Similarly, the columns show the 12 times when the green die displays either 3 or 6. However, there are 4 times which appear in _both_ the rows _and_ the columns. Thus, there are 20, not 24, outcomes in which the product is divisible by 3. The probability is $\frac{20}{36}$ or $\frac{5}{9}$.

METHOD 3: _Strategy: Count the number of products which are NOT divisible by 3._

If the product is not divisible by 3, each die shows one of the four numbers: 1, 2, 4, or 5. With two dice there are $4 \times 4 = 16$ outcomes in which the product is _not_ a multiple of 3. This is shown by the empty spaces in the chart on page 10. Thus there are $36 - 16 = 20$ outcomes in which the product _is_ a multiple of 3. As above the probability is then $\frac{20}{36}$ or $\frac{5}{9}$.

Olympiad 4

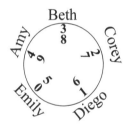

4A METHOD 1: _Strategy: Count up._

With five people in the circle, the person who says "1" will also say 6, 11, 16, 21, 26, and 31. If Amy says 34, and Beth says 33, then Corey says 32, and Diego says 31. Therefore, **the person who says "1" is Diego.**

METHOD 2: _Strategy: Count down, noticing the units digits._

There are five students, so after counting twice around the table, they have counted down ten numbers. After that, the students count the same units digits as they did the first two rounds. The student who says "1" is the same student who says "31", Diego.

> **FOLLOW-UP:** _Suppose the counting numbers 1 through 1000 alternate direction in every other row as indicated in the table at the right. In which column does 49 appear? 1000?_ [A, D]

A	B	C	D	E	F
1	2	3	4	5	6
12	11	10	9	8	7
13	14	15	...		

... and so on.

4B _Strategy: Find a common denominator._

The least common denominator is 35, which is the least common multiple of 5 and 7. Raising the terms, the statement becomes $\frac{21}{35} < \frac{5 \times \square}{35} < \frac{28}{35}$. The numerator of the middle fraction is a multiple of 5. The only multiple of 5 between 21 and 28 is 25. If $5 \times \square$ is 25, **the whole number used for $\square$ is 5.**

4C _Strategy: Make a table._

Consider the house Mr. Sullivan might live in, the houses "before" his, and then the first few houses that come after that.

Beginning of Street		Mr. Sullivan	End of Street	
1 + 2 + 3	= **6**	4	5 + 6 = **11**	_Too big_
1 + 2 + 3 + 4	= **10**	5	6 + 7 = **13**	_Too big_
1 + 2 + 3 + 4 + 5	= **15**	6	7 + 8 = **15**	_Equal sums_

Therefore, **there are 8 houses on Bay Street.**

FOLLOW-UP: _Suppose the product of the house numbers before Mr. Sullivan's is the same as that of the house numbers after his. How many houses are on Bay Street?_ [10]

4D **METHOD 1:** _Strategy: Count the number of cubes painted on 4 faces._
Since every one of the eight cubes is painted on four of its six faces, 32 square faces are painted. The area of each face is $3 \times 3 = 9$ sq cm, so a total of $32 \times 9 = $ **288 sq cm are covered in paint.**

METHOD 2: _Strategy: Count the number of cube faces that are exposed._
The front of the figure has 8 faces of cubes and the back has 8 faces. The top, bottom, and two sides each have 3 faces. The middle "hole" has 4 exposed faces. Therefore, a total of $(2 \times 8) + (4 \times 3) + 4 = 32$ exposed faces are painted. The area of each face is 3×3 or 9 sq cm, so $32 \times 9 = 288$ sq cm are covered in paint.

METHOD 3: _Strategy: Count the number of cube faces that are not exposed._
Each cube has 6 faces and there are 8 cubes in the figure for a total of 48 faces. There are 8 places where 2 cube faces are glued together; thus 8×2 faces are not painted. Then $48 - 16 = 32$ faces are painted. As above, 288 sq cm are covered in paint.

4E **METHOD 1:** _Strategy: Use the least common multiple._
N leaves a remainder of 1 when divided by 2, 3, 4, or 5. Suppose we subtract 1 from N to eliminate the remainder. The result is a multiple of 2, 3, 4, and 5, which have a least common multiple of 60. Moreover, _all_ common multiples of 2, 3, 4, and 5 are multiples of 60. Then N is 1 more than a multiple of 60. N is in the set {61, 121, 181, 241, 301, 361, ...}. Divide each of these by 7. The first multiple of 7 in this set is 301. **The smallest value that N can be is 301.**

METHOD 2: _Strategy: Determine the units digit and then the possible multiples of 7._
N leaves a remainder of 1 when divided by 5, so N has a units digit of 1 or 6. N leaves a remainder of 1 when divided by 2, so N is odd and its units digit is 1. The multiples of 7 that have a units digit of 1 are the product of 7 and a number with a units digit of 3; i.e. 7×3, 7×13, etc. Then N is one of the numbers in the set {21, 91, 161, 231, 301, 371, ...}. The smallest of these that leaves a remainder of 1 when divided by 3 or by 4 is 301.

FOLLOW-UPS: *(1) A class has more than 10 students. The teacher tries to group them for a game. If she forms groups of 3, 4, 6, or 8, one student is left out. How many students are in the class?* [25]   *(2) What is the smallest number that leaves a remainder of 1 when divided by 2, a remainder of 2 when divided by 3, a remainder of 3 when divided by 4, a remainder of 4 when divided by 5, a remainder of 5 when divided by 6, and a remainder of 6 when divided by 7?* [419; Hint: What happens if 1 is added to the number?]

Olympiad 5

5A   METHOD 1: *Strategy: Use reasoning.*

1. *"Mr. Red and Mr. White are older than the man in gray."* Neither Mr. Red nor Mr. White wears gray. Mr. Gray does not wear gray. So Mr. Blue wears the gray shirt.
2. *"The man in red is next to Mr. White."* Mr. White does not wear red, Mr. Red does not wear red, and Mr. Blue is known to be wearing gray. So Mr. Gray wears the red shirt.
3. Mr. White does not wear white, so he is wearing the blue shirt.
4. Then **Mr. Red wears a white shirt.**

Some students may find it convenient to organize their thoughts by using a table, entering **X** for a combination that is ruled out by the clues and **O** for a match. One way to develop the table is shown below. The darkened boxes show new entries.

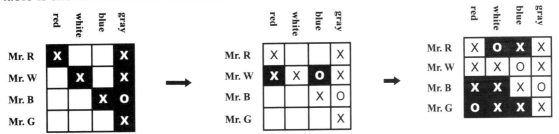

5B   *Strategy: Minimize the numerator; maximize the denominator.*
A fraction has minimum value if the numerator is as small as possible and the denominator is as large as possible. **The least possible value of the fraction is** $\frac{3}{9+7}=\frac{3}{16}$.

FOLLOW-UP: *What is the largest possible value of the fraction?* $[\frac{9}{8}]$

5C   *Strategy: Find the total area of the missing pieces.*
The original area of the piece of paper is $60 \times 20 = 1200$ sq cm. The total area of the regions cut out is then $1200 - 980 = 220$ sq cm. Then:

METHOD 1: _Strategy: Change the figure to create a simpler problem._
"Slide" the two shaded cutout rectangles together, as shown. None of the areas will change.

The total area of the cutouts is the same as the area of a single rectangle with base 12 + 8 = 20 cm. The area of this single rectangle is 220 so **the height of each cut is** 220 ÷ 20 = **11 cm.**

METHOD 2: _Strategy: Use algebra._
Let h = the height of each cut.
The areas of the cutout rectangles are $12h$ and $8h$. $12h + 8h = 220$
Add $12h$ and $8h$: $20h = 220$
Divide each side of the equation by 20: $h = 11$

The height of each cut is 11 cm.

5D   For ease, call a pizza cut into large slices a _large pie_ and call one cut into small slices a _small pie_.

METHOD 1: _Find a relationship between the numbers of large and small pies._
Each small pie is cut into 8 slices, so the number of small slices is a multiple of 8. With 5 small slices for each 3 large slices, the number of small slices is also a multiple of 5. Then the number of small slices is a multiple of 40, the LCM of 8 and 5. Now, group the small slices by 40s. For each (8 × 5) = 40 small slices there are (8 × 3) = 24 large slices. But 40 small slices form 5 small pies and 24 large slices form 4 large pies. That is, of every 9 pies, 5 are small and 4 are large. Alexis has 10 groups of 9 pies, so **there are** 10 × 5 = **50 small pies** (and 40 large pies).

METHOD 2: _Strategy: Guess and check._
With 5 small slices for every 3 large slices, then $\frac{1}{5}$ of the number of small slices equals $\frac{1}{3}$ of the number of large slices. In the table at the right we try first 45 pies of each size and then adjust by fives.

There are 50 small pies.

Number of small pies	45	**50**
Number of large pies	45	**40**
Number of small slices	360	**400**
Number of large slices	270	**240**
$\frac{1}{5}$ of the number of small slices	72	**80**
$\frac{1}{3}$ of the number of large slices	**No**	**YES**

FOLLOW-UPS: _(1) Suppose there are equal numbers of small and large slices. What is the smallest possible number of whole pizzas?_ [7] _(2) Is it possible to have 90 pizzas with the same number of small slices as large slices?_ [No; the number of pizzas would have to be a multiple of seven]

5E *Strategy: Find three different counting numbers with a sum of 8.*
The numbers of each type of marble can be 1, 3, and 4, or they can be 1, 2 and 5. To get the least possible total weight, assign the greatest weight to the least number of marbles and the second greatest weight to the second least possible number of marbles. Then the least total weight occurs when Lin has one 50 gram marble, two 40 g marbles, and five 20 g marbles. **The smallest possible total weight of Lin's marbles is** $(1 \times 50) + (2 \times 40) + (5 \times 20) = $ **230 g.**

FOLLOW-UP: *What is the largest possible weight of Lin's marbles?* [350 g]

Set 2   Olympiad 1

1A METHOD 1: *Strategy: Rearrange the numbers to simplify the problem.*
Since the only operations are addition and subtraction, the number chosen is subtracted out. It is only necessary to start with 20, subtract 17 and add 13.
■ $+ 20 - 17 + 13 - $ ■ $ = 20 - 17 + 13 = 16$. **The result is 16.**

METHOD 2: *Strategy: Choose a number between 32 and 56.*
Choose any number (such as 40) between 32 and 56 and perform the indicated operations:
$$40 + 20 - 17 + 13 - 40 = 16.$$
It is wise to repeat, choosing at least two other numbers, in order to make sure 16 is the only result regardless of the number you choose.

1B METHOD 1: *Strategy: Find the sum of the two smaller numbers.*
Since the sum of the three numbers is 15 more than the greatest of them, then the sum of the two smaller numbers is 15. The numbers are consecutive, so the two smaller numbers are 7 and 8. **The greatest** (third) **number is 9.**

METHOD 2: *Strategy: Use algebra.*
Let M denote the least number. The 3 consecutive numbers are M, $M + 1$, and $M + 2$.

English: The sum of the three numbers is 15 more than the greatest of them.
Equation: $(M) + (M + 1) + (M + 2) = 15 + (M + 2)$

Subtract $M + 2$ from each side of the equation:	$(M) + (M + 1)$ $= 15$
Replace $M + M$ by $2 \times M$:	$(2 \times M) + 1$ $= 15$
Subtract 1 from each side of the equation:	$2 \times M$ $= 14$
Divide each side of the equation by 2:	M $= 7$
Find the values of $M + 1$ and $M + 2$:	$M + 1$ $= 8$
	$M + 2$ $= 9$

The greatest of 7, 8, and 9 is 9.

METHOD 3: _Strategy: Guess, check and revise in an organized way._
Test 1, 2, 3: The difference between $1 + 2 + 3$ and $15 + 3$ is 12, so add 6 to each number. This results in $7 + 8 + 9 = 15 + 9$ and the greatest number is 9.

> **FOLLOW–UPS:** _(1) If the sum of three consecutive even numbers is 18 more than the smallest number, what are the three numbers? [6,8,10]   (2) The sum of seven consecutive counting numbers is 56. Find the fourth (middle) number. [8]_

1C   _Strategy: First determine the order of the cups._
From statement (1) the order of the cups, from left to right is RWG, RGW, or GRW. From statement (3) the gray cup is not leftmost and from statement (4) it is not rightmost. These eliminate GRW and RWG, respectively. Then the cup order is RGW. Statement (3) says that the shell is to the left of the gray cup, so **the shell is under the red cup.**
(_A similar method would start by first determining the order of the objects._)

1D   _Strategy: Express all distances in the same unit of measure._
The perimeter of the rectangle is 2 meters = 200 cm. Thus the sum of the length and width (called the semiperimeter) is 100 cm. Since the length is 70 cm, the width is 30 cm. **The area of the rectangle is** $70 \times 30 = $ **2100 sq cm.**

1E   METHOD 1: _Strategy: Pair each 30¢-stamp with a 40¢-stamp._
All but five of the 40¢-stamps can be paired with 30¢-stamps. These five "extra" 40¢-stamps account for $2.00 of the given $5.20. Then the total difference of all the pairs is the remaining $3.20. Since each pair differs by 10¢, there are 32 pairs. Then **Asha has** thirty-two 30¢-stamps and **thirty-seven 40¢-stamps.**

Checking, $(37 \times 40¢) - (32 \times 30¢) = \$14.80 - \$9.60 = \$5.20$.

METHOD 2: _Strategy: Make an organized list of simpler cases and find a pattern._

1	Number of 30¢ stamps	1	2	3	...	
2	Number of 40¢ stamps	6	7	8	...	**?**
3	Value of 30¢ stamps	$0.30	$0.60	$0.90	...	
4	Value of 40¢ stamps	$2.40	$2.80	$3.20	...	
5	Difference in value	$2.10	$2.20	$2.30	...	**$5.20**

For each additional 30¢-stamp, the difference in value increases by 10¢, as indicated by line 5. To change the difference in value from $2.30 to $5.20, $290¢ \div 10¢ = 29$ additional stamps of each type are needed. Asha has $(3 + 29) = $ thirty-two 30¢-stamps and $(8 + 29) = $ thirty-seven 40¢-stamps.

METHOD 3: _Strategy: Use algebra._

Let x = the number of 30¢-stamps that Asha has.

Then $x + 5$ = the number of 40¢-stamps.

$30x$ = the value (in cents) of the 30¢-stamps and

$40(x + 5)$ = the value (in cents) of the 40¢-stamps.

The value of the 40¢ stamps is 520¢ more than the value of the 30¢ stamps.

$$40(x + 5) = 30x + 520$$

Multiply both x and 5 by 40:	$40x + 200 = 30x + 520$
Subtract $30x$ from each side of the equation:	$10x + 200 = 520$
Subtract 200 from each side of the equation:	$10x = 320$
Divide each side of the equation by 10:	$x = 32$
Find the number of 40¢-stamps:	$x + 5 = 37.$

Thus, Asha has thirty-seven 40¢-stamps.

> ***FOLLOW-UP:*** *Monica has $10.00 in quarters, nickels, and dimes. She has 6 more quarters than dimes and 10 more nickels than dimes. How many of each coin does she have?* [30 nickels, 20 dimes, 26 quarters]

Olympiad 2

2A METHOD 1: _Strategy: Count by complete circuits of the circle._

The letter E is touched every 5 points beginning with the fifth point. Thus E is the 25th touch and **C is the 28th point the ant touches.**

METHOD 2: _Strategy: Count by individual points._

The points in order are **ABCDE ABCDE ABCDE …** . The 28th point that the ant touches is C.

> ***FOLLOW-UPS:*** *(1) What is the 528th point the ant touches?* [C]   *(2) Suppose the ant touches every second point, beginning with A. The first four points are A, C, E, B. What is the 28th point the ant touches? The 2006th?* [E, A]

2B METHOD 1: _Strategy: Draw a diagram._

Letters farther to the right represent taller people.

- ■   Gina is taller than Henry but shorter than Jennie: _ H _ G _ J _
- ■   Ivan is taller than Katie but shorter than Gina: _ K _ I _ G _

Gina appears on both lines. Only Jennie is to the right of Gina, so **Jennie is the tallest.**

METHOD 2: _Strategy: Compare Gina's height to that of each of the others._
From the first sentence, Jennie is the tallest of the three people named. From the second sentence, Gina is the tallest of the three people named. Since Jennie is taller than Gina, Jennie is the tallest.

2C   _Strategy: Start with the difference in their ages._
1992 – 1970 = 22. Mr. Jackson is 22 years older than Lea. Then:

METHOD 1: _Strategy: Express this difference in terms of Lea's age._
In the year in question, Mr. Jackson's age can be expressed as (Lea's age) + (Lea's age) + (Lea's age). The difference in their ages, 22 years, is then twice Lea's age, so Lea is 11 years old. Mr. Jackson is 11 + 22 = 33 years old. Eleven years after 1992 is 2003, as is 33 years after 1970. **The year was 2003.**

METHOD 2: _Strategy: Make a chart listing their ages each year._
Mr. Jackson's age in the required year is 3 times Lea's age. The chart lists multiples of 3 for his ages and then subtracts 22 years to get her corresponding ages.

Mr. Jackson's age	24	27	30	**33**
Lea's age	2	5	8	**11**
Is Mr. J 3 times as old?	No	No	No	**Yes**
Year	1994	1997	2000	**2003**

The only time that his age was three times hers was when he was 33 years and she was 11 years. The year was 2003.

METHOD 3: _Strategy: Use algebra._
Let L be Lea's age when Mr. Jackson's age is 3 times as great.

When Lea is L years old, Mr. Jackson's age can be expressed two ways: $L + 22$ and $3L$.
Equate the two ways: $\qquad\qquad\qquad 3L = L + 22$

Subtract L from each side of the equation:	$2L =$	22
Divide each side of the equation by 2:	$L =$	11

Lea is 11 years old in the year 1992 + 11 or 2003.

FOLLOW-UP: _Dave is four times as old as Jeff. In 10 years, he will be twice as old. How old are they now?_ [Dave is 20; Jeff is 5.]

2D _Strategy_: _Consider the possible dimensions of the small rectangles._
Rectangle **I**, with area 21 sq cm, is either 1 cm by 21 cm, or 3 cm by 7 cm. Rectangle **II**, with area 35 sq cm, is either 1 cm by 35 cm, or 5 cm by 7 cm. The common side, $\overline{GJ}$, of both rectangles is then either 1 cm or 7 cm in length. If $GJ = 1$ cm, then $EJ = 21$ cm. But 21 is not a factor of 48 and cannot be the length of a side of rectangle **III**. Thus each of GJ, AE, and DF measure 7 cm and each of AG, EJ, and BH measure 3 cm. Then EB, JH, and FC each measure $48 \div 3 = 16$ cm, GD, JF, and HC each measure 5 cm. Finally $AB = 23$ and $AD = 8$.

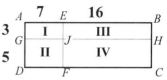

With a length of 23 and width of 8, **the area rectangle ABCD is 184 sq cm.**

2E **METHOD 1:** _Strategy_: _Group the marbles two different ways._
Before the exchange: group all the marbles by 8s, of which 5 are Amy's and 3 are Tara's. After the exchange: group the marbles by 5s, of which 3 are Amy's and 2 are Tara's. Thus, the total number of marbles remains constant and is a multiple of both 8 and 5, that is, of 40: 40, 80, 120, and so on.

Assume the minimal total of 40 marbles, Amy having 25 and Tara 15. After Amy gives 1 marble to Tara, Amy has 24 and Tara has 16 marbles. Amy's marbles can be arranged in 8 groups of 3 and Tara's in 8 groups of 2. This satisfies all conditions of the problem. **Amy started with 25 marbles.** There is no need to check 80, 120, and so on.

METHOD 2: _Strategy_: _Make a table of possible numbers of marbles for each girl._
Consider all number pairs in a ratio of 5 to 3 ("before"). In each case, look for a ratio of 3 to 2 after trading 1 marble ("after").

Number before exchange		Number after exchange	
Amy	**Tara**	**Amy**	**Tara**
5	3	4	4
10	6	9	7
15	9	14	10
20	12	19	13
25	15	24	16

This occurs when Amy ends with 24 and Tara with 16 marbles. Amy started with 25 marbles.

METHOD 3: _Strategy_: _Use algebra._
Represent the two numbers in a 5:3 ratio as $5a$ and $3a$.
The ratio will become 3:2:

$$\frac{5a-1}{3a+1} = \frac{3}{2}.$$

Cross-multiply: $2(5a - 1) = 3(3a + 1)$
Use the distributive law on each side of the equation: $10a - 2 = 9a + 3$
Add 2 to each side of the equation: $10a = 9a + 5$
Subtract $9a$ from each side of the equation: $a = 5$
Since $5a = 25$, Amy started with 25 marbles.

SET 2   SOLUTIONS

FOLLOW-UP: *Louise has $\frac{7}{8}$ as many grapes as Cindy. After Louise eats 10 grapes, she has $\frac{2}{3}$ as many grapes as Cindy. How many grapes does Cindy have?* [48; Hint: what number does not change?]

Olympiad 3

3A METHOD 1: *Strategy: Divide the larger factor by 4.*
As a result, the two numbers are equal with a product of 9. Then the smaller number is 3, the larger number is 12, and **the sum of the two numbers is 15.**

METHOD 2: *Strategy: List the factor pairs of 36.*
The factor pairs of 36 are: 1 & 36, 2 & 18, 3 & 12, 4 & 9, 6 & 6. The only pair in which one factor is four times the other is 3 and 12. Their sum is 15.

METHOD 3: *Strategy: Apply the Associative Property of Multiplication.*

Use 4 as one of the factors of 36:	$36 = 4 \times 9$
Split 9 into two equal factors:	$36 = 4 \times (3 \times 3)$
Use the associative property:	$36 = (4 \times 3) \times 3$
Multiply 4 and 3:	$36 = 12 \times 3.$

The sum of the numbers is 15.

3B METHOD 1: *Strategy: Consider Mrs. Saada's age last year.*
Last year her age was a multiple of both 9 and 4 and thus a multiple of 36. The only multiple of 36 between 50 and 80 is 72. Then this year **Mrs. Saada is 73 years old.**

METHOD 2: *Strategy: List the numbers that satisfy one of the conditions.*
It is faster to divide by 9 than by 4 because 9 produces fewer results. The only numbers between 50 and 80 that are 1 more than a multiple of 9 are 55, 64, and 73. Of these, only 73 is one more than a multiple of 4. Mrs. Saada is 73 years old.

FOLLOW-UP: *Kai and his mother are younger than 10 and 50 years old, respectively. When the sum of their ages is divided by 5, the remainder is 2. When each of their ages is divided by 7, there is no remainder. How old is Kai's mother?* [35]

3C METHOD 1: *Strategy: Measure the perimeter of the room in tiles.*
The perimeter of the room is $2 \times 9 + 2 \times 5 = 28$ tiles. This counts each of the four corner tiles twice. To compensate, subtract 4. **24 tiles touch the walls.**

METHOD 2: _Strategy: Draw a diagram, and count the tiles that touch the edges._

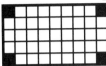

24 tiles touch the walls.

3D   _Strategy: Determine how many people are in each group._
$\frac{5}{5}$ represents a whole amount. Of the 50 cars, the remaining $\frac{4}{5}$ contain just one person. Then of these $\frac{4}{5} \times 50 = 40$ cars, the remaining $\frac{2}{5}$ are driven by men. $\frac{4}{5} \times 40 = 16$: Thus, **16 cars are driven by men.**

> **FOLLOW-UP:** _One day, Sharon goes to the mall and spends $\frac{1}{2}$ her money on a pair of jeans. She spends $\frac{1}{3}$ of what she has left on a CD and then $\frac{1}{4}$ of what's left on lunch. If she returns home with $15.00, how much did she start with?_ [$60]

3E   **METHOD 1:** _Strategy: Determine whether the result is even or odd._
Find a way to avoid all that computation. The product of two odd numbers is odd, and the sum of two odd numbers is even. Therefore, $(13 \times 17) + (19 \times 23)$ is even. The least prime number, 2, is a factor of every even number. **The smallest prime number that divides the given expression is 2.**

METHOD 2: _Strategy: Do the arithmetic and then factor._
$(13 \times 17) + (19 \times 23) = 221 + 437 = 658$. $658 = 2 \times 7 \times 47$. Observe that once the factor of 2 is found, it is not necessary to factor further: the least prime number that divides the sum is 2.

> **FOLLOW–UPS:** _(1) What is the greatest prime number that divides $(17 \times 13) + (17 \times 23)$?_ [17]   _(2) What is the greatest prime number that divides $(17 \times 25) + (17 \times 20) + (17 \times 12)$?_ [19; the expression = 17×57]   _(3) What prime numbers divide $(14 \times 31) - (7 \times 17)$?_ [7, 5, 3; think $14 \times 31 = 7 \times 62$]

Olympiad 4

4A   **METHOD 1:** _Strategy: Determine the number of whole weeks._
Every 7 days from "today" will be a Tuesday. In 49 days from today, 7 weeks will have passed, which includes 7 Fridays. Since the 49th day from today is a Tuesday, the 52nd day from today is another Friday. **There are 8 Fridays in the next 53 days.**

METHOD 2: *Strategy: Count Fridays.*
Since "today" is Tuesday, the 3rd day will be a Friday, as will the 10th, 17th, 24th, ... , 52nd days from today. There are 8 Fridays in the next 53 days.

4B   *Strategy: Consider the effect of place value on H.*
The largest possible sum of three single-digit numbers is 27, so H is either 1 or 2 (since 0 cannot be a leading digit). Suppose H is 2. Then $A + A + 2$ is $20 + A$. This is impossible for any digit A. So H is 1. Since $A + A + 1 = 10 + A$, A is 9. **The two-digit number HA is 19.**

$$\begin{array}{r} A \\ A \\ + \; H \\ \hline H\,A \end{array}$$

> ***FOLLOW-UPS:*** *(1) EM and ME are each two-digit numbers whose product is 252. EM is 9 more than ME. Find the values of E and M.* [E= 2, M = 1; the difference of 9 is not needed.] *(2) See pages 115-118 of Creative Problem Solving in School Mathematics, 2nd Edition, for more cryptarithms.*

4C   **METHOD 1:** *Strategy: Count the odd numbers from 11 to 59 inclusive.*
There are 49 whole numbers from 11 through 59. Since the list starts and ends with an odd number, it contains one more odd number than even number. Thus there are 25 odd and 24 even numbers. There are five odd multiples of 5 between 11 and 59: 15, 25, 35, 45, and 55. **The probability of Kristen being in an odd-numbered room is $\frac{5}{25}$ or $\frac{1}{5}$.**

METHOD 2: *Strategy: Split the room numbers up into decades.*
Consider the five decades 11-19, 21-29, 31-39, 41-49, and 51-59. Each decade has 5 odd room numbers, for a total of 25 odd-numbered rooms. In each decade only the room number ending in 5 is divisible by 5. The probability of Kristen being in an odd-numbered room is $\frac{5}{25}$ or $\frac{1}{5}$.

4D   *Strategy: Consider each possible pair of figures separately.*
A circle may cross each side of a square in at most 2 points, for a total of 8 points.

A circle may cross each side of a triangle in at most 2 points, for a total of 6 points.

Each side of a triangle may cross in at most 2 sides of a square, for a total of 6 points.

It is possible to draw the figures so that all points are different, so **the greatest number of points where two or more of them may cross is $8 + 6 + 6 = 20$.**

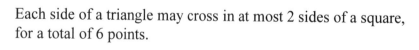

4E   _Strategy: Count the digits used for one-digit numbers first, then two-digit numbers, etc._

Page	# of digits used	# of digits remaining
1-9	$9 \times 1 = 9$	$258 - 9 = 249$
10-99	$90 \times 2 = 180$	$249 - 180 = 69$

The remaining 69 digits form 23 three-digit numbers and the last page of the book is the 23rd number following 99. **The last page number is 122.**

>   **FOLLOW-UPS:** _(1) How many digits are used to number 1200 pages? [3693]   (2) How many 2's are used to number pages 1 through 227 of a book? [79]_

Olympiad 5

5A   **METHOD 1:** _Strategy: Find the average._
The page numbers in a book are consecutive. Half of 245 is 122.5, so the page numbers that you see are 122 and 123. **The next page number is 124.**

5B   **METHOD 1:** _Strategy: Find the total of the four heights._
The four heights have an average of 180, so their total is $180 \times 4 = 720$ cm. The sum of the three known heights is 525 cm, so **the fourth adult's height is** $720 - 525 = \textbf{195 cm}$.

METHOD 2: _Strategy: Compare each height with the average._
Each of the heights of the first two adults are 10 cm less than the given average. The height of the third adult is 5 cm _more_ than the average. The sum of these three heights is 15 cm less than the average. The fourth adult is then 15 cm more than the average, or 195 cm tall, as illustrated by the diagram.

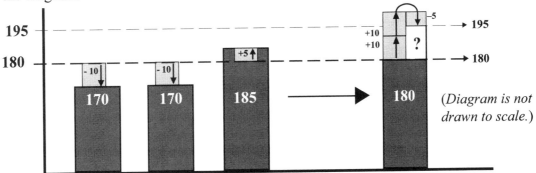

(Diagram is not drawn to scale.)

>   **FOLLOW-UPS:** _(1) Four of Samantha's jars contain an average of 35 pennies and the other three contain an average of 42 pennies. What is the average number of pennies in all seven jars? [38] (2) In a recipe for a certain three-bean salad, you mix 4 ounces of a 20¢ bean, 5 ounces of a 38¢ bean, and 3 ounces of a 50¢ bean. What is the cost per ounce of the salad? [35¢]_

SET 2   SOLUTIONS

5C   **METHOD 1:** *Strategy: List all numbers whose digit-sum is 19.*

List the digits in each potential plate number in descending order to make the resulting number as great as possible. Then select the plate number whose product is 216.

Plate number	991	982	973	**964**	955	883	874	865	775	766
Product of digits	81	144	189	**216**	225	192	224	240	245	252

The greatest license plate number is 964.

METHOD 2: *Strategy: Examine the factors of 216.*

$216 = (2 \times 2 \times 2) \times (3 \times 3 \times 3) \times 1$. The only single-digit products of 1s, 2s and 3s are 1, 2, 3, 4, 6, 8, and 9. For the largest plate number, write the digits in descending order.

First check this list to see if 9 can be the hundreds digit: $216 = 9 \times 24 = 9 \times 8 \times 3$ or $9 \times 6 \times 4$. Since the sum of its digits is 19 for 964 but not for 983, the greatest license plate number is 964.

> **FOLLOW-UPS:** *(1) For how many three-digit plate numbers is the product of the digits 216 and the sum of the digits 19?* [6]   *(2) For how many three-digit numbers is the product of the digits 336? 96?* [6; 15]   *(3) For how many numbers is the product of the digits 12 if 1 is not a digit and it may have any number of digits?* [7]

5D   *Strategy: Use the differences between the terms.*

$32 - 11 = 21$ and $46 - 32 = 14$. Thus, the number by which Josh is counting — call that his "jump" — is a factor of both 14 and 21. The only two common factors are 1 and 7. The jump cannot be 1, or else 24 would be one of his numbers. So Josh's jump is 7. Since his starting number is a whole number other than 11, the second number is 11, and therefore **the whole number Josh starts with is 4.**

> **FOLLOW-UP:** *The first number that is in both Ana's and Josh's lists is 18. What is the second number that is in both lists?* [53] *The fifth number?* [158]

5E   *Strategy: Find a box for which only one value is possible.*

There are many ways to do this problem. Here is one. Each entry in a black box is derived from those in the shaded boxes.

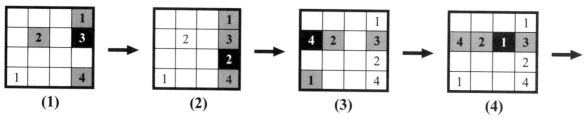

(1)   (2)   (3)   (4)

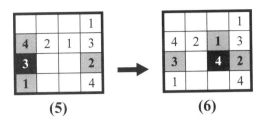

(5) → (6)

(Completed table)

2	4	3	1
4	2	1	3
3	1	4	2
1	3	2	4

The number in the square originally marked "X" is 4.

Set 3   Olympiad 1

1A *Strategy: Use the pattern in the numbers to simplify the arithmetic.*
$(81 + 18) + (72 + 27) + (63 + 36) + (54 + 45) + 4 = 99 + 99 + 99 + 99 + 4 = 4 \times 99 + 4 \times 1$.
Rewrite as $4 \times (99 + 1) = 4 \times 100 = 400$. **The sum is 400.**

> **FOLLOW–UPS:** *All possible 4-digit numbers are formed using the digits 1, 2, 3, and 4. Each digit is used once in each number. (1) What is the sum of all these numbers?* [66,660] *(2) The digits of each 4-digit number are added. What is the sum of all these sums?* [240]

1B **METHOD 1:** *Strategy: Pair each man with a woman.*
There are 12 women who can't be paired with men, and so, $100 - 12 = 88$ people can be paired. Then there are $88 \div 2 = 44$ men. Thus $44 + 12 =$ **56 women are on the plane.**

METHOD 2: *Strategy: Start with equal numbers of men and women.*
Suppose the plane has 50 men and 50 women. To get 12 more women than men, replace 6 men by 6 women. This results in 6 fewer men and 6 more women. Then 44 men and 56 women are on the plane.

METHOD 3: *Strategy: Use algebra.*
Let m be the number of men. Then $m + 12$ is the number of women.

All together there are 100 men and women: $(m) + (m + 12) = 100$

Combine like terms:	$2m + 12 = 100$
Subtract 12 from each side of the equation:	$2m = 88$
Divide each side of the equation by 2:	$m = 44$

There are 44 men and $100 - 44 = 56$ women on the airplane.

> **FOLLOW–UP:** *There are a total of 60 men and women in a club. If the number of men is two-thirds of the number of women, find the number of women in the club.* [36].

1C   METHOD 1: *Strategy: Count in an organized way.*
The table organizes each type of rectangle in the diagram by the number of regions and the number of times each occurs.

# of regions	1	2		3		4	6
# of rectangles	8	4	5	2	2	2	2

There are $8 + 4 + 5 + 2 + 2 + 2 + 1 = $ **24 rectangles of all sizes in the picture.**

METHOD 2: *Strategy: Label each region and list in an organized way.*

1 bit:	A, B, C, D, E, F, G, H
2 bits:	AB, BC, DE, FG, GH; BD, DG, CE, EH
3 bits:	ABC, FGH; BDG, CEH
4 bits:	BDCE, DGEH
6 bits:	BDGCEH. There are 24 rectangles.

A		F
B	D	G
C	E	H

1D   METHOD 1: *Strategy: Determine the numbers and then their placement.*
The smallest possible sum for six different counting numbers is $1 + 2 + 3 + 4 + 5 + 6 = 21$. The sum is given as 21, so the numbers are 1, 2, 3, 4, 5, and 6.

Two given sums are each 8 and the only sets of these numbers with that sum are $\{1, 3, 4\}$ and $\{1, 2, 5\}$.

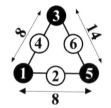

These numbers are in the five circles along the left and bottom sides of the triangle, and the number they share, 1, is in the bottom left shaded circle. 6 can only be in the unshaded circle in the center of side 14. The other two shaded circles on side 14 sum to 8, and must be 3 and 5, in either order. The three shaded circles contain the numbers 1, 3, and 5, and **their sum is 9.**

METHOD 2: *Strategy: Find the sum of the numbers along the three sides.*
The sum of the three given sums (8, 8, 14) is 30. As above the sum of the first 6 counting numbers is 21. However, each number in the three shaded circles was counted *twice*. The sum of the numbers in the three shaded circles is $30 - 21 = 9$. (Note: we do not need to place the numbers in circles.)

SET 3   SOLUTIONS

1E METHOD 1: _Strategy_: _Build a table using multiples of 6._

The fact that the mother's age is a multiple of Rebekah's age both now and in 6 years suggests that each age is originally a multiple of 6.

AGE NOW	Rebekah	6	12	18
	Mother (4 times as much)	24	48	72
AGE IN 6 YEARS	Rebekah	12	18	24
	Mother	30	54	78
Is mother's age 3 times as much?		no	**YES**	no

Rebekah is 12 years old now.

METHOD 2: _Strategy_: _Start with a simpler problem._

Instead of 6 years, suppose 1 year elapses. The first two columns show some possible related ages now for Rebekah and her mother. The next two columns show their resulting ages one year from now. The last column, setting aside common sense for the moment, checks if her mother will then be 3 times as old as Rebekah.

Age now		Age in 1 year		Is mother's age 3 times Rebekah's?
Rebekah	Her mother	Rebekah	Her mother	
1	4	2	5	no
2	8	3	9	YES

To increase the elapsed time from 1 year to 6, while preserving the age ratios (i. e., Now the mother is 4 times as old and in the future will become 3 times as old), multiply each age by 6. That makes their ages now 12 and 48, in 6 years 18 and 54. Because 54 is 3 × 18, Rebekah now is 12.

> **FOLLOW–UPS:** _(1) Chandra is twice as old as Nora. Nora is 6 years younger than Lian. The sum of all their ages is 62. How old is Nora? [14]. (2) The length of a rectangle is 5 times its width. Its length and width are both increased by 3 cm. The length of the new rectangle is 4 times its width. Find the perimeter of the original rectangle. [108 cm]_

Olympiad 2

2A METHOD 1: _Strategy_: _Do the indicated arithmetic operations._

220 – 22 = 198 and 198 ÷ 22 = 9. **9 makes the statement true.**

METHOD 2: _Strategy_: _Simplify the problem._

Since 220 = 10 × 22, then 220 – 22 = 9 × 22. 9 makes the statement true.

2B *Strategy: First determine the order in which the students sit.*
Abby sits next to both Ben and Colin in either order.

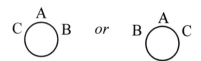

Dalia sits next to both Ben and Sara in either order.

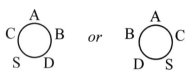

Thus Abby and Colin are seated next to each other. Because the chair numbers are in numerical order and theirs add up to 6, Abby and Colin are seated in chairs 1 and 5, whether counted clockwise or counterclockwise. In both cases, **Dalia is in chair number 3.**

> *FOLLOW-UPS: Suppose the chairs are not numbered. In how many ways can 5 people be arranged at a circular table? 6 people? 7?* [24; 120; 720]

2C **METHOD 1:** *Strategy: Consider possible values of the repeated prime factor.*
The following are organized according to the repeated factor. Products between 30 and 60 are **underlined and bold**.

2×2×3, 2×2×5, 2×2×7, **2×2×11**, **2×2×13**, 2×2×17, …
3×3×2, **3×3×5**, 3×3×7, …
5×5×2, 5×5×3, …
7×7×2, …   No other funny numbers between 30 and 60 are possible.

In all, there are 4 funny numbers, 44, 45, 50, and 52, **between 30 and 60.**

METHOD 2: *Strategy: Factor all the numbers between 30 and 60.*
Factor 30, 31, 32, 33, …, 60. Only four numbers turn out to be funny:

$$44 = 2 \times 2 \times 11,$$
$$45 = 3 \times 3 \times 5,$$
$$50 = 2 \times 5 \times 5,$$
$$52 = 2 \times 2 \times 13.$$

> *FOLLOW–UPS: (1) How many different divisors does each funny number have?* [6] *(2) What number between 30 and 60 has this same number of divisors but is not funny?* [32] *(3) What is the next smallest number that has exactly 6 divisors but is not funny?* [243]

SET 3   SOLUTIONS

2D *Strategy: Express the desired area in terms of the areas of simpler figures.*

METHOD 1: *Strategy: Embed the given figure in a larger rectangle.*
Wrap the figure in a rectangle, as shown. The rectangle is 14 m by 11 m, and its area is 154 sq m. The areas of the shaded rectangles are 9 × 3 = 27 sq m and 2 × 4 = 8 sq m. Subtracting 27 and 8 from 154, **the area of the given figure is 119 sq m.**

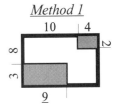
Method 1

METHOD 2: *Strategy: Split the figure into smaller rectangles.*
One possibility is shown in diagram A.

Opposite sides of a rectangle have the same length. This produces segments of 1 cm and 6 cm as shown in diagram A. Then diagram B shows the separation of the rectangles and the lengths of all sides. Then:

- Rectangle I: Its area is 1 × 3 = 3 sq m.
- Rectangle II: Its area is 9 × 4 = 36 sq m.
- Rectangle III: Its area is 8 × 10 = 80 sq m.

Method 2

diagram A   *diagram B*

The area of the given figure is then 80 + 3 + 36 = 119 sq m.

2E **METHOD 1:** *Strategy: Count the number of digits in an organized way.*
Count the digits from 1 through 9, then 10 through 19, and so on.

Counting numbers	1 ⇨ 9	10 ⇨ 19	20 ⇨ 29	30 ⇨ 39	40 ⇨ 49
Number of digits	9	20	20	20	20
Cumulative number of digits	9	29	49	69	89

The numbers 1 through 49 require 89 digits. The remaining 100 − 89 = 11 digits form the numbers 50, 51, 52, 53, 54, and the first digit of 55. **The 100th digit in the string is 5.**

METHOD 2: *Strategy: Look for a pattern.*
Write the first 100 digits of the string in a 10 by 10 array. After the first 9 numbers, all the remaining numbers are two-digit, requiring two boxes. Each decade (the 10s, 20s, etc.) has twenty digits and takes exactly two rows of the array to complete, starting in the tenth column. Then the digits in the tenth column, read top to bottom, are two 1's, then two 2's, and so on. The digit in the tenth row and tenth column, which is the 100th digit, is a 5.

1	2	3	4	5	6	7	8	9	1
0	1 1	1 2	1 3	1 4					1
5	1 6	1 7	1 8	1 9					2
0	2 1	2 2	2 3	2 4					2
5	2 6	2 7	2 8	2 9					3
0	3 1	3 2	3 3	3 4					3
5	3 6	3 7	3 8	3 9					4
0	4 1	4 2	4 3	4 4					4
5	4 6	4 7	4 8	4 9					5
0	5 1	5 2	5 3	5 4					5

Division E   155

SET 3 SOLUTIONS

FOLLOW-UPS: *(1) Look at the shaded column of the table shown in method 2. The first zero to appear in this column is a digit of what number?* [103]

Olympiad 3

3A *Strategy: Fulfill one requirement at a time.*

3 is the only prime number given ....3 _ _ _
9 is 3 more than 6........................... 3 9 6 _
1 is the only digit left....................... 3 9 6 1
The number is 3,961.

(1 is not a prime number. See *What Every Young Mathlete Should Know.)*

3B METHOD 1: *Strategy: Pair each nickel with a quarter.*

After the nickels are paired with quarters, there are 4 quarters left over, worth a total of $1.00. The paired coins are worth $3.10 – $1.00 = $2.10. Each pair is worth $.05 + $.25 = $.30. The number of pairs is 210 ÷ 30 = 7, so **Emma has 7 nickels.**

METHOD 2: *Strategy: Make a table. Find a pattern.*

Number of coins	Nickels	1	2	3	...	?
	Quarters	5	6	7	...	
Value of coins	Nickels	$0.05	$0.10	$0.15	...	
	Quarters	$1.25	$1.50	$1.75	...	
Total value		**$1.30**	**$1.60**	**$1.90**	...	**$3.10**

Each time a nickel is added, a quarter is also added and this increases the total value by $.30. When there is 1 nickel, the total value is $1.30. Emma has $3.10 which is $1.80 more than $1.30. Then 180 ÷ 30 is 6. After the first nickel, 6 more are needed. Emma has 7 nickels.

METHOD 3: *Strategy: Work down from the maximum number of quarters.*

Emma can't have more than $3.00 in quarters. Suppose she has 12 quarters. Then she would have 8 nickels, for a total value of $3.40, which is too high. If, instead, she has 11 quarters, she would have 7 nickels for a total value of $3.10. Emma has 7 nickels.

FOLLOW-UP: *Cary's bank contains quarters, nickels and dimes. The number of nickels is 3 times the number of quarters. The number of dimes is 3 times the number of nickels. The bank has 39 coins in all. What is the total value of Cary's coins?* [$3.90]

3C METHOD 1: _Strategy: Start with the area of MATH._

Rectangle _MATH_ is either 1 by 30, 2 by 15, 3 by 10, or 5 by 6 cm. _TH_ is one of these eight lengths.

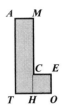

The area of square _ECHO_ is between 5 and 24, and _TH_ = _HO_. Then _HO_ can only be 3 because each of the other seven choices produces an area that is too large or too small. Then _TH_ = 3, _HO_ = 3, _OE_ = 3, _EC_ = 3, _CH_ = 3, _AM_ = 3, _AT_ = 10. Then _MH_ = 10, so _MC_ = 7.

The perimeter of the shaded figure, _MA_ + _AT_ + _TH_ + _HO_ + _OE_ + _EC_ + _CM_, **is 32 cm.**

METHOD 2: _Strategy: Start with the area of ECHO._

The area of _ECHO_ could be 9 or 16 sq cm, so _HO_ would be 3 or 4 cm. Since _H_ is the midpoint of $\overline{TO}$, _TH_ is either 3 or 4 cm.

The area of _MATH_ is 30 sq cm. Of 3 and 4, only 3 is a factor of 30, so each side of _ECHO_ is 3 cm long.

Thus, _TH_ = 3 cm and _AT_ = 10 cm. Further, _MA_ = 3 and _MC_ = 10 − 3 = 7 cm.

Then the perimeter of the shaded figure is 32 cm, which is the sum of its sides.

> **FOLLOW-UPS:** _All lengths in the figure are in cm and all angles are right angles._ (1) _What is the perimeter of the figure?_ [46 cm]   (2) _What is its area?_ [58 sq cm]

3D _Strategy: Find the common difference (the number by which Sequence B counts down)._
Represent Sequence B visually: __, 35, __, __, __, 23, __, __, … .

The sequence counts down from 35 to 23 in 4 steps, so each step counts down by 3. Keep counting down by 3 until a single-digit number is reached. Sequence B is 38, 35, 32, 29, 26, 23, 20, 17, 14, 11, 8. **There are 11 numbers in Sequence B.**

3E METHOD 1: _Strategy: Find all sample space entries that meet the conditions given._
Each has a choice of 3 letters. Amy and Brett could have the same letter. The sample space has 3 × 3 × 3 = 27 possibilities. Write them out as a chart as follows or as a tree diagram. The instances when Cate's letter is different from both Amy's letter and from Brett's letter are boldfaced.

Cate chooses Z	ZZZ	ZZU	ZZT	ZUZ	**ZUU**	**ZUT**	ZTZ	**ZTU**	**ZTT**
Cate chooses U	**UZZ**	UZU	**UZT**	UUZ	UUU	UUT	**UTZ**	UTU	**UTT**
Cate choosesT	**TZZ**	**TZU**	TZT	**TUZ**	**TUU**	TUT	TTZ	TTU	TTT

The probability that Cate's letter is different from both Amy's and Brett's is $\frac{12}{27}$ or $\frac{4}{9}$.

METHOD 2: <u>Strategy</u>: *Compare Cate's letter with each of the others, one at a time.*
For each letter Cate might choose, the probability that Amy chooses a different letter is $\frac{2}{3}$. In $\frac{1}{3}$ of *those* cases Brett's letter will match Cate's letter, and thus in $\frac{2}{3}$ of the cases Brett's letter will differ from Cate's letter. That is, Brett's letter will differ from Cate's letter $\frac{2}{3}$ of $\frac{2}{3}$ of the time. Therefore, the probability that Cate's letter is different from both Amy's and Brett's is $\frac{4}{9}$.

> **FOLLOW-UP:** *Amy, Brett, Cate, and David each write down 1, 2, 3, or 4. What is the probability that each writes down a different number?* $[\frac{3}{32}]$

Olympiad 4

4A <u>Strategy</u>: *Find the number of full weeks in January.*
January has 31 days, which is 4 weeks and 3 days. Four weeks after Monday, January 1, is another Monday, January 29. Three days later is a Thursday. **February 1, 1990, was on a Thursday.**

4B **METHOD 1:** <u>Strategy</u>: *Work backwards, using a number line.*
Start with Ava. Then place Olivia, Christopher, and Ethan in that order.

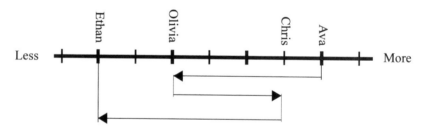

Counting spaces, **Ava got 6 more votes than Ethan.**

METHOD 2: <u>Strategy</u>: *Choose an arbitrary number of votes for Ethan.*
Because the four vote totals differ by fixed amounts, assigning any random value to Ethan's total will not change the difference between his total and Ava's. Suppose Ethan received 10 votes. Then Christopher had 15 votes, Olivia had 12 votes and Ava had 16 votes. Thus Ava beat Ethan by 16 – 10 = 6 votes. Check by assigning two other random values to Ethan's vote total.

> **FOLLOW-UP:** *Tom read six times as many books as Nia, who read one-quarter as many as Jeff, who read twice as many as Paula. Paula read 10 books. Who read more books, Jeff and Paula combined, or Tom?* [The sums are equal.]

4C **METHOD 1:** *Strategy: Represent the fractions visually.*
In the first diagram, the cross-hatching represents the $\frac{3}{5}$ of Mrs. Allen's original sum that she spent at the grocery store, so $\frac{2}{5}$ of the starting sum remained, as shown by the unshaded boxes.

Next, the solid shading in the second diagram represents what she spent at the gas station, which is $\frac{3}{5}$ of the first remainder. The 4 unshaded boxes represent her final remainder, $8. Then each box represents $2. The original large box contains 25 of these small boxes and so represents $25 \times 2 = \$50$. **Mrs. Allen started with $50.**

METHOD 2: *Strategy: Work backwards.*
When Mrs. Allen spends $\frac{3}{5}$ of her money, then $\frac{2}{5}$ of it remains. Her final $8 is $\frac{2}{5}$ of what remained after the first purchase. Thus after the first purchase $8 \div \frac{2}{5} = \$20$ remained. That $20 is $\frac{2}{5}$ of what she started with. Therefore she started with $20 \div \frac{2}{5} = \$50$.

4D *Strategy: Find the distance each rides.*
At 5 miles per hour for 1 hour, Jan travels 5 miles. Then at 10 miles per hour for a half hour, she travels half of 10 miles, which is another 5 miles. So Jan travels a total of $5 + 5 = 10$ miles.

That means Nika also travels 10 miles. After 1 hour, she has traveled 8 miles. Her remaining 2 miles is $\frac{1}{4}$ of the distance she has already traveled and so takes $\frac{1}{4}$ as much time. Nika needs 60 minutes to cover the first 8 miles and an additional 15 minutes to cover the last 2 miles, so **Nika rides for 75 minutes.**

FOLLOW-UP: *What was Jan's average speed, in mph?* $[6\frac{2}{3}]$

4E *Strategy: List and examine each possibility for **B** and **Y**.*
Since **SAY** is less than 1000, **BABY** is less than 3000 and **B** can only be 2 or 1. The product of **Y** and 3 has a ones digit of **Y**, so **Y** can only be 5 or 0. Then there are just four choices to test for (**B**,**Y**): (2,5) or (1,5) or (2,0) or (1,0).

$$\begin{array}{r} S\,A\,Y \\ \times\quad 3 \\ \hline B\,A\,B\,Y \end{array}$$

(1) Suppose **B** = 2 and **Y** = 5. Thus 1 more than $3 \times$ **A** ends in 2, so **A** = 7. Then 2 more than $3 \times$ S is 27, which is impossible.

$$\begin{array}{r} S\,A\,5 \\ \times\quad 3 \\ \hline 2\,A\,2\,5 \end{array}$$

(2) Suppose **B** = 1 and **Y** = 5. Thus 1 more than $3 \times$ **A** ends in 1, so **A** = 0. Then $3 \times$ S is 10. This is also impossible.

$$\begin{array}{r} S\,A\,5 \\ \times\quad 3 \\ \hline 1\,A\,1\,5 \end{array}$$

(3) Suppose **B** = 2 and **Y** = 0. Thus $3 \times$ **A** ends in 2, so **A** = 4. Then 1 more than $3 \times$ S is 24, which is again impossible.

$$\begin{array}{r} S\,A\,0 \\ \times\quad 3 \\ \hline 2\,A\,2\,0 \end{array}$$

(4) The only remaining possibility is **B** = 1 and **Y** = 0. Thus $3 \times$ **A** ends in 1, so **A** = 7. Then 2 more than $3 \times$ S is 17, so **S** = 5. Checking, $570 \times 3 = 1710$.

$$\begin{array}{r} S\,A\,0 \\ \times\quad 3 \\ \hline 1\,A\,1\,0 \end{array}$$

The three-digit number represented by SAY is 570.

Olympiad 5

5A *Strategy: Minimize the other numbers.*

To put as many marbles as possible in one cup, place as few as possible in the other cups. The four cups with the least number contain $1 + 2 + 3 + 5 = 11$ marbles. With a total of 20 marbles, **the greatest number any one cup can have is 9.**

5B *Strategy: Look for a pattern in the last numbers in each row.*

Examine the last number in each row. Figure 1 shows that it is the sum of that row number and all the row numbers preceding it. These numbers (1, 3, 6, 10, …) are called "triangular numbers".

Row 1: **1**
Row 2: **2 3**
Row 3: **4 5 6**
and so on …

The last number in the 16th row is the 16th triangular number, $1 + 2 + 3 + 4 + \ldots + 15 + 16$. To add them quickly, use the symmetry shown in figure 2. Pair the numbers from the outside in: add 1 and 16, 2 and 15, 3 and 14, and so on. There are 8 pairs of numbers, each adding to 17, and the total is $8 \times 17 = 136$.

Counting back three numbers, **the 13th number in row 16 is 133.**

Figure 1

Row	Last number
1	1 = 1
2	3 = 1+2
3	6 = 1+2+3
⋮	⋮
16	? = 1+2+3+ …+16

Figure 2

$$1 + 2 + 3 + \ldots + 14 + 15 + 16$$

17
17
17

FOLLOW-UP: *What is the last number in the 11th row of the pattern below?* [131]

Row 1:	1			
Row 2:	3	5		
Row 3:	7	9	11	
Row 4:	13	15	17	19

5C METHOD 1: *Strategy: List the numbers that satisfy each condition.*

Numbers that are greater than 250 and 2 more than a multiple of:

7:   254, 261, 268, 275, 282, …, 310, **317**, 324, …
5:   252, 257, 262, 267, 272, 277, 282, …, 307, 312, **317**, 322, …
3:   251, 254, 257, 260, 263, 266, …, 314, **317**, 320, …

The least number of toy soldiers that Joshua may have is the least number to appear in all 3 lists, **317**.

METHOD 2: _Strategy: Use common multiples._
In each case 2 toy soldiers were left over. Suppose Joshua had 2 fewer toy soldiers. Then their number would be a multiple of 3, of 5, and of 7. No two of these numbers have a common factor, so their least common multiple is their product, 105. The number of soldiers is thus 2 more than a multiple of 105. The first multiple of 105 that is more than 250 is 315, so the least number of toy soldiers Joshua may have is 315 + 2 = 317.

> **FOLLOW-UPS:** _(1) What is the least four-digit number divisible by 5, 7, 15, and 21? [1050] (2) What is the least number that leaves a remainder of 3 when divided by 5, a remainder of 4 when divided by 6, and a remainder of 5 when divided by 7? (Hint: Find a nearby number that is a multiple of 5, 6, and 7.) [208]_

5D _Strategy: Split the figure into more familiar shapes._
Draw the three diagonals of the hexagon.

METHOD 1: _Figure 1_: The three diagonals divide the hexagon into six congruent triangles. Two of the triangles are completely shaded. The other four triangles are half shaded and half clear.

Figure 1

Figure 2: The halves of the partly shaded triangles can be rearranged to form two clear triangles and two additional completely shaded ones. The four shaded triangles have a total area of 60 sq cm, so each the area of each is 15 sq cm. This is also the area of each clear triangle, so **the area of the entire hexagon is** $6 \times 15 = $ **90 sq cm.**

Figure 2

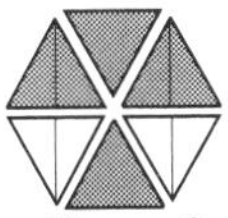

METHOD 2: _Figure 3_: In addition to the diagonals, draw three vertical lines as shown. These lines split the hexagon into twelve congruent triangles, eight of which are shaded. The shaded area is 60 sq cm, so each shaded triangle has an area of $60 \div 8 = 7\frac{1}{2}$ sq cm and the area of the entire hexagon is $7\frac{1}{2} \times 12 = 90$ sq cm.

Figure 3

5E _Strategy: Work backwards._
The last term, 60, is the sum of the preceding term, 37, and the term before that, 23. Writing the sequence in reverse order and subtracting each term from the preceding one gives 60, 37, 23, 14, 9, 5, 4. **There are 7 entries in the sequence.**

> **FOLLOW-UP:** _Exploration: These numbers are based on the Fibonacci Sequence, which is 1, 1, 2, 3, 5, 8, 13, 34, 55, and so on. Investigate its properties, history (bee or rabbit births), and applications (where in nature this sequence occurs)._

1A *Strategy: Rearrange the numbers to simplify the arithmetic.*
$55 - 11 + 44 - 22 + 33 - 33 + 22 - 44 + 11 - 55 =$
    $(55 - 55) + (44 - 44) + (33 - 33) + (22 - 22) + (11 - 11) = 0$
The value is 0.

> **FOLLOW–UP:** *What is the value of the following?*
> $(1 - \frac{1}{2}) + (\frac{1}{2} - \frac{1}{3}) + (\frac{1}{3} - \frac{1}{4}) + (\frac{1}{4} - \frac{1}{5}) + (\frac{1}{5} - \frac{1}{6}) + (\frac{1}{6} - \frac{1}{7})$ [ans. $\frac{6}{7}$]

1B *Strategy: Consider the ones and tens digits separately*
Any number with a ones digit of 4 is a multiple of 2 and is therefore not prime. If the tens digit is 4, the number could be 41, 43, 45, 47, or 49. But $45 = 9 \times 5$, and $49 = 7 \times 7$. The others are prime. **There are 3 two-digit prime numbers that have a digit of 4.**

> **FOLLOW-UP:** *The sum of two prime numbers is 63. Find their product.* [122]

1C **METHOD 1:** *Strategy: Find the dimensions of the shaded area.*
Since the area of the large square is 49 sq cm, each side is 7 cm. The area of the small square is 25 sq cm, and each side is 5 cm. The lengths of the sides of the larger and smaller squares differ by 2 cm. Therefore the sides of the shaded region are 7, 7, 5, 5, 2, and 2 cm and its **perimeter is 28 cm.**

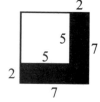

METHOD 2: *Strategy: Find a simpler equivalent problem.*
The area of the large square is 49 sq cm, so each side is 7 cm. The opposite sides of the small square are congruent, as indicated by the arrows. Thus, the distance "traveled" around the shaded region is the same as the distance traveled around the large square, and their perimeters are equal. Then the perimeter of the shaded region **is** $4 \times 7 = 28$ cm.
(*Note that the size of the small square is irrelevant!*)

1D *Strategy: Determine which digits satisfy each condition.*
The single digit prime numbers are 2, 3, 5, and 7. The single digit perfect squares are 0, 1, 4, and 9, leaving 6 and 8 as neither prime nor perfect square. Choose the largest digit in each group and arrange from greatest to least to get the largest possible number, 987. But 987 is divisible by 3. To get the next greatest number, choose the next greatest digit from the group containing 7. **The greatest possible value of Janine's number is 985.**

1E   **METHOD 1:**   *Strategy*: *Find the number of multiples of 9 less than each given value.*
Since $600 \div 9 = 66\frac{2}{3}$, there are 66 numbers less than 600 that are divisible by 9. Since $400 \div 9 = 44\frac{4}{9}$, there are 44 numbers less than 400 that are divisible by 9. Because neither 400 nor 600 is divisible by 9, **there are** $66 - 44 =$ **22 numbers between 400 and 600 that are divisible by 9.**

METHOD 2:   *Strategy*: *Split the numbers in the interval into groups of 9.*
Between 400 and 600, there are 199 whole numbers, excluding 400 and 600. Dividing 199 by 9 yields 22 with a remainder of 1. Thus there are 22 complete groups of 9 consecutive numbers. Each group contains exactly one multiple of 9. The "leftover" number, 599, is not a multiple of 9, so there are 22 numbers in the interval that are divisible by 9.

METHOD 3:   *Strategy*: *Find the first number and repeatedly add 9.*
$400 \div 9 = 44\frac{4}{9}$, so the first number greater than 400 that is divisible by 9 is $45 \times 9 = 405$.

Then 405, 414, 423, 432, 441, 450, 459, 468, 477, 486, 495, 504, 513, 522, 531, 540, 549, 558, 567, 576, 585, and 594 are all divisible by 9, 22 numbers in all.

> ***FOLLOW-UPS:*** *How many numbers between 401 and 599 are divisible (1) by 2 _and_ 5? (2) by 2 _or_ 5?* [19; 119]

Olympiad 2

2A   *Strategy*: *Use reasoning.*
Aaron is not wearing yellow and Chris is wearing white, so Aaron is wearing pink and **Becky's shirt is yellow.**

2B   **METHOD 1:**   *Strategy*: *Make two lists and look for a common member.*
Three-digit multiples of 5: 100, 105, 110, 115, **120**, ...
Three-digit multiples of 6: 102, 108, 114, **120**, ...
The least number to leave a remainder of 1 when divided by 5 or by 6 is 121.

METHOD 2:   *Strategy*: *Use the least common multiple.*
The number sought is 1 more than a multiple of 5 and also 1 more than a multiple of 6. Since 5 and 6 have no factors in common, their least common multiple is $5 \times 6 = 30$. The smallest three-digit multiple of 30 is 120, so the least such number is 121.

> ***FOLLOW-UP:*** *What is the smallest number greater than 1 which leaves a remainder of 1 when divided by 2,3,4,5,6,7,8, or 9?* [2521]

2C   **METHOD 1:**   _Strategy: Find the interval between consecutive multiples._
Draw four blanks to represent the four consecutive multiples. 28 is midway between the first two multiples and 44 is midway between the last two.

$$\underline{}\overset{28}{\downarrow}\underline{} \quad \underline{}\overset{44}{\downarrow}\underline{}$$

It takes two equal "jumps" in value to go from 28 to 44, so each jump is 8. It takes half a jump, 4, to go from 44 to the greatest multiple, so **the greatest multiple on Abby's list is 48.**

METHOD 2:   _Strategy: Examine number pairs that average 28._
Number pairs that average 28: (27,29), (26,30), (25,31), (24,32), and so on. Of these pairs, only 24 and 32 are <u>consecutive</u> multiples of a number, namely 8. The next two multiples of 8 are 40 and 48, which do average 44. The greatest multiple is 48.

METHOD 3:   _Strategy: Find the number of which each is a multiple._
The sum of the first two multiples is $28 \times 2 = 56$. The sum of the last two multiples is $44 \times 2 = 88$. If the list of multiples is extended, both sums would also appear on the list. The greatest common factor of 56 and 88 is 8, so that the numbers on the list are 24, 32, 40, and 48, of which 48 is greatest.

> **FOLLOW-UPS:** _(1) On a list of ten numbers, the average of the first 2 is 20, the average of the next 3 is 30, and the average of the last 5 is 50. What is the average of all ten numbers?_ [38]   _(2) List any four consecutive multiples of your favorite number. What is the difference between the sum of the last two and the sum of the first two?_ [4 times your favorite number] _How could this have been used in the solution of the problem?_

2D   _Strategy: Find the dimensions of the overlap (PQRS)._
Because the area of rectangle _ABCD_ is 14 sq cm and _AD_ = 7 cm, then _AB_ = 2 cm. Thus the length of $\overline{PQ}$ also is 2 cm. Likewise, _EH_ = $33 \div 11 = 3$ cm, so that the length of $\overline{PS}$ also is 3 cm.

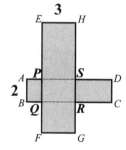

METHOD 1:   _Strategy: Eliminate the duplication of the overlap._
The area of the overlap _PQRS_ is 6 sq cm. It is included in the areas of both rectangles, _ABCD_ and _EFGH_. The sum of the given areas, 14 sq cm and 33 sq cm, include the 6 sq cm counted twice. **The area of the shaded region is $14 + 33 - 6 = 41$ sq cm.**

METHOD 2:   _Strategy: Draw a simpler diagram._
Move rectangle _ABCD_ so that _A_ coincides with _E_ as shown. The total area and the area of the overlap are unchanged. As above, _AB_ = 2 cm and _EH_ = 3 cm. Then _HD_ = $7 - 3 = 4$ cm. The area of the shaded region = the area of _EFGH_ + the area of _HTCD_ = $33 + (4 \times 2) = 41$ sq cm.

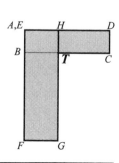

2E _Strategy:_ _Find the area of one face of a cube._

The surface of the stack consists of 14 squares (the top of the stack, the bottom of the stack, and the 12 vertical squares on the sides of the stack). The area of each square is $350 \div 14 = 25$ sq cm. If the cubes are wrapped separately, each cube has to be covered on 6 square faces, a total of $3 \times 6 = 18$ faces. That is 4 more faces than were covered originally and therefore $4 \times 25 =$ **100 sq cm of additional paper is needed.**

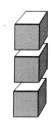

> **FOLLOW-UP:** _Five cubes, whose edges measure 1,2,3,4, and 5 cm, respectively, are stacked so that each of them except the largest rests on top of the next largest one. How many sq cm of paint are needed to cover the exposed surface of the pile? (Include the bottom face of the largest cube.)_ [270]

Olympiad 3

3A **METHOD 1:** _Strategy:_ _Use the test for divisibility by 11._

If a number is divisible by 11, the difference of the sums of alternating digits is either 0 or some other multiple of 11. $(4 + 9) - (8 + A)$ is divisible by 11 if **A represents the digit 5.**

METHOD 2: _Strategy:_ _Do the division._

```
        4 4 ?
1 1 ) 4 8 9 A
      4 4
        4 9
        4 4
          5 A
          5 5
            0
```

Since the final subtraction produces a 0, A represents 5.

> **FOLLOW-UP:** _(1) What digit might A represent if 87A4 is divisible by 8?_ [0, 4, or 8]. _(2) Find all values for A and B for which the five digit number 16A3B is divisible by 44._ [There are 2 solutions: $(A,B) = (6,2)$ or $(2,6)$.]

3B **METHOD 1:** _Strategy:_ _Equalize the number of each type of coin._

After she gets an additional quarter, Emma has $\$1.85 + \$.25 = \$2.10$. Pair each nickel with a quarter. Each pair is worth $\$.30$, so there are $210¢ \div 30¢$ pairs. **Emma has 7 nickels.**

Note: Instead of adding a quarter, you could just subtract a nickel, and then follow the above reasoning.

METHOD 2: _Strategy: Start with the maximum number of quarters._

Since Emma began with $1.85, she began with 7 quarters at most. The table uses the number of quarters and the corresponding number of nickels to find the total value.

# of quarters to start	7	6	5
# of nickels to start	8	7	6
Value of these coins	$2.15	$1.85	$1.55

If Emma has 6 quarters and 7 nickels, the conditions of the problem are satisfied. Emma has 7 nickels.

> **FOLLOW-UP:** _A farm has 8 more chickens than cows. The cows and chickens have a total of 166 legs. How many chickens are on the farm?_ [33]

3C METHOD 1: _Strategy: Minimize the perimeter after each fold._

To reduce the perimeter as much as possible at each step, fold the longer side in half.

Start with an 8 cm by 12 cm rectangle. After one fold it is 8 cm by 6 cm. After two folds it is 4 cm by 6 cm. After 3 folds it is 4 cm by 3 cm. **The least possible perimeter after 3 folds is** $2 \times 4 + 2 \times 3 =$ **14 cm.**

METHOD 2: _Strategy: Examine all the possibilities._

Denote by A a fold that halves the vertical side and by B a fold that halves the horizontal side. Note that the final perimeter is determined by the number of folds in each direction but not the order of the folds.

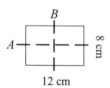

Folds	AAA	AAB	ABB	BBB
Dimensions after 1 fold	12×4	12×4	12×4	6×8
2 folds	12×2	12×2	6×4	3×8
3 folds	12×1	6×2	3×4	1.5×8
Final perimeter	26 cm	16 cm	14 cm	19 cm

The least possible perimeter after 3 folds is 14 cm.

3D METHOD 1: _Strategy: First adjust the number of fences._

Two fences can be painted by 4 people in 5 hours, so 8 fences takes those same 4 people 4 times as long, or 20 hours. If 4 people need 20 hours to paint the 8 fences, then 8 people will take only half as long to do the job. **It takes 10 hours for 8 people to paint 8 fences.**

METHOD 2: _Strategy: First adjust the number of people._

If 4 people need 5 hours to paint the 2 fences, then 8 people need only half as long ($2\frac{1}{2}$ hours) to paint the 2 fences. To paint 8 fences, the 8 people need 4 times as long, 10 hours.

METHOD 3: *Strategy: Find the number of "person-hours" needed to paint a fence.*
If 4 people can paint 2 fences in 5 hours, then one person working alone takes 4 times as long, 20 hours, to paint those 2 fences. Then to paint 1 fence, one person needs 10 hours. Thus 8 people can paint 8 times as many fences, 8 fences, in the same 10 hours.

3E   METHOD 1: *Strategy: Start with simpler cases and look for a pattern.*
To form the sequence of units (ones) digits start with 7, 9, 3, and 1. Then repeatedly multiply the units digit of the last term by 7 and continually discard the tens digit to find each succeeding term. The first eight terms are 7, 9, 3, 1, 7, 9, 3, 1, and a pattern appears.

The product of four factors of 7 has a units digit of 1. So does the product of eight, twelve, sixteen factors of 7, and so on. Thus, every fourth term is 1. The 48th term, which is the units digit of the product of 48 factors of 7, is also 1. Since $1 \times 7 \times 7$ ends in 9, the 50th term, which is **the units digit of the product of 50 factors of 7, is 9.**

METHOD 2: *Strategy: Find an equivalent but simpler problem.*
Group the 50 factors of 7 into 25 pairs: $(7 \times 7) \times (7 \times 7) \times \cdots \times (7 \times 7)$. Thus 7^{50} equals 25 factors of 49. Only the units digit is important, so we can use 9 instead of 49. That is, examine the ones digit of the product of 25 factors of 9. But the product of an *even* number of 9s ends in 1, and the product of an *odd* number of 9s ends in 9. The ones digit in the product of 25 factors of 9 is 9, so 7^{50} ends in 9 after all the multiplication is done.

> ***FOLLOW-UPS:*** *(1) Repeated multiplication by 7 produces 4 different ones digits: 7,9,3,1. What other numbers when repeatedly multiplied also produce 4 different ones digits? [2,3,8] (2) What is the tens digit in the product of fifty factors of 7? [4]*

Olympiad 4

4A   *Strategy: List the single-digit primes.*
The single-digit prime numbers are 2, 3, 5, and 7. Select the 3 greatest numbers from this list and write them from largest to smallest. **The last time before noon when all 3 digits are prime is 7:53.**

> ***FOLLOW-UP:*** *At how many times between midnight and noon will the digits be 3 different primes? [18]*

SET 4 SOLUTIONS

4B <u>Strategy</u>: *Make an organized list.*
List all the ways four different numbers can add to 15. Starting with the largest number reduces the number of trials necessary. Because $3 + 2 + 1 = 6$ is the least possible sum for 3 of the numbers, the greatest number can't exceed $15 - 6 = 9$.

$15 = 9 + 6 = 9 + 3 + 2 + 1$
$15 = 8 + 7 = 8 + 4 + 2 + 1$
$15 = 7 + 8 = 7 + 5 + 2 + 1$ or $7 + 4 + 3 + 1$
$15 = 6 + 9 = 6 + 5 + 3 + 1$ or $6 + 4 + 3 + 2$

15 can be written as the sum of four different counting numbers in 6 different ways.

4C **METHOD 1:** <u>Strategy</u>: *Count horizontally, from the top layer down.*
Make a table that counts cubes separately for each layer. In each case, add the number of hidden cubes to the number of visible cubes.

Layer	Cubes in layer (visible + hidden)
1 (top)	1 = 1
2	2 + 1 = 3
3	3 + 3 = 6
4 (bottom)	4 + 6 = 10

$1 + 3 + 6 + 10 = $ **20 cubes are used to form the tower.**

METHOD 2: <u>Strategy</u>: *Count vertically, stack by stack.*
This table counts cubes separately for each stack (column), from the shortest to the tallest. Both hidden and visible cubes are counted.

Height of each stack	No. of stacks	Total cubes by height
1 cube high	4	4
2	3	6
3	2	6
4	1	4
	Total	**20**

A total of 20 cubes are used to form the tower.

> **FOLLOW-UPS:** *(1) How many cubes would be in a similar tower of 5 layers? 6? 7?* [35, 56, 84] *(2) Suppose the bottom layer of a similar tower has 91 cubes. How many layers would there be?* [13]

168   *Division E*

4D *Strategy: Consider the clues one at a time, starting with the most restrictive clue.*
Clue 3: The only prime factor of the 4-digit number is 11, so the number = 11×11 or $11 \times 11 \times 11$ or $11 \times 11 \times 11 \times 11$, etc. Of these, only $11 \times 11 \times 11 = 1331$ has 4 digits, so the 6-digit number is _1331_.

Clue 1: The number reads the same right to left, so the first and last digits are the same. Call the number A1331A.

Clue 2: The number is a multiple of 9, so the sum of its digits is a multiple of 9. $A + 1 + 3 + 3 + 1 + A = A + 8 + A$ must equal 9 or 18. No digit A satisfies $A + 8 + A = 9$, but if $A + 8 + A = 18$, $A = 5$. **Hannah's number is 513 315.**

4E *Strategy: Make the figure as compact as possible.*
The area of one L-shape is 3 sq cm. A figure made up of 5 L-shapes has an area of 15 sq cm. The fact that all the angles in each shape are right angles suggests trying to pack the 5 shapes into a square of area 16 sq cm. This can be done as shown in the figure.

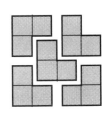

The least possible perimeter is $4 + 4 + 3 + 3 + 1 + 1 = $ **16 cm.**

Olympiad 5

5A **METHOD 1:** *Strategy: Use a diagram to show what happens.*
The upper box shows Sara's age divided by 3 and then increased by 8. This restores her age, so 8 is the remaining $\frac{2}{3}$ of her age. Then $\frac{1}{3}$ of her age is 4, and **Sara is 12 years old.**

←	Sara's age	→
age ÷ 3		8

4	4	4

METHOD 2: *Strategy: Compare her age and 8 more than one-third of it.*
Sara's age is divisible by 3, so it is one of 3, 6, 9, 12, 15, and so on. Since this is 8 more than $\frac{1}{3}$ of her age, she is at least 9 years old. Build a table to compare her age with 8 more than $\frac{1}{3}$ of it.

Sara's age, possibly	9	12	15	18	21	...
$\frac{1}{3}$ of Sara's age	3	4	5	6	7	...
8 more than $\frac{1}{3}$ of Sara's age	11	12	13	14	15	...

In all but one case, dividing her age by 3 and then adding 8 produces a different number. Sara is 12 years old.

METHOD 3: _Strategy: Use algebra._

Let a represent Sara's age in years. Then $\frac{1}{3}a$ represents Sara's age divided by 3.

Sara's age is equal to 8 more than her age divided by 3: $a = \frac{1}{3}a + 8$

Multiply each side of the equation by 3: $3a = a + 24$
Subtract a from each side of the equation: $2a = 24$
Divide each side of the equation by 2: $a = 12$

Sara is 12 years old.

> **FOLLOW-UP:** _Three times my age is equal to 2 years more than my father's age. In 11 years, my age will be half of his age. How old am I?_ [13]

5B   METHOD 1: _Strategy: Use the fact that the common difference is 3._

The increase of 3 in each successive term suggests comparing the numbers to the multiples of 3.

The given list is 5, 8, 11, 14, … and the multiples of 3 are 3, 6, 9, 12, … Each number in the list is 2 more than a multiple of 3. The greatest multiple of 3 that is less than 100 is 99 and 99 + 2 = 101. **The first number in the list that is greater than 100 is 101.**

METHOD 2: _Strategy: Determine some number in the list that is near 100._

Begin with 14, the last number given. Since each term is 3 more than the term before it, adding a convenient multiple of 3, say 30, to 14 will produce other numbers in the list : 14, …, 44, …, 74, …, 104. Then count backwards from 104 by 3s to get other members of the list: 101 and then 98. The least number in the list that is greater than 100 is 101.

5C   _Strategy: Use the algorithms for addition and multiplication._

Since zero is never a leading digit, the letter O does not represent zero.
In the addition, O + O does not produce a "carry", so O = 1, 2, 3, or 4.
In the multiplication, 4 × O + a possible "carry" of 0, 1, 2, or 3 gives the
two-digit number ending in FO.

$$\begin{array}{r} O\,N\,E \\ +\,F\,O\,U\,R \\ \hline F\,I\,V\,E \end{array}$$

Suppose O = 1. Then 4 × 1 + the carry = F1. No carry works.
Suppose O = 2. Then 4 × 2 + the carry = F2. No carry works.
Suppose O = 3. Then 4 × 3 + the carry = F3. This works if the carry is 1.
Suppose O = 4. Then 4 × 4 + the carry = F4. No carry works.

$$\begin{array}{r} O\,N\,E \\ \times\,4 \\ \hline F\,O\,U\,R \end{array}$$

The letter O represents the digit 3.

> **FOLLOW-UP:** _Complete the solution of the cryptarithm. What is the four-digit number FIVE?_ [1725]

5D _Strategy_: Determine the possible pairs of numbers on each tile.
As shown in figure 1, list the 25 possible pairings, with the first letter representing the front of the tile.

Eliminate the circled tiles because they have the same letter on the front and back.

This leaves two of each pairing. Cross out the second listing of each pairing. Figure 2 shows the ten remaining pairings.

Now consider the four tiles that have E on the back. Each row must have exactly one such tile, or else two tiles would be identical. The DE tile, however, is the _only_ tile in the bottom row. You can point to the tile that shows the D and _know_ the back has an E. **The fewest tiles you can point to is 1.**

figure 1

AA, AB, AC, AD, AE
BA, BB, BC, BD, BE
CA, CB, CC, CD, CE
DA, DB, DC, DD, DE
EA, EB, EC, ED, EE

figure 2

AB, AC, AD, AE
BC, BD, BE
CD, CE
→ DE

> _FOLLOW-UPS_: (1) Suppose the letter on the back does not have to be different from the letter on the front. Would the complete set still consist of 10 tiles? [No. 15 are needed] (2) Would you still be able to point to one tile and know the back contains an E? [Yes. The E on the front would have to have an E on the back.] (3) Suppose there are more than 5 letters. Would you still be able to find the F (or G or ...) on the back in one try? [Yes.Use the above reasoning.]

5E **METHOD 1:** _Strategy_: Evaluate each expression.
$8 \odot 5 = (8 \times 8) - (5 \times 5) = 64 - 25 = 39$
$5 \odot 2 = (5 \times 5) - (2 \times 2) = 25 - 4 = 21$.
The sum is $39 + 21 = $60.

METHOD 2: _Strategy_: Eliminate unnecessary terms.
$(8 \odot 5) + (5 \odot 2) = (8 \times 8) - (5 \times 5) + (5 \times 5) - (2 \times 2)$.
Notice that you are both subtracting and adding (5×5).
$(8 \odot 5) + (5 \odot 2) = (8 \times 8) - (2 \times 2) = 64 - 4 = 60$.

> _FOLLOW-UPS_: (1) Suppose $(27 \odot 23) + (23 \odot 12) = (27 \odot N)$. What is the value of N? [12] (2) What is the sum of $(100 \odot 97) + (97 \odot 94) + (94 \odot 91) + ... + (4 \odot 1)$? [9,999]

Set 5   Olympiad 1

1A   METHOD 1: _Strategy: Simplify using the Distributive Property._
$(8 \times 4) + (8 \times 3) + (8 \times 2) + (8 \times 1) = 8 \times (4 + 3 + 2 + 1) = 8 \times 10.$ **The value is 80.**

METHOD 2: _Strategy: Perform the operations as indicated._
$(8 \times 4) + (8 \times 3) + (8 \times 2) + (8 \times 1) = 32 + 24 + 16 + 8 = 80.$

1B   _Strategy: Consider the worst case._
We must avoid picking a second blue jelly bean as long as we can. Suppose Amanda picks all the red and white jelly beans first. She then has used 10 picks and her next two picks must be blue. **Without looking, she knows that among the 12 jelly beans she has picked, at least two must be blue.**

> **FOLLOW-UPS:** _(1) Suppose she wants two jelly beans of the same color, regardless of which color it is. What is the fewest jelly beans she must pick in this case?_ [4]   _(2) How many jelly beans would she need to pick to ensure that she has at least two of each color?_ [16]

1C   _Strategy: Examine each number in the sequence._
Use divisibility tests to determine whether each number in the sequence, taken in ascending order, is prime or composite. The first five numbers (2, 5, 11, 23, and 47) are each prime. The next number, 95, ends in a 5 and is divisible by 5. **Thus, 95 is the first number in the sequence that is _not_ a prime number.**

> **FOLLOW-UP:** _Consider all the prime numbers less than 100. How many pairs of consecutive prime numbers have an odd difference?_ [1]

1D   METHOD 1: _Strategy: Count in an organized way._
The table on the next page shows the total count-down time separated into one-minute intervals. The second column specifies which times contain a "2" and the third column counts the total number of seconds "2" is displayed in each interval.

Time intervals	Seconds showing a "2"	Number of such times
4:59 to 4:00	4:29 through 4:20; also 4:52, 4:42, 4:32, 4:12, 4:02	15
3:59 to 3:00	3:29 through 3:20; also 3:52, 3:42, 3:32, 3:12, 3:02	15
2:59 to 2:00	2:59 through 2:00	60
1:59 to 1:00	1:29 through 1:20; also 1:52, 1:42, 1:32, 1:12, 1:02	15
0:59 to 0:00	0:29 through 0:20; also 0:52, 0:42, 0:32, 0:12, 0:02	15
	Total number of seconds	**120**

Thus, one of the digits shows a "2" for 120 seconds.

METHOD 2: *Strategy: Count the number of seconds that a 2 is _not_ showing.*
Consider the times from 4:59 through 0:00, a total of 300 seconds.

• The minute digit is 4, 3, 2, 1, or 0. There are 4 values other than 2.
• The 10-second digit is 5, 4, 3, 2, 1, or 0. There are 5 values other than 2.
• The second digit is 9, 8, 7, 6, 5, 4, 3, 2, 1, or 0. There are 9 values other than 2.

We can form a reading that does not show 2 by choosing a non-2 for each of the 3 digits. This can be done in $4 \times 5 \times 9 = 180$ different ways. There are then 180 seconds in which no 2 is showing and therefore $300 - 180 = 120$ seconds in which at least one 2 is showing.

> **FOLLOW-UPS:** *(1) Which of the other digits will also be displayed for exactly 120 seconds?*
> [4,3,1]   *(2) How many numbers between 200 and 600 are _not_ divisible by 5?* [320]

1E   *Strategy: Minimize the use of the longest sides.*
By touching all 4 front corners first and then all 4 rear corners as shown, the ant can travel along a 20-cm side only once. If the ant starts along a 4-cm side when touching the 4 front corners, it travels only once along a 15 cm side. The same is true when the ant touches the 4 rear corners. **The shortest distance that the ant may travel is** $(4 \times 4) + (2 \times 15) + (1 \times 20) =$ **66 cm.** The diagram shows one of several possible paths.

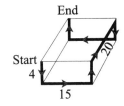

> **FOLLOW-UP:** *How many different paths are 66 cm long?* [8, one starting at each corner]

SET 5 SOLUTIONS

Olympiad 2

2A **METHOD 1:** _Strategy: Work from right to left._
In the ones column, $5 + 8 + T$ ends in 5, so $T = 2$ (with a "carry" of 1). Then $1 + 4 + 7 + A$ ends in 0, so $A = 8$ (with a carry of 2). Finally, $2 + 3 + 6 + C$ is 12, so $C = 1$. **The three-digit number _CAT_ is 182.**

$$\begin{array}{r} 3\ 4\ 5 \\ 6\ 7\ 8 \\ +\ C\ A\ T \\ \hline 1\ 2\ 0\ 5 \end{array}$$

METHOD 2: _Strategy: Add the first two numbers and subtract from the sum._
$1205 - (345 + 678) = 1205 - 1023 = 182$.

> **FOLLOW-UP:** _Find digits A and B in the following multiplication:_ $12{,}345{,}679 \times A = BBB{,}BBB{,}BBB$. [$A = 9$, $B = 1$; the digits of BBB,BBB,BBB add to $9 \times B$, a multiple of 9.]

2B _Strategy: List the prime numbers._
The first few primes are 2, 3, 5, 7, 11, 13, 17, 19… . A "twinner" is surrounded by primes, so look for pairs of primes that differ by 2 (these are called _twin primes_). The first three pairs are 3 & 5, 5 & 7, and 11 & 13. The three least "twinners" are 4, 6 and 12, and **their sum is 22.**

> **FOLLOW-UPS:** _(1) Find three primes such that the sum of two of them equals the third._ [2 and any pair of twin primes] _(2) Can you find a solution to (1) without using 2 as one of the numbers? Explain._ [No. All primes except 2 are odd, and the sum of two odd numbers is even.]

2C _Strategy: Find the range of possible sums._
If each die shows 1, the total is 5. If each die shows 6, the total is 30. All integral sums from 5 to 30 inclusive are possible. These are all the counting numbers up to 30, except for 1 through 4. Then **26 different sums are possible.**

2D _Strategy: Determine the length of the common side._
$\overline{DC}$ is a side of both rectangles _ABCD_ and _DCFE,_ and its length is then a factor of both 63 and 35. The only common factors of 63 and 35 are 1 and 7. _DC_ cannot be 1, or else _AB_ would be 1 and _DE_ would be 35. But since _AB_ is given as longer than _DE_, _DC_ must be 7. Then $AD = 9$, $DE = 5$, and **_AE_ is 14 cm long.**

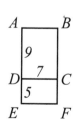

Division E

2E _Strategy: Working backwards, find the winner of each round._

The winner of a round receives as many marbles as she already has from each of the others. For example, if she has 4, she would get 8 more, 4 from each player, for a total of 12. **This triples what she has.** That is, after each round, the winner's total is a multiple of 3.

At the end of Round 2, the only multiple of 3 is Brenda's total, 6, so she won Round 2. Brenda must have started Round 2 with 2 marbles and received 2 more from each of the others. The table below shows how many marbles each had at the end of each round.

Similarly, at the end of Round 1, the only multiple of 3 is Cate's highlighted total, 9, so she won Round 1. Cate had started Round 1 with 3 marbles and received 3 more from each of the others. **At the start of the game, Ashley had** $7 + 3 = $ **10 marbles** as highlighted in the table.

Round	Ashley	Brenda	Cate
End of Round 2 — Brenda won 2 marbles from each	5	**6**	7
End of Round 1 — Cate won 3 marbles from each	7	2	**9**
Start	**10**	5	3

Olympiad 3

3A _Strategy: Consider each condition in turn._

Since $3 + 9 = 5 + 7$, the last two digits are either 39, 93, 57, or 75. Because Joshua's number is a multiple of 5, the last two digits are 75. The thousands digit is greater than the hundreds, so the first two digits are 93. **Joshua's number is 9375.**

3B **METHOD 1:** _Strategy: Combine the given information._

Suppose Megan has enough money to buy 1 hat and 2 shirts for $21 and then another 2 hats and 1 shirt for $18. In total, she would have bought 3 hats and 3 shirts for $39. But actually she can afford only 1 hat and 1 shirt, and so **Megan has** $39 \div 3 = $ **$13.**

METHOD 2: _Strategy: Make a table._

Try different values for the cost of 1 shirt: $5, $6, $7, and so on. Use the first statement to find the cost of a hat. See which value also gives $18 for the second statement.

Costs:

1 shirt:	$5	$6	$7	$8
2 shirts:	$10	$12	$14	$16
1 hat:	21 − 10 = $11	21 − 12 = $9	21 − 14 = $7	21 − 16 = $5
2 hats + 1 shirt:	2×11 + 5 = $27	2×9 + 6 = $24	2×7 + 7 = $21	2×5 + 8 = $18

A shirt costs $8 and a hat costs $5. Megan has $13.

3C   METHOD 1: _Strategy: Find the time 1 painter needs to paint 1 room._

For three painters to paint one classroom, 4 hours are needed. So for one painter to paint that classroom, $3 \times 4 = 12$ hours are needed. **Then for one painter to paint <u>two</u> classrooms, it would take** twice as long, or **24 hours.**

METHOD 2: _Strategy: Find the part of a room done per hour by 1 painter._

In 4 hours, 3 painters can paint 1 classroom, so in 1 hour the 3 painters can paint $\frac{1}{4}$ of a room. Then in 1 hour each painter paints $\frac{1}{12}$ of a room. So each painter working alone needs 12 hours to paint 1 classroom and therefore 24 hours to paint 2 classrooms.

METHOD 3: _Strategy: Draw a picture._

In the pictures, each small square represents 1 painter's work for 1 hour. The first picture shows that 3 painters (rows) need 4 hours (columns) to paint 1 classroom. The next picture, to show the time the 3 painters need for 2 classrooms, doubles the number of squares (by doubling the number of columns). The third picture rearranges the small squares into 1 column (1 painter) and shows that 1 painter needs 24 hours to paint the 2 classrooms.

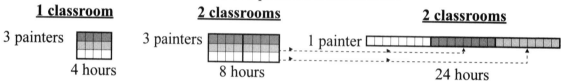

1 classroom	**2 classrooms**	**2 classrooms**
3 painters	3 painters	1 painter
4 hours	8 hours	24 hours

3D   _Strategy: Place the largest tiles first._

Start with a 3 by 3 tile. No matter where it is placed, the greatest number of squares remaining in a row or column is two. So only one 3 by 3 tile can be used. Put it in a corner position to allow maximum space for the 2 by 2 tiles.

Then three of the 2 by 2 tiles can be placed. One placement is shown. The remaining spaces must be filled by the 1 by 1 tiles. There are four of those spaces. **The fewest number of tiles is** $1 + 3 + 4 = \mathbf{8}.$

> **FOLLOW-UP:** _What would be the fewest number of tiles Mr. Wright would need if his floor measured 6 ft by 6 ft? 7 ft by 7 ft? 8 ft by 8 ft?_ [4; 12; 11]

3E   METHOD 1: _Strategy: Find a large factor first._

Note that 111,111 consists of 2 blocks of the digits "111". Then 111 is a factor of 111,111. Upon division, $111{,}111 = 111 \times 1001$. First factor 111. Because the sum of the digits of 111 is 3, 3 is a factor of 111. Upon division, $111 = 3 \times 37$. Both 3 and 37 factors are prime numbers.

The problem states that there are 3 more prime factors. 1001 satisfies the divisibility test for 11 (See _What Every Young Mathlete Should Know_). Then $1001 \div 11 = 91$. 11 is prime, so 91 must be the product of the last 2 primes. To find them, you only need to test primes that are less than 10: 2, 3, and 5 don't work, but 7 does: $91 = 7 \times 13$, both of which are prime.

The sum of the 5 prime factors of 111,111 is $3 + 37 + 11 + 7 + 13 = \mathbf{71}.$

METHOD 2: *Strategy: Find a small factor first.*
The sum of the digits in 111,111 is 6, a multiple of 3, so 3 is a factor of 111,111. Then 111,111 = 3 × 37,037. To factor 37,037, try 37: 37,037 = 37 × 1001. Proceed as in Method 1 to find the other 3 prime factors 11, 7, and 13. The sum of the five prime factors is 71.

METHOD 3: *Strategy: Divide by each prime in order, starting with 2.*
111,111 ÷ **2** is not a whole number. 111,111 ÷ **3** = 37, 037. 37,037 ÷ **5** is not a whole number. 37,037 ÷ **7** = 5291. 5291 ÷ **11** = 481. 481 ÷ **13** = 37. 37 is prime. Then 3 + 7 + 11 + 13 + 37 = 71. (Note: Divide again by 3, 7, and 11 to ensure that no factor appears another time.)

> **FOLLOW-UP:** *(1) In Method 1, we said that in order to factor 91, it suffices to test primes less than 10. Why is this so?* [If both factors are 10 or more, the product is 100 or more.] *(2) To determine whether 421 is a prime number, you try to factor it. What is the greatest factor you have to try to show that it is prime?* [19]

Olympiad 4

4A **METHOD 1:** *Strategy: Work backwards.*
Shauna has $1, so Emma has 1 × 5 = $5, Ben has 5 + 3= $8, and Allie has half of 8 = $4. **Allie and Ben have** 8 + 4= **$12 together.**

> **FOLLOW-UP:** *Lauren went to the mall with all of her birthday money. She spent half of it on a pair of designer jeans, a third of what was left on a T-shirt, and a sixth of what was left after that on a slice of pizza and a soda. She returned home with $25. How much money did she get for her birthday?* [$90]

4B **METHOD 1:** *Strategy: Count paths to each letter separately.*
For each of the 4 paths from *A* to *B*, there is 1 path from *B* to *C* and then 3 paths from *C* to *D*.

There are 4 × 1 × 3 = **12 different paths that go from *A* to *B* to *C* to *D*** and touch each point once.

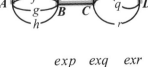

METHOD 2: *Strategy: Make an organized list.*
Label the individual paths by naming the three segments traveled. One such path, shown by the thick lines is *exp*. Paths from *A* to *B* to C to *D* can be represented by a tree diagram or by the list at the right:

There are 12 different paths in all.

exp	*exq*	*exr*
fxp	*fxq*	*fxr*
gxp	*gxq*	*gxr*
hxp	*hxq*	*hxr*

4C   **METHOD 1:** _Strategy: Compare the distances they ride each hour._

Each hour, Sarah rides 5 miles more than Tyler. **Sarah will be 30 miles ahead of Tyler in** $30 \div 5 =$ **6 hours.**

METHOD 2: _Strategy: Use algebra._

Sarah rides for t hours at 20 mph, so Sarah's distance is $20t$ miles. Likewise, Tyler's distance is $15t$ miles.

Sarah | $\longmapsto\!\!\!-\!\!20t\!\!\longrightarrow$
Tyler | $\longmapsto\!\!-\!15t\!\longrightarrow\!\mid\!\longleftarrow\!30\!\longrightarrow$

Sarah's distance is 30 miles more than Tyler's distance: $20t = 15t + 30$
Subtract $15t$ from each side of the equation: $5t = 30$
Divide each side of the equation by 5: $t = 6$

Sarah will be 30 miles ahead of Tyler in 6 hours.

> **FOLLOW-UP:** _Neighbors Jake and Mary drive to the same ski lodge 270 miles away, but Mary starts one hour before Jake. If Mary's average speed is 45 miles per hour and both people arrive at the same time, what is Jake's average speed?_ [54 mph]

4D   **METHOD 1:** _Strategy: Use the pattern in the given information._

Note that in each case the number of cards left over is 2 less than the number of piles. Suppose Michael gets 2 more cards. He can now put the cards into 3, 4, or 5 equal piles. Therefore the new number of cards is a multiple of 60, the Least Common Multiple (LCM) of 3, 4, and 5. Then before getting the extra 2 cards, **Michael has 58 cards.**

METHOD 2: _Strategy: Consider one condition at a time._

1. The number of cards is 3 more than a multiple of 5, so it ends in 3 or 8.
2. This number is also 2 more than a multiple of 4, so it is even. The number ends in 8.
3. The number is 1 more than a multiple of 3; the multiple of 3 itself must end in 7.
4. Add 1 to the multiples of 3 that end in 7: 28, 58, 88, 118, … and test each.
5. 28 satisfies two conditions, but is not 2 more than a multiple of 4. However, 58 satisfies all three conditions. Michael has 58 cards.

> **FOLLOW-UP:** _What is the least number that leaves a remainder of 3 when divided by 5, a remainder of 2 when divided by 6, a remainder of 1 when divided by 7, and is greater than 200? (Hint: Take some away.)_ [218]

4E   _Strategy: Find the length of one side of the box._

The perimeter of the figure is made up of 14 congruent segments. Each segment is $42 \div 14 = 3$ cm. Folding the figure forms a box 3 cm high with a 3 cm by 3 cm base. $3 \times 3 = 9$ one-cm cubes can fit in one layer on the bottom and 3 such layers can fit in the box. In all, **27 one-cm cubes can fit in the box.**

Olympiad 5

5A **METHOD 1:** <u>Strategy</u>: *Look for a pattern.*
Notice that the numbers in the first shaded box and the last shaded box add to 25. Similarly, $3 + 22 = 25$, $6 + 19 = 25$, and so on. Six pairs of numbers each add to 25, so **the sum of the numbers in the shaded boxes is** $6 \times 25 = $ **150.**

METHOD 2: <u>Strategy</u>: *Add in an organized way.*
Add each row:
The sum $18 + 50 + 82 = 150$.

Check by adding each column:
$9 + 20 + 22 + 12 + 13 + 28 + 30 + 16 = 150$.

1	2	3	4	5	6	7	8	*18*
9	10	11	12	13	14	15	16	*50*
17	18	19	20	21	22	23	24	*82*
9	*20*	*22*	*12*	*13*	*28*	*30*	*16*	**150**

> ***FOLLOW-UP:*** *What is the sum $1 + 2 + 4 + 8 + 16 + 32 + 64 + 128 + 256 + 512$? (Hint: Look for a pattern in the partial sums as terms are added left to right.)* [1023]

5B **METHOD 1:** <u>Strategy</u>: *Start with a specific number of each vehicle.*
Suppose all 200 vehicles were cars. The toll total would be $4 \times 200 = \$800$, which is $60 too low. Each car that is replaced by a truck increases the toll total by $2. To increase the total by $60, replace $60 \div 2 = 30$ cars by trucks. Then **30 of the vehicles were trucks.** Check the answer: $(30 \times \$6) + (170 \times \$4) = \$860$.

METHOD 2: <u>Strategy</u>: *Use algebra.*
Let $T = $ the number of trucks. They paid a total of $6T$ dollars.
Then $200 - T = $ the number of cars. They paid a total of $4(200 - T)$ dollars.

Together, all the cars and trucks paid a total of $860.

Multiply $(200 - T)$ by 4:
Add $6T$ to $-4T$:
Subtract 800 from each side of the equation:
Divide each side of the equation by 2:

$$4(200 - T) + 6T = 860$$
$$800 - 4T + 6T = 860$$
$$800 \qquad + 2T = 860$$
$$2T = 60$$
$$T = 30$$

30 of the vehicles were trucks.

Check as in method 1.

5C METHOD 1: _Strategy: Make two tables: BEFORE and AFTER._

The first table shows various combinations of candies before Zach eats. The second table shows the results of eating the candies and compares the numbers of blue and red candies.

BEFORE eating the 3 candies							
Blue	2	4	6	... 14	16	18	20
Red	1	2	3	... 7	8	9	10

AFTER eating the 3 candies							
Blue – 1	1	3	5	... 13	**15**	17	19
Red – 2	—	0	1	... 5	**6**	7	8

Zach ends with 15 blue and 6 red candies, which is 5 blues for every 2 reds. Then **Zach starts with** 16 blues and 8 reds for a total of **24 candies.**

METHOD 2: _Strategy: Group the candies two different ways._

At first, Zach can form groups of 3 candies with 2 blue and 1 red in each group. The total number of candies is a multiple of 3. After he eats 3, the total is still a multiple of 3, but now the candies can also be grouped by 7s with 5 blues and 2 reds in each group. Thus the new total is now a multiple of both 3 and 7; that is, a multiple of 21. Test 21, 42, 63, ... to see which multiple satisfies all conditions of the problem.

First test 21 candies. There are 3 groups of 7 and in each group 5 are blue and 2 are red. Thus there are 15 blue and 6 red candies. Adding back the 1 blue and 2 red candies that were eaten, there were originally 16 blue and 8 red candies. This is 2 blues for every red, so all conditions of the problem are satisfied. Zach starts with 16 + 8 = 24 candies.

Adding back the eaten candies to 42, 63, 84, and so on does not produce 2 blues for each red. Thus 24 is the only answer.

5D _Strategy: Draw a picture. First consider the vertical sides of the box._
The box has four vertical sides. For each, exactly 12 cubes (shown with an **X**), have just one face touching a side of the box. Only 9 cubes have exactly one face touching the bottom of the box, since each border cube on the bottom also touches one or two vertical sides. (To visualize it, sketch of the bottom of the box.) In all **a total of** $4 \times 12 + 9 =$ **57 one-cm cubes touch exactly one face of the box.**

FOLLOW-UPS: _(1) How many of the 125 unit cubes do not touch the box?_ [36]   _(2) Suppose the box had a closed top. How many unit cubes would touch exactly one face?_ [54] _(3) Now, suppose the closed box measured 4 cm on each edge. How many unit cubes would touch exactly one face?_ [24]   _(4) Suppose the closed box measured 6 cm on each edge. How many unit cubes would touch exactly one face?_ [96] _Can we generalize these results?_

5E **METHOD 1:** _Strategy: Work from the middle outward._
Consider the numbers listed in order from least to greatest.   __, __, __, __, __, __

Since 50 is the average, and all numbers are equally spaced,
the two consecutive odd numbers in the middle are 49 and 51.   __, __, 49, 51, __, __

Once these are in place, write the odd numbers that precede
49 and that follow 51 to complete the list.   45, 47, 49, 51, 53, 55

The least of these numbers is 45.

METHOD 2: _Strategy: Add the same amount to each member of the simplest possible set._
The sum of any 6 numbers is equal to 6 times their average, so the sum of the required numbers
is $6 \times 50 = 300$. Suppose the six consecutive odd numbers were 1, 3, 5, 7, 9, and 11. Their sum
would be 36, which is 264 short of 300. Add $264 \div 6 = 44$ to each of 1, 3, 5, …, 11: The least
number in the set {45, 47, 49, 51, 53, 55} is 45.

Set 6   Olympiad 1

1A _Strategy: Find the elapsed time in days._
Every 24 hours, the time is again 4:00 PM. Because $245 \div 24 = 10$ R5, **in 245 hours it will be**
10 days and 5 hours later, or **9 PM.**

> **FOLLOW-UP:** _If it is noon now, what time was it 161 hours and 27 minutes ago?_ [6:33 PM]

1B **METHOD 1:** _Strategy: Find the ones digit first._
Ashley's locker number ends in 0 or 5. It cannot be 0 because then the hundreds digit and
the tens digit would be the same. The only other choice for the ones digit is 5. Since the tens
digit is 5 more than the hundreds digit, her locker number is one of the following: 165, 275,
385, 495. Of these numbers, only for 385 is the sum of the digits equal to 16. **Ashley's locker**
number is 385.

METHOD 2: _Strategy: Find the tens digit first._
The sum of the digits is 16 and the tens digit is the sum of the other 2 digits, so the tens digit is
half the sum, 8. As above, the ones digit is 0 or 5, giving possibilities of 880 or 385. The three
digits must be different, so Ashley's locker number is 385.

1C **METHOD 1:** *Strategy: Use the definition of an average.*
The ten friends have a total of $10 \times 5 = 50$ toy soldiers. When Lee joins the group, the 11 friends have a total of $11 \times 6 = 66$ toy soldiers. Then **Lee has** $66 - 50 = $ **16 toy soldiers.**

METHOD 2: *Strategy: Increase each friend's total by the same amount.*
Suppose Lee also has 5 soldiers. The average for all 11 friends would still be 5. To increase the average to 6, add 1 to each friend's total. This increases the total by 11. Then transfer those 11 toy soldiers to Lee's total, which keeps the new average at 6. Lee has 16 toy soldiers.

> ***FOLLOW-UP:*** *On a math test, the average of the 8 girls in the class was 85, and the average of the 12 boys in the class was 80. What was the average of all the students in the class?* [82]

1D **METHOD 1:** *Strategy: Figure why GABRIEL costs more than CAROL.*
GABRIEL has 1 more consonant and 1 more vowel than CAROL. Then 1 consonant and 1 vowel together cost $43 - 31 = \$12$. 2 consonants and 2 vowels together cost twice as much, $24. But CAROL has 3 consonants and 2 vowels. So the 1 extra consonant costs $31 - 24 = \$7$. Then the 3 consonants in CAROL cost $21, and the 2 vowels cost $31 - 21 = \$10$. 1 vowel costs **$5. BRIDGET**, with 5 consonants and 2 vowels, **costs** $5 \times 7 + 2 \times 5 = $ **$45 to engrave.**

METHOD 2: *Strategy: Make a chart. Use number properties to limit the guesses.*
CAROL, with 3 consonants and 2 vowels, costs $31, an odd number. Since the cost of 2 vowels must be even, the cost of 3 consonants must be odd, and therefore the cost of 1 consonant is odd. The table below tests different odd costs for a consonant to see which one produces the $43 cost for GABRIEL.

one consonant	CAROL CRL	AO	one vowel	GABRIEL GBRL	AIE	total cost
$3	9	$31 - 9 = $ 22	$11	$4 \times \$3 = $ 12	$3 \times 11 = $ 33	$12 + 33 = $ $45
$5	15	$31 - 15 = $ 16	$8	$4 \times \$5 = $ 20	$3 \times 8 = $ 24	$20 + 24 = $ $44
$7	21	$31 - 21 = $ 10	$5	$4 \times \$7 = $ 28	$3 \times 5 = $ 15	$28 + 15 = $ $43

Then each consonant costs $7, each vowel costs $5, and BRIDGET costs $45 to engrave.

1E *Strategy: Count in an organized way.*
1×1 squares: 24 of the 25 unit squares have no shading.

2×2 squares: Twelve 2×2 squares do not include the shaded square. The following diagrams show the twelve possible positions of the small squares, row by row from left to right.

3×3 squares: Three 3×3 squares do not include the shaded square.

4×4 squares: None: all possible 4×4 squares include the shaded square.

In all **there are 39 squares in the diagram that do not include the shaded square.**

FOLLOW-UP: *On a 5 × 5 unshaded checkerboard, how many 1 × 2 rectangles are there?* [40]

Olympiad 2

2A <u>*Strategy*</u>*: Simplify the expression.*
$10 + 20 + 30 + 40 + 50 = 150$.
$150 + \underline{\quad} = 220$
***N* represents 70.**

2B **METHOD 1:** <u>*Strategy*</u>*: Divide and find the quotient.*
$150 \div 9 = 16$ with a remainder. Therefore, multiplying 17 by 9 produces **the least multiple of 9 that is greater than 150** which **is 153.**

METHOD 2: <u>*Strategy*</u>*: List the multiples of 9.*
Start with a known multiple of 9. Continue adding 9 until the sum first exceeds 150. For example: 99, 108, 117, 126, 135, 144, 153. 153 is the least multiple of 9 greater than 150.

METHOD 3: <u>*Strategy*</u>*: Use the test of divisibility for 9.*
The sum of the digits of any multiple of 9 is also a multiple of 9. The sum of the digits of 150 is 6, so if 3 is added to 150, the result is a multiple of 9. 153 is the least multiple of 9 greater than 150.

FOLLOW-UP: *What is the greatest multiple of 8 less than 150?* [144]

2C **METHOD 1:** <u>*Strategy*</u>*: Start with a different number of people in each car.*
If the number of people in every car is different and no car is empty, the minimum number of people would be $1 + 2 + 3 + 4 + 5 = 15$. But there are only 12 people, and no car has 5 people. Take 3 of the 5 people out of that last car, leaving $1 + 2 + 3 + 4 + 2 = 12$ people. Only the two red cars have the same number, so **each red car has 2 people.**

METHOD 2: *Strategy: Start with 1 person in each car.*

First place 1 person, the driver, in each car. The five cars must contain the remaining 7 people, with the 2 red cars having the same number of people. There are two ways to place the 7 people: {0,0,1,2,4} and {0,1,1,2,3}. However, using {0,0,1,2,4} we would place 5 people in one car. This leaves {0,1,1,2,3}, which places 1, 2, 2, 3, and 4 people in the cars. Each red car has 2 people.

> ***FOLLOW-UPS:*** *In how many ways can 5 identical tee shirts be distributed among 3 students if: (1) each student gets at least 1 tee shirt? (2) some students might not get any tee shirts? [6, 21]*

2D METHOD 1: *Strategy: Find the total number of games won.*

The team won $\frac{3}{4}$ of its first 24 games. Therefore, it won 18 games and lost 6 of its first 24 games. If in the end the team has won just half of its games, the team must have lost 18 games. Thus $G + 6 = 18$ and **G represents 12.**

METHOD 2: *Strategy: Represent the fraction visually.*

Represent the first 24 games:

| W | W | W | L | = 24.

Thus each box represents 6 games.

Now represent all the games:

| W | W | W | L | **L** | **L** | The shaded boxes represent the G games.

Since each box represents 6 games, G represents 12.

2E METHOD 1: *Strategy: Form sequences (lists) using the given rule.*

Beginning with 10, 11, 12, etc., write out possible sequences and look for one that contains 44. Begin each new sequence with the least two-digit number that doesn't appear in a previous sequence. End the sequence once 44 is reached or passed.

Start	Sequence	44?
10	10,11,13 (11+2), 17, 25, 32, 37, **47**	No
12	12, 15, 21, 24, 30, 33, 39, **51**	No
14	14, 19, 29, 40, **44**	**YES**

Because 44 is the third number in the sequence, **the first number is 29.**

METHOD 2: _Strategy_: _Work backwards_.

Try a few numbers. Since 40 + 4 = 44, the second number is 40.

The first number plus the sum of its digits is 40. Choose a few numbers in the thirties. Notice in each case that adding the number to the sum of its digits produces an odd number. Therefore, start with 29. In fact, 29 + 11 = 40, so the first number is 29.

> **FOLLOW-UPS:** _(1) The first numbers in the Fibonacci Sequence are 1, 1, 2, 3, 5, 8, and 13. What is the sum of the first ten numbers in the sequence?_ [143] _(2) Other than 1, what is the least number in the Fibonacci Sequence that is a perfect square?_ [144] _(3) Consider the answers to FOLLOW-UPS (1) and (2). In the Fibonacci Sequence, what pattern emerges as you compare the sums of the terms to the terms themselves?_ [Each sum is 1 less than the Fibonacci Number two terms later.]

Olympiad 3

3A **METHOD 1:** _Strategy_: _Work backwards, using opposite operations._

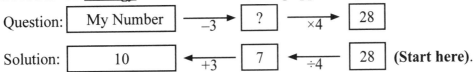

The result is (28 ÷ 4) + 3 = 10. **My number is 10.**

METHOD 2: _Strategy_: Use algebra.

Let _N_ represent my number.

Then	$4(N-3)$	$= 28$
Divide both sides of the equation by 4:	$N-3$	$= 7$
Add 3 to each side of the equation:	N	$= 10.$ My number is 10.

> **FOLLOW-UPS:** _(1) When you multiply my number by 4, then divide by 2, then multiply by 4 and then divide by 8, the answer is 1. What is my number?_ [1] _(2) (A mental arithmetic challenge) Without using a calculator or paper, find the product of 99 × 43._ [4257 ; think 100 × 43 – 1 × 43]

3B **METHOD 1:** _Strategy_: _Use the Least Common Multiple (LCM)._

The LCM of 6 and 15 is 30. Because the only multiple of 30 between 104 and 140 is 120, **the number is 120,**

METHOD 2: _Strategy: Use divisibility rules._

Multiples of 15 end in 0 or 5. Multiples of 6 are even. Then the number ends in 0. The possibilities are 110, 120, or 130. Any multiple of 6 is a multiple of 3, and so the sum of its digits is a multiple of 3. Of 110, 120, and 130, this is true only for 120. **The number is 120.**

METHOD 3: _Strategy: Use a table to compare multiples of 6 and 15._

Only three multiples of 15 (the greater number) are between 104 and 140: 105, 120, and 135. Of these, only 120 is also divisible by 6 (the lesser number).

Variation: Make two lists of multiples in the interval, the first of 15 and the other of 6, and select the number that appears on both lists.

3C The clock shows that the power outage ended 3 hours and 50 minutes ago. To determine the time, subtract 3 hours and 50 minutes from 9:35.

METHOD 1: _Strategy: Use a convenient time, then adjust._

Because 4 hours earlier the time was 5:35, then 3 hours and 50 minutes earlier the time was 5:45. **The power outage ended at 5:45 AM.**

METHOD 2: _Strategy: Regroup._

9 hours 35 minutes		8 hours 95 minutes
−3 hours 50 minutes	⟶	− 3 hours 50 minutes
		5 hours 45 minutes.

The power outage ended at 5:45 AM.

> **FOLLOW-UP:** _At 3:00 pm a clock shows the correct time. If it loses 12 minutes every hour, in how many hours will it next show the correct time?_ [60 hours]

3D **METHOD 1:** _Strategy: Change the figure to a simpler one with the same perimeter._

Sliding segments to different locations does not change their lengths. Slide the vertical sides (or segments of sides) left or right as shown. Similarly, slide the horizontal segments up or down, also as shown. This creates a square that is 10 cm on a side. The perimeter of the square, and therefore **the perimeter of the original figure, is 40 cm.**

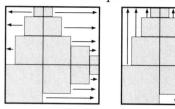

METHOD 2: _Strategy: Add the lengths of the sides of the figure._

Note that each side of the figure that is not the side of one of the squares is 1 cm in length. Starting at the bottom left and going clockwise, the perimeter of the figure is 4+1+3+1+2+1+1+1+1+1+1+2+1+1+2+1+1+1+1+1+2+1+3+1+4 = 40 cm.

FOLLOW-UP: *What is the area of region A in this diagram?*
[$4 \times 6 - 1^2 - 2^2 - 3^2 = 10$ sq cm; other methods are possible.]

3E   METHOD 1: *Strategy: Compare the distances the two bugs walked.*
The second bug covers 16 cm in the same time the first bug covers 24 cm. Because the second bug covers only $\frac{2}{3}$ the distance of the first bug, it travels at $\frac{2}{3}$ the speed. The speed of the first is 3 cm per sec. **The speed of the second bug is 2 cm per sec.**

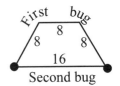

METHOD 2: *Strategy: Find the time that each bug traveled.*
The first bug needed 8 seconds to travel the 24 cm. Its rate was 3 cm per second. The second bug traveled 16 cm in the same 8 seconds, so its rate was 2 cm per second.

Olympiad 4

4A   METHOD 1: *Strategy: Subtract the cost of the drinks.*
Three drinks cost $6. Therefore 2 hot dogs cost $8. **One hot dog costs $4.**

METHOD 2: *Strategy: Use algebra*
Let *h* represent the price of a hot dog. Then:
2 hot dogs plus 3 $2-drinks cost $14.

	$2h + 3(2) = 14$
Multiply $2 by 3	$2h + 6: = 14$
Subtract $6 from each side of the equation :	$2h = 8$
Divide each side of the equation by 2	$h = 4$ One hot dog costs $4.

4B   METHOD 1: *Strategy: Draw a diagram to compare their amounts.*
Represent each person by an initial. Rank them from most to least, top to bottom.

1 Michael has $5 less than Samantha.

2 Samantha has $10 more than Rob.

3 Rob has $15 less than Hailey.

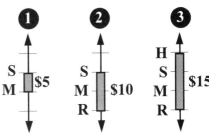

The picture shows that **Hailey has $10 more than Michael.**

METHOD 2: *Strategy: Assign a convenient amount to Michael.*
Suppose Michael has $50. Then Samantha has $55. Rob has $45 and Hailey has $60. Hailey has $10 more than Michael.

> ***FOLLOW-UP:*** *In Method 2, choose other amounts for Michael. Why does this method work?*

4C *Strategy: Add 1 number at a time to the list, starting with the least.*
Omit 1 from the list since every number is a multiple of 1. Put 2 on the list. Omit all multiples of 2 greater than 2. Put 3 on the list and omit all its multiples greater than 3. Put 5 on the list and omit all its multiples greater than 5. Continue the process until the list contains 6 numbers. *In this case* they happen to be the first 6 primes: 2, 3, 5, 7, 11, and 13. **The least possible total is 41.**

> ***FOLLOW-UPS:*** *(1) What is the greatest prime number less than 100?* [97] *(2) If the digits of the prime number 13 are reversed, the result, 31, is also a prime number. What is the next pair of reversible prime numbers?* [17, 71] *Can you find 2 more?* [37, 73] [79, 97] *(3) Research information on the Sieve of Eratosthenes.*

4D *Strategy: Find the total number of marbles.*
Since $\frac{2}{5}$ of the marbles show some red, the number of marbles is a multiple of 5. Likewise, the total number of marbles is also a multiple of 4 and of 7. The least common multiple of 4, 5, and 7 is 140. The next common multiple is 280, which is too large. Mia has 140 marbles. Because $\frac{6}{7}$ of 140 is 120, **120 marbles show some blue.**

4E **METHOD 1:** *Strategy: Show the number of ways to reach each point.*
To clarify the listing, use circled italicized letters for the points in the top path and bolded lower case letters for those in the middle path.

Figure 2 is the same as Figure 1. Figure 2 shows the number of paths from C to each point. From C there is only one way to reach points **H**, **h**, and ⓔ. There are only two ways to reach points **E**, **R**, **Y**, and **e**. With three ways to reach point ⓡ and four ways to reach point **r**, there are seven ways to reach point **y**. Thus, **there are 9 paths that spell Cheryl.**

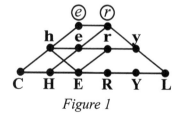

Figure 1

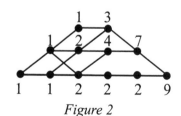

Figure 2

METHOD 2: *Strategy: Use a tree diagram to list each path.*
Trace each path that starts at **C** and leads to **L**.

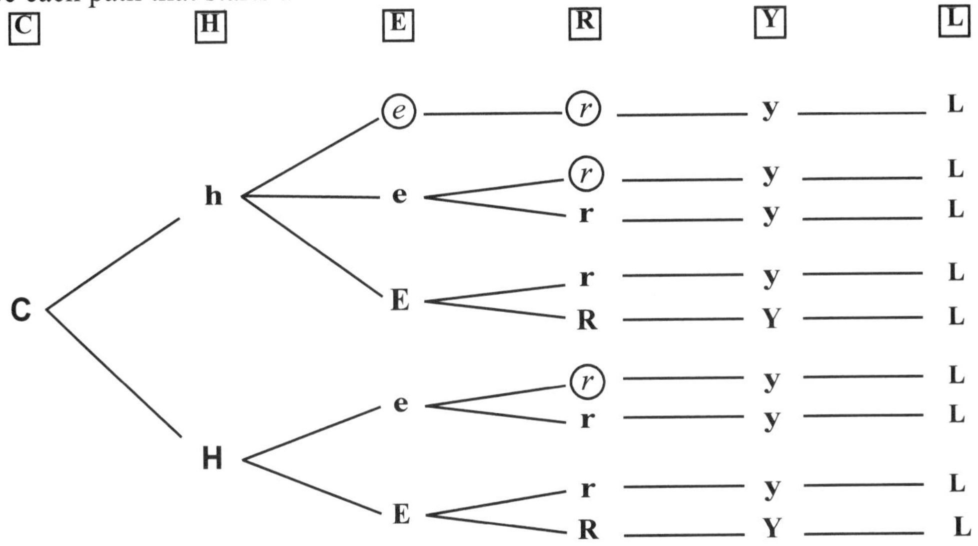

| C | H | E | R | Y | L |

As shown above, **9 paths trace her name.**

> ***FOLLOW-UPS:*** *(1) Using the letters in MATH, how many different 3-letter passwords can be made if no letter is repeated? [24]   (2) How many different 3-digit numbers can be written using the digits 3, 5, 7, and 9? [24]   (3) Why are both answers the same?*

Olympiad 5

5A *Strategy: Group the factors to simplify the multiplication.*
METHOD 1: $(2 \times 3 \times 5) \times (2 \times 3 \times 5) \times (2 \times 3 \times 5) = 30 \times 30 \times 30 = 27,000$. **There are 5 digits in the product.**

METHOD 2: $3 \times 3 \times 3 \times (2 \times 5) \times (2 \times 5) \times (2 \times 5) = 27 \times 10 \times 10 \times 10 = 27,000$. There are 5 digits in the product.

> ***FOLLOW-UP:*** *The number 10,000 is written as the product of two numbers, neither of which has 10 as a factor. What is the sum of these two numbers? [641]*

5B   *Strategy: List the possibilities for each digit.*
The hundreds digit is 4 or 8.

The tens digit could be 1 or 4 or 9. Since the tens digit is less than the hundreds digit, it cannot be 9. The tens digit is 1 or 4.

The ones digit could be 3 or 6 or 9. Again, since the ones digit is less than the tens digit, it cannot be 6 or 9. The ones digit must be 3.

Working backward, since the tens digit must be greater than 3, the tens digit is 4. The hundreds digit is then 8.

Lisa's secret number is 843.

5C   *Strategy: Find the length of a side of a small square.*
All eight small squares are congruent, and their total area is 8 square centimeters. Thus, each small square has an area of 1 square centimeter, and each small square is 1 cm by 1 cm. Count the number of small square edges going around the outside the figure. **The perimeter of the figure is 18 cm.**

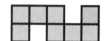

> **FOLLOW-UPS:** *(1) Suppose the perimeter of the given figure is 72 cm. What is its area?* [128 sq cm]   *(2) Exploration: How many different figures can you form from the 8 original squares? What are their perimeters?* [results will vary.]

5D   **METHOD 1:** *Strategy: Break the problem into cases.*
Numbers with exactly two digits the same look like ABB or BAB or BBA, where A and B represent two different digits.

(a) First consider numbers of the form ABB. A may not equal 0 in this arrangement. If A = 1, there are nine such numbers (100, 122, 133, …, 199). There are also nine such numbers for each of A = 2, 3, 4, …, 9. Thus, there is a total of 9 × 9 = 81 numbers of the form ABB.

(b) Consider numbers of the form BAB. If A = 0, there are nine such numbers (101, 202, 303, …, 909). Since B may not equal 0, there are only eight such numbers for each of A = 1, 2, 3, …, 9. Thus, there is a total of 9 + 8 × 9 = 81 numbers of the form BAB.

(c) A similar argument shows that there is also a total of 81 numbers of the form BBA.

Therefore, a total of 3 × 81 = **243 three-digit numbers have exactly two digits the same.**

METHOD 2: _Strategy: Count the numbers that don't have exactly two digits the same._
The digits of a 3-digit number are in 3 classes. Either all are the same, just two of them are the same, or all are different.

(a) **All the same:** These numbers have the form AAA. There are 9 such numbers (111, 222, 333, ..., 999).

(b) **All different:** These numbers have the form ABC. There are 9 choices for the digit A, since A cannot be 0. For each value of A, there are 9 choices left for B (since B could be 0). For each pair of values of A and B, 8 choices remain for C. Thus, there are 9 × 9 × 8 = 648 numbers of the form ABC.

(c) Since there are 999 numbers less than 1000, of which 99 have two digits, there are 900 three-digit numbers. Then 900 – 648 – 9 = 243 three-digit numbers have exactly two identical digits.

METHOD 3: _Strategy: Make a list._

Repeated digit	List of numbers	Quantity	
2 zeros	**1**00, 200, 300, ..., 900		**9**
2 ones	**11**0, 112, 113, ..., 119 (_not 111_)	9	
	101, 121, 131, ..., 191 (_not 111_)	9	**26**
	2**11**, 311, 411, ..., 911 (_not 111_)	8	
2 twos	**22**0, 221, 223, ..., 229 (_not 222_)	9	
	202, 212, 232, ..., 292 (_not 222_)	9	**26**
	1**22**, 322, 422, ..., 922 (_not 222_)	8	

As shown in the table, 2 zeroes appear in nine numbers. Also, 2 ones and 2 twos each appear in another 26 numbers. Similarly, 2 threes, 2 fours, ..., and 2 nines each appear in 26 numbers. This is a total of 9 + (26 × 9) = 243 numbers. In all, there are 243 three-digit numbers with two identical digits.

5E _Strategy: Determine the possible numbers of normal leaves._
The number of normal clovers is a multiple of 5, since there are 5 times as many normal clovers as lucky clovers. The number of normal clovers is also even, since there are twice as many of them as there are of broken clovers. The number of normal clovers is therefore a multiple of 10.

For each 10 normal clovers, there are 2 lucky clovers and 5 broken clovers.

Split the collection of N clovers into groups so that each group has 10 normals, 2 luckies, and 5 brokens. The number of leaves in each group is (10 × 3) + (2 × 4) + (5 × 2) = 48.

The total number of leaves is a multiple of 48, and the least multiple of 48 that is greater than 200 is 5 × 48 = 240. **The least value of N is 240.**

Set 7   Olympiad 1

1A   METHOD 1: _Strategy_: *Find a pattern.*

$$(20 + 40 + 60 + 80 + 100 + 120)$$
$$- (10 + 30 + 50 + 70 + \ \ 90 + 110)$$
$$10 + 10 + 10 + 10 + \ \ 10 + \ \ 10.$$

The value is 60.

METHOD 2: _Strategy_: *Perform the operations as indicated.*

$20 + 40 + 60 + 80 + 100 + 120 = 420$
$10 + 30 + 50 + 70 + \ \ 90 + 110 = \underline{360}$
$\qquad\qquad\qquad$ Difference $= \ \ 60.$ The value is 60.

1B   METHOD 1: _Strategy_: *Start with an extreme case.*

Suppose all 20 creatures are owners. There would then be a total of 40 legs. The extra 24 legs must be accounted for by the dogs. Since each dog has 2 more legs than its owner, **there are** $24 \div 2 = $ **12 dogs in the group.**

METHOD 2: _Strategy_: *Set up a table and look for a pattern.*

The number of legs is 2 times the number of owners plus 4 times the number of dogs.

Number of owners	20	19	18	17	...	?
Number of dogs	0	1	2	3	...	?
Number of legs	40	42	44	46	...	?

Each increase of 1 in the number of dogs increases the number of legs by 2. To increase from 40 legs to 64 legs, a total of 24, requires an increase of 12 in the number of dogs. There are 12 dogs in the group.

METHOD 3: _Strategy_: *Use algebra.*

Let D = the number of dogs. They have $4D$ legs.
Then $20 - D$ = the number of owners; they have $2(20 - D)$ legs.
$\qquad$ The total number of legs is $4D + 2(20 - D)$.

Equation: The total number of legs is 64:	$4D + 2(20 - D)$	$= 64$
Multiply $20 - D$ by 2:	$4D + (40 - 2D)$	$= 64$
Combine $4D$ and $-2D$:	$2D + \ 40$	$= 64$
Subtract 40 from each side of the equation:	$2D$	$= 24$
Divide each side of the equation by 2:	D	$= 12$

$\qquad$ There are exactly 12 dogs in the group.

FOLLOW–UP: *In a room there are three-legged stools and four-legged chairs. There are total of 14 seats and 47 legs. How many chairs are in the room?* [5]

1C **METHOD 1:** _Strategy: Determine how many times Keri came in first._
Keri could not have finished first 3 or more times because that would give her more than 20 points. Suppose she finished first twice, a total of 16 points. Any remaining points must have come from finishing second, scoring 3 points each time. She can't have scored 4 points.

The same reasoning shows she can't have finished first 0 times since 20 is not a multiple of 3. So Keri finished first once, for 8 points. The remaining 12 points came from 4 second place finishes. She played 8 games, so **Keri finished last in** the remaining **3 games.**

METHOD 2: _Strategy: List multiples of 8 and of 3 that are less than 20._

Possible scores from first place finishes:	0, **8**, 16
Possible scores from second place finishes:	0, 3, 6, 9, **12**, 15, 18

Only 8 and 12 sum to 20. This is 1 first place and 4 second places, so Keri finished last in 3 games.

> **FOLLOW-UPS:** _(1) Suppose the winner of each game scored 5 points instead of 8. How many games might Keri have won? [1 or 4]. (2) Suppose the winner scored 6 points. Is it possible for Keri to earn 20 points? [No! — why?]_

1D _Strategy: Count in an organized way._
Four-sided figures can be formed by combining (_or by eliminating_) triangles in the picture.

Combine 2 triangles
  (_or eliminate 2 unconnected triangles_):

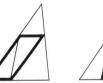

Combine 3 triangles
  (_or eliminate 1 triangle_):

6 four-sided figures can be traced.

1E _Strategy: Use reasoning and number properties._
The sum of three 3-digit numbers must be less than 3000, so S is 1 or 2.

Suppose S = 1. In the ones column, D + D + D ends in 1 so D = 7. In the tens column, 7 + 7 + 7 + 2 ends in 3 so M = 3 and there is a "carry" of 2. In the hundreds column, A + A + A + 2 = 1U. A is even and can't be 2 (too small) or 6 or 8 (both too large). But if A = 4, U is also 4, so A and U do not represent different digits. Thus there is no solution if S = 1.

```
    A D D
    A D D
  + A D D
  ───────
  S U M S
```

Try S = 2. In the ones column, D + D + D ends in 2 so D = 4 and there is a carry of 1. In the tens column, 4 + 4 + 4 + 1 ends in 3 so M = 3, with a carry of 1. In the hundreds column, A + A + A + 1 = 2U. Only if A is 8 is the sum greater than 20, and then U = 5. **SUMS is 2532.**

> **FOLLOW-UP:** *Different letters represent different digits. Find the sum CDD5 if ABB + BAB + BBA = CDD5. There are 2 solutions.* [1665 and 2775]

What is the next larger number whose digits also add up to 3?

Olympiad 2

2A _Strategy: Make the smallest possible increase in the number._
Since the sum of the digits must remain 3, move the 1 one place to the left. **The next larger number with 3 as the sum of the digits is 2100.**

> *FOLLOW-UPS: (1) For how many 4-digit numbers is 3 the sum of the digits?* [10 (1110, 1101, 1011, 1002, 1020, 1200, 2001, 2010, 2100, 3000)] *(2) For how many 4-digit numbers do the digits add up to 4?* [20]

2B _Strategy: Determine the number of letters in the repeating part._
In the sequence ABBCCDABBCCD…, there are 6 letters before the pattern repeats itself. The first 78 terms of the sequence contain 13 complete repetitions of the pattern and no additional letters. **The 78th letter is** the same as the 6th letter, which is **D.**

> *FOLLOW-UPS: (1) In the sequence of letters ABBCCCDDDDEEEEEFFFFFF…, what is the 100th letter?* [N] *(2) A letter is chosen in FOLLOW-UP (1) from the first 50 letters. What is the probability that it is a vowel?* [$\frac{15}{50}$ or $\frac{3}{10}$]

2C **METHOD 1:** _Strategy: Draw a diagram._
On the number line, point *J* represents Jen's age, point *2J* represents twice her age and point *3J* represents three times her age. Point *N* represents the number that is both 8 more than *2J* and 16 less than *3J*.

The distance from *2J* to *3J* is the same as the distance from zero to *J*; that is Jen's age. Thus **Jen's age is** 8 + 16 = **24.**

METHOD 2: *Strategy: Use algebra.*

The variables J, $2J$, $3J$, and N are as defined in METHOD 1.

Because $N = 3J - 16$ and $N = 2J + 8$, then: $3J - 16 = 2J + 8$

Add 16 to each side of the equation: $3J = 2J + 24$

Subtract $2J$ from each side of the equation: $J = 24$

Jen's age is 24.

2D   *Strategy: List all possible areas for the two squares.*

List the square numbers: 1,4,9,16,25,36,49,64,81,100. Only 36 and 64 add to 100. Then the larger square is 8 cm on each side and the smaller is 6 cm on each side. Now find the perimeter of the figure.

METHOD 1: *Strategy: Find the total perimeter of the 2 squares, and adjust.*

The total perimeter of the squares is $(4 \times 8) + (4 \times 6) = 56$ cm. But this counts the length of segment AB twice, for each of the two squares. But AB should not be counted at all. **The perimeter of the figure is** $56 - (2 \times 6) = $ **44 cm.**

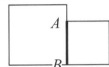

METHOD 2: *Strategy: Find the length of each segment.*

The two squares have 6 cm in common, so the larger square contributes an extra $8 - 6 = 2$ cm to the perimeter. Then the perimeter of the figure is $2 + (3 \times 8) + (3 \times 6) = 44$ cm.

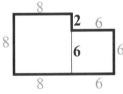

METHOD 3: *Strategy: Slide segments to make the figure into a rectangle.*

While the area changes, the perimeter stays the same. The diagram on the left indicates the two segments to be moved. The resulting diagram on the right indicates that the same lengths will be added to find the perimeter, but in a more convenient fashion.

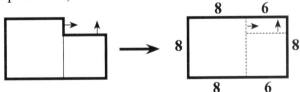

Thus, the perimeter of the figure is $(2 \times 14) + (2 \times 8) = 44$ cm.

FOLLOW-UP: 2 squares whose side-lengths are whole numbers are placed so that one is entirely inside the other. If the area of the region between the two squares is 45, what are two possible pairs of lengths of the sides? [There are 3 pairs. (7,2) and (9,6) are the most readily found, but (23,22) also works.]

2E *Strategy: Work backwards.*

The table below shows actions in reverse. The first column names each person, last to first. The second column shows the actions each person took. The third column states the number of coins on the table as each person approached.

NAME	ACTION	MUST HAVE STARTED WITH
Selena	Took 5, left 4	9 coins
Joe	Took 2, left 9	11
Joe	Took half, left 11	22
Nick	Took 2, left 22	24
Sara	Took 4, left 24	28
Sara	Took half, left 28	56

56 coins were on the table to start with.

Olympiad 3

3A *Strategy: Make a list.*

If the ones digit is twice the tens digit, the only possibilities are 12, 24, 36, and 48. Tens digits of 5 through 9 would produce two digits in the ones place; zero can't be a leading digit. If the tens digit is twice the ones digit, the only possibilities are 21, 42, 63, and 84. Thus, **8 two-digit numbers have one digit that is twice the other.**

3B *Strategy: Find the sum of each row and each column.*

If only one number needs to be changed, it must sit in a row and column that has a different sum from the others. The diagram shows the sum of each row and column.

columns

22	1	16	**39**
9	13	19	**41**
10	25	4	**39**
41	**39**	**39**	

rows

The middle row has a different sum from the other two. The sum of the first column is different from the other two. **The number that must be changed is** in the middle row, first column, **9.** (If the 9 is replaced by 7, the result is a magic square.)

3C *Strategy: Work from left to right.*

Use the letters **A** through **G** to designate the seven digits.

E = 1, since the sum of two 2-digit numbers is less than 200.

$$\begin{array}{r} A\,B \\ +\,C\,D \\ \hline E\,F\,G \end{array}$$

This means that the tens digits must add up to at least 10, including a carry from the ones column if a carry exists.

There are 4 cases for the tens column:
- 6 and 5 plus a carry, because **F** and **E** cannot both be 1;
- 6 and 4 and no carry;
- 6 and 3 plus a carry; and
- 5 and 4 plus a carry.

In all three cases in which the units place needs to produce a carry, the remaining digits are too small to do so. This leaves 6 and 4 in the tens place, and the ones column must add 2 and 3 to get 5. **The answer to the addition problem is 105.**

3D **METHOD 1:** *Strategy: Set up a table. Use number properties to limit choices.*

The cost of 1 green plus 2 red marbles is an odd number of cents but the cost of 2 red marbles is even. So the cost of 1 green marble is odd.

The top row of the table lists each possible cost of 1 green. The other rows use this number to figure the cost of 1 red and 1 blue marble.

Suppose 1 green costs	3¢	5¢	7¢	9¢
Then 2 red = 13¢ – 1 green, so 2 red cost	10¢	8¢	6¢	4¢
Therefore, 1 red would cost	5¢	4¢	3¢	2¢
Next, 2 blue = 16¢ – 1 red, so 2 blue cost	11	12	13	14
Therefore, 1 blue would cost	——	6¢	——	7¢
CHECK: 1 blue + 2 green costs	——	16¢	——	25¢

1 blue and 2 green cost 16¢, not 25¢. Therefore, **a green marble costs 5 cents.**

METHOD 2: *Strategy: Combine the given information.*

Suppose all 3 purchases are made. Then 3 green marbles, 3 blue marbles, and 3 red marbles cost a total of 45 cents. So 1 green marble, 1 blue marble, and 1 red marble cost 15 cents. The first and second sentences show that 1 blue and 2 green marbles cost as much as 1 red and 2 blue marbles. If we imagine a balance scale with 1 blue and 2 green marbles on one side and 1 red and 2 blue marbles on the other, we could remove 1 blue marble from each side and see that 2 green marbles balance 1 red and 1 blue marble. Thus, we could replace 1 red and 1 blue with 2 green marbles. So we know that 3 green marbles cost 15 cents, so each green marble costs **5 cents**.

> **FOLLOW-UP:** *At a movie theater, 2 popcorns and a soda cost $13, while 5 popcorns and 4 sodas cost $37. Julia orders a popcorn and a soda. How much does Julia spend?* [$8]

3E   METHOD 1: _Strategy: Add the areas of triangle ADE and square DBCE._

The _semi_-perimeter of the rectangle (that is $DA + AB$) is 18 cm.

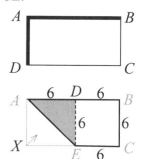

After folding on crease $\overline{AE}$, $\overline{AD}$ lies on $\overline{AB}$ with D touching the midpoint of $\overline{AB}$. Then AB is twice AD, and the original rectangle is 12 cm by 6 cm. Thus $DBCE$ is a 6 cm by 6 cm square and its area is 36 sq cm. Look at triangle ADE: it actually is half of square $ADEX$, also a 6 cm by 6 cm square; its area is half of 36 sq cm = 18 sq cm. **The area of trapezoid $ABCE$ is $36 + 18 =$ 54 sq cm.**

METHOD 2: _Strategy: Subtract the area of the shaded region from the rectangle._

As before, the original rectangle is 12 cm by 6 cm. Its area is 72 sq cm. $\overline{AD}$ and $\overline{DE}$ are each 6 cm long and the area of the shaded region (again half of a 6×6 square) is 18 sq cm. Then the area of $ABCE$ is $72 - 18 = 54$ sq cm.

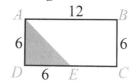

Olympiad 4

4A   _Strategy: Count how many times each digit appears._
There are sixteen 4s, twelve 3s, eight 2s, four 1s, and one 0. **The sum of the digits is** $(16 \times 4) + (12 \times 3) + (8 \times 2) + (4 \times 1) = 64 + 36 + 16 + 4 =$ **120.**

```
            4
          4 3 4
        4 3 2 3 4
      4 3 2 1 2 3 4
    4 3 2 1 0 1 2 3 4
      4 3 2 1 2 3 4
        4 3 2 3 4
          4 3 4
            4
```

> _Follow-Ups: (1) Suppose the diagram above is surrounded by a border of 5s. What is the sum of the digits in the new picture? [220]   (2) Suppose the pattern is continued with a border of 6s, then 7s, and then 8s. What is the sum of the 8s in the new picture? [256]_

4B   METHOD 1: _Strategy: Find the average of the page numbers._
The sum of the first and fourth page numbers is 47. This is also the sum of the second and third page numbers. The average of the 4 page numbers is $23\frac{1}{2}$. $23\frac{1}{2}$ is immediately between the second and third page numbers. The page numbers are 22, 23, 24, and 25. **The chapter begins on page 22.**

METHOD 2: _Strategy: Use algebra._
Let P represent the first page number. The other numbers are $P + 1$, $P + 2$, and $P + 3$. Then $P + (P + 3) = 47$. Solving, $P = 22$. The chapter begins on page 22.

FOLLOW-UPS: *(1) Max just finished reading 7 consecutive pages for homework. The sum of the page numbers he read is 392. What page numbers did he read? [pp. 53-59]   (2) Four brothers are each born one year apart. The sum of their ages is the father's age which is two less than five times the youngest's age. How old is the father? [38]*

4C   *Strategy: List the digits that satisfy each condition.*
Place the prime numbers {2, 3, 5, 7} in the corner boxes.

Place the squares {1, 4, 9} in the middle column.

Place the remaining digits {6, 8} in the remaining boxes of the middle row.

2,3,5,7	1,4,9	2,3,5,7
6,8	1,4,9	6,8
2,3,5,7	1,4,9	2,3,5,7

Read the middle row, left to right, and choose the least unused number in each box. **The least number is 618.**

> ***FOLLOW-UPS:*** *What is the least three-digit number that can be formed if the first digit is prime, the second digit is square, the third digit is even, and no digit is repeated?[204]*

4D   **METHOD 1:** *Strategy: Find the factors.*
Write the problem as a multiplication: M × AB = EEE. If all three digits of a number are the same, it is a multiple of 111. 111 is a multiple of 3 because the sum of its digits is 3. The prime factors of 111 are 3 and 37. AB must be a multiple of 37, inasmuch as M is only one digit. Since AB is an even 2-digit number, **AB is** 2 × 37 = **74.**

METHOD 2: *Strategy: Use number properties to reduce the possible guesses.*
As above, EEE is a multiple of 3. Further, since M × AB = EEE and AB is even, EEE = 222, 444, 666, or 888. Divide each by 3, 6, and 9: 222 ÷ 3, 444 ÷ 6 and 666 ÷ 9 each produce a quotient of 74. 222 ÷ 6 = 37, which is not even. Each of the other choices produces a nonzero remainder or a three-digit quotient. The only even possible value for AB is 74.

> ***FOLLOW-UPS:*** *(1) Find C if AB × C = AAA. [9]   (2) Replace each letter with a different digit to make the division at the right correct. [BET=247, THAT=7657, ON=31]*

$$
\begin{array}{r}
O\,N \\
B\,E\,T\,\overline{)T\,H\,A\,T} \\
-T\,E\,N \\
\hline
B\,E\,T \\
-\underline{B\,E\,T} \\
\end{array}
$$

4E   *Strategy: Draw a diagram.*
Draw the rectangular solid showing how it was cut into 2-cm cubes.
Eliminate the 8 corner cubes (3 faces painted) and the 12 edge cubes
(2 faces painted.) **4 of these cubes have only one face painted.**

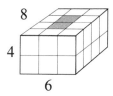

> **FOLLOW-UPS:** *Suppose the rectangular solid in 4E is cut into 1-cm cubes. (1) How many cubes have three faces painted?* [8]   *(2) No faces painted?* [48]   *(3) Into how many 1-cm by 2-cm by 3-cm rectangular solids can the figure in 4E be cut?* [32]

Olympiad 5

5A   **METHOD 1:** *Strategy: Use divisibility rules for 3 and 5.*
A number is divisible by 15 if it is divisible by both 3 and 5. Because the number 3367N is divisible by 3, the sum of its digits is divisible by 3. Thus, 19 + N is divisible by 3 and N is 2, 5, or 8. If a number is divisible by 5, its units digit, N, is 0 or 5. Thus **the digit N is 5.**

METHOD 2: *Strategy: Do the division.*

$$
\begin{array}{r}
2\ 2\ 4\ ? \\
1\ 5\,\overline{)\ 3\ 3\ 6\ 7\ N} \\
-3\ 0 \\
\hline
3\ 6 \\
-3\ 0 \\
\hline
6\ 7 \\
-6\ 0 \\
\hline
7\ N \\
-7\ 5 \\
\hline
0
\end{array}
$$

The final remainder is 0, so 7N is 75 and the digit N is 5.

> **FOLLOW-UP:** *If the number 51A6B is divisible by 36, what numbers could 51A6B represent?*
> [51660 or 51264 or 51768]

5B   *Strategy: First find the number of pounds needed.*
Each tray needs $\frac{2}{3}$ pound of carrots, so 25 trays need $25 \times \frac{2}{3} = \frac{50}{3}$ or $16\frac{2}{3}$ pounds. Since carrots come in 2-pound bags, 8 bags won't suffice, so **Vera must buy 9 bags of carrots.**

5C **METHOD 1:** _Strategy: Set up a table of the differences in their amounts._
Each has at least 4 grapes.

If Dom gives Hannah 4 grapes, she gains 4 and he loses 4. For their totals to become equal, he must have 8 more grapes than she.

In this table, the first two columns show how many grapes he and she could have now: 12 and 4, 13 and 5, 14 and 6, and so on. The other two columns show the results in each case after Hannah gives Dom 4 grapes.

CURRENT STATUS		AFTER HANNAH GIVES DOM 4 GRAPES	
Dom	Hannah	Dom	Hannah
12	4	16	0
13	5	17	1
14	6	18	2
15	7	19	3
16	8	20	4

Since $20 = 5 \times 4$, **Hannah** really **has 8 grapes** and Dom 16.

METHOD 2: _Strategy: Use a diagram to show the results._
As in method 1, Dom has 8 more grapes than Hannah. If she gives him 4 grapes, he would have 16 more than she, by the same reasoning as in method 1. The diagram at the right shows why the 16 is four times her final quantity. Then her final quantity would be 4 grapes. Thus, when they speak Hannah has 8 grapes.

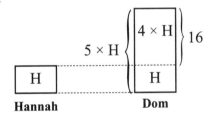

5D **METHOD 1:** _Strategy: Find the perimeter of 1 small rectangle._
Each small rectangle has a length that is half the length of the large rectangle and a width that is also half as large. The perimeter of a small rectangle is then half the perimeter of the large rectangle, 25 cm. **The total of the perimeters of the 4 smaller rectangles is** $4 \times 25 = 100$ **cm.**

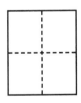

METHOD 2: _Strategy: Assign numerical values to the length and width._
The perimeter of the paper is 50 cm, so the sum of length and width is 25 cm. Suppose the length is 20 cm and the width is 5 cm. Each small rectangle then has a length of 10 cm and a width of $2\frac{1}{2}$ cm. The perimeter of each small rectangle is $20 + 5 = 25$ cm, and the total of the four perimeters is 100 cm.

> **FOLLOW-UPS:** _(1) Suppose one cut were 8 cm lower and the other 3 cm to the right as shown. How would the sum of the perimeters be affected?_
> [It wouldn't.]   _(2) The perimeter of a checkerboard is 100 cm. What is the sum of the perimeters of its 64 squares?_ [800 cm]

5E _Strategy_: _Minimize the denominator. Then maximize the numerator._
The smallest possible denominator is 1, which can be obtained by using $20 - 19$, $30 - 29$, etc.
To save as many large digits as possible for the numerator, use $20 - 19$ for the denominator.
The digits remaining are those from 3 through 8. To make the numerator as large as possible,
use 8, 7, and 6 as the tens digits (in any order) and 3, 4, and 5 as the ones digits (in any order).
The greatest possible value is $\frac{83 + 74 + 65}{20 - 19} =$ **222.**

FOLLOW-UP: _What is the least possible positive value of the fraction?_ $\left[\frac{27}{22}\right]$

Set 8   Olympiad 1

1A _Strategy_: _Use the pattern in the numbers to simplify the arithmetic._
Group the numbers in pairs:
$$87 - 76 + 65 - 54 + 43 - 32 + 21 - 10 \qquad =$$
$$(87 - 76) + (65 - 54) + (43 - 32) + (21 - 10) =$$
$$11 \quad + \quad 11 \quad + \quad 11 \quad + \quad 11 \quad = \textbf{44}$$

1B **METHOD 1:** _Strategy_: _Start with the greatest number._
To get the greatest sum, start by choosing 10. Then 9 can't be used so choose 8. 7 can't be used,
and neither can 6 because it's adjacent to 5 which is given as one of the numbers. 4 and 5 must
be included, so 3 can't be used. Choose 2 as the final number. **The greatest possible sum of
Grace's numbers is $10 + 8 + 5 + 4 + 2 = 29.$**

METHOD 2: _Strategy_: _Start with the known numbers._
Two of the numbers are 4 and 5. Neither 3 nor 6 can be used because they are adjacent to the
two numbers already used. The other three numbers must be chosen from 1, 2, 7, 8, 9, and 10.
Only two numbers can be chosen from 7, 8, 9, and 10, and therefore either 1 or 2 must be used.
The greatest possible sum of Grace's numbers is $10 + 8 + 5 + 4 + 2 = 29.$

1C **METHOD 1:** _Strategy_: _Draw a picture._
Draw the 7×7 square. Shade the small squares on the edges and count
them. **24 of the small squares are painted blue.**

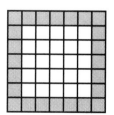

METHOD 2: _Strategy_: _Count the small squares along one edge._
7 small squares along each of the 4 sides of the large square give a total
of 28. But each of the 4 corner squares has been counted twice. Thus
there are a total of $28 - 4 = 24$ squares that are painted blue.

METHOD 3: <u>*Strategy*</u>: *Count the squares that are not painted.*
The unpainted squares form a 5×5 array of 25 squares inside the large square. Then 49 – 25 = 24 squares are painted blue.

> ***FOLLOW-UPS:*** *(1) A 10 × 6 rectangle is marked off into 60 small squares. Each of the squares along the edges of the rectangle and each of the squares adjacent to those border squares is painted red. How many of the small squares are painted red?* [48]   *(2) A rectangular photo that is 16 cm by 20 cm is surrounded by a frame that is 2 cm in width. What is the area of the frame?* [160 sq cm]

1D   <u>*Strategy*</u>: *Find all sets of 3 numbers with the given sums.*
The only sets of 3 different numbers chosen from the given values that have a sum of 13 are {2,5,6} and {3,4,6}. These are the numbers along sides A and B in the diagram. **The circle at the top** is on both sides and therefore **contains 6**.

To check, note that the only 3 numbers that have a sum of 6 are 1, 2, and 3. These must be along the bottom. This leads to the solution to the right.

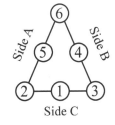

Side C

(Sides A and B may be interchanged.)

1E   <u>*Strategy*</u>: *Draw the picture and count carefully.*
In order to have the maximum number of regions, every new line must be drawn in such a way that three lines do not meet at the same point.

If 2 straight lines are drawn and they intersect, 4 regions are created.

If 3 intersecting lines are drawn, 7 regions at most may be created.

If 4 lines are drawn, the greatest number of regions we can create is 11.

> ***Follow-Ups:*** *(1) What is the greatest number of intersection points of 4 lines in the plane?* [6]   *(2) Can you find a pattern in the number of regions inside the circle formed by 1, 2, 3, or 4 lines? How many regions inside the circle can be formed by 5 lines?* [16] *By 6 lines?* [22]

Olympiad 2

2A **METHOD 1:** _Strategy: Use the distributive property of multiplication over addition._
$(47 \times 8) + (8 \times 27) + (26 \times 8) = (47 + 27 + 26) \times 8 = 100 \times 8 = \textbf{800.}$

METHOD 2: _Strategy: Perform the operations as indicated._
$(47 \times 8) + (8 \times 27) + (26 \times 8) = 376 + 216 + 208 = 800.$

2B _Strategy: Maximize the minuend; minimize the subtrahend._
Use the three greatest digits in the minuend and arrange them from greatest to
least. Arrange the other three digits from least to greatest in the subtrahend. Then
531 is the greatest possible difference.

$$\begin{array}{r} 654 \\ -123 \\ \hline 531 \end{array}$$

> _**FOLLOW-UP:** The ten digits are each used once to form two 5-digit even numbers whose difference is a maximum. What are the numbers?_ [98,756 – 10,234 = 88,522]

2C **METHOD 1:** _Strategy: Find how much 4 volunteers can do in 1 hour._
If 4 volunteers can pack 12 boxes every 30 minutes, then 4 volunteers can pack 24 boxes
every hour (60 minutes). In order to pack 72 boxes in an hour, since $72 \div 24 = 3$, three times as
many volunteers are needed. So 12 volunteers are needed to do the job; therefore, **8 additional
volunteers are needed.**

METHOD 2: _Strategy: Find how many boxes 1 volunteer can pack in an hour._
If 4 volunteers can pack 12 boxes every 30 minutes, then 1 volunteer can pack $\frac{1}{4}$ as many in
30 minutes, or 3 boxes. One volunteer can then pack 6 boxes in an hour. To pack 72 boxes
requires 12 volunteers, and so 8 additional volunteers are needed.

> _**FOLLOW-UP:** If 8 volunteers can pack 12 boxes in 30 minutes, how long would it take 6 volunteers to pack 24 boxes?_ [80 minutes]

2D **METHOD 1:** _Strategy: Find the least and greatest 3-digit multiples of 21._
(1) Because $999 \div 21 = 47$ R12, there are 47 three-digit multiples of 21.
(2) Because $100 \div 21 = 4$ R16, there are 4 two digit multiples of 21.

(3) Of the 47 multiples of 21 that are less than 1000, 4 of them have only 2 digits, so **there are
43 three-digit numbers that are multiples of 21.**

METHOD 2: *Strategy: List the multiples of 21.*
List all the multiples of 21 until all 3-digit multiples are discovered.

The multiples of 21 that have 3 digits are:
~~21, 42, 63, 84,~~
105, 126, 147, 168, 189, 210, 231, 252, 273, 294
315, 336, 357, 378, 399, 420, 441, 462, 483, 504
525, 546, 567, 588, 609, 630, 651, 672, 693, 714
735, 756, 777, 798, 819, 840, 861, 882, 903, 924
945, 966, 987, ~~1008.~~

In all there are 43 multiples of 21 that have 3 digits.

> **FOLLOW-UP:** *How many 3-digit odd numbers are not multiples of 5?* [360; any 3-digit number which ends with 1, 3, 7 or 9]

2E **METHOD 1:** *Strategy: Determine the dimensions of the overlapping region.*
Label the overlapping region I. Label the other two regions II and III as shown.

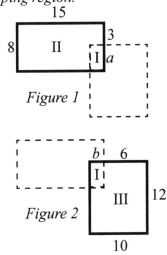

Figure 1: Regions II and I form a rectangle whose area is $15 \times 8 = 120$ sq cm.

Figure 2: Regions I and III form a rectangle whose area is $10 \times 12 = 120$ sq cm.

Thus the sum of regions (II + I) + (I + III) = 240 sq cm.

However this counts the area of region I twice. The area of the entire region is then 240 – the area of region I.

Because region I is a rectangle, its opposite sides are congruent. Thus, in figure 1, $8 = 3 + a$, so $a = 5$. In figure 2, $b + 6 = 10$, so $b = 4$. Then the area of region I is $5 \times 4 = 20$ sq cm, and **the area of the entire region is** $240 - 20 =$ **220 sq cm.**

METHOD 2: *Strategy: Wrap the figure in a rectangle and then subtract the excess.*
Draw rectangle *ABCD*. The sides of rectangle IV have lengths of 3 and 6, and an area of 18. As shown at the right, $AB = 15 + 6$, so $DC = 21$. Also, $BC = 3 + 12$, so $AD = 15$. Then the sides of rectangle V have lengths of $21 - 10 = 11$ and $15 - 8 = 7$, and its area is 77. Then the area of *ABCD* is $21 \times 15 = 315$.

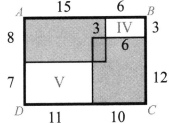

To find the area of the original region, subtract the excess areas (of rectangles IV and V) from that of rectangle *ABCD*. Thus $315 - 18 - 77 = 220$ sq cm.

> **FOLLOW-UP:** *What is the perimeter of the shaded region?* [72 cm]

Olympiad 3

3A _Strategy: Solve for △ first._
△ + △ = 24. Therefore, △ = 12.
△ + ◊ = 20, so 12 + ◊ = 20.
Therefore, ◊ **represents 8**.

> **FOLLOW-UP**: _What whole numbers have a product of 144 and a sum of 25?_ [16 and 9]

3B _Strategy: Make an organized table._
For each possible tens digit, 1 through 9, determine each possible units digit (that differs by 3 from the tens digit). The units digit could be either 3 more than the tens digit or 3 less than it.

Tens digit	1	2	3	4	5	6	7	8	9
2-digit number (units digit is greater)	14	25	36	47	58	69			
2-digit number (tens digit is greater)			30	41	52	63	74	85	96

No number appears twice on the list, so **there are 13 numbers between 10 and 99 whose digits differ by 3**.

> **FOLLOW-UPS**: _(1) How many 2-digit numbers have a tens digit that is less than the ones digit?_ [36]   _(2) How many 3-digit numbers have a tens digit that is less than the ones digit and a hundreds digit that is less than the tens digit?_ [84]

3C _Strategy: Label each individual box in order to organize the counting._
Use the numbers 1-6 as the six labels. Combinations of labels (say, 34) identify combinations of individual boxes.

One-box rectangles: 1, 2, 3, 4, 5, 6
Two-box rectangles: 34
Three-box rectangles: 345
Four-box rectangles: 3456
Five-box rectangles: 23456
Six-box rectangles: 123456

There are 11 different rectangles in this diagram.

3D **METHOD 1:** _Strategy: Draw a diagram._
Draw 24 boxes to represent the students. Put N in 2 boxes to represent those who like neither. Then put V in the next 18 boxes to represent those who like video games.

Now, starting at the end of the list of boxes, put M in 15 boxes to represent those who like to go to the movies. Count the boxes with both V and M in them.

11 students like both.

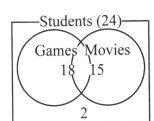

METHOD 2: _Strategy: Use a Venn diagram._
Ignore the 2 students who liked neither. The remaining 22 students liked at least one of the activities. If the number who liked video games and the number who liked movies are added, the total, 33, is greater than the 22 students who liked one or more of them. Some of the students must have been counted twice. These are the students who liked both. 33 − 22 = 11 students like both.

> **FOLLOW UP:** _Suppose in the given problem students are also asked whether they like to play basketball. One liked none of the 3 activities, one liked movies and basketball but not video games, four liked movies and video games but not basketball and two liked video games only. How many liked basketball?_ [14]

3E _Strategy: Consider possibilities._
First, note that the missing digits are 1, 2, 3, 4, 8, and 9. We cannot place either 8 or 9 in the missing addend or else we will have to repeat a digit. So the sum includes both 8 and 9 and either 8 or 9 occupies the hundreds place. Then where do we place the digit 1? There are four choices.

$$\begin{array}{r} 5\,6\,7 \\ +\,\square\,\square\,\square \\ \hline \square\,\square\,\square \end{array}$$

Case 1: 567 + __ __**1** = 9__8.   Reject. The tens place must include a carry from the ones place and that's impossible.

Case 2: 567 + __**1**__ = 98__ or 89__.   Reject. Adding 2, 3, or 4 to the 7 does not produce a 2, 3, or 4 in the sum. Also a sum of 8__9 or 9__8 does not allow a possible addition in the tens place.

Case 3: 567 + __4__ = __**1**__.   Reject. For the same reason as case 2, the addition in the units place is again impossible (7 + __ = __). Also, using the 9 in the units place yields a 6 in the sum, but 6 was already used.

Case 4: 567 + __ __4 = __ __**1**. Now this works as shown at the right.

$$\begin{array}{r} 5\,6\,7 \\ +\,3\,2\,4 \\ \hline 8\,9\,1 \end{array}$$

The sum is 891.

Olympiad 4

4A *Strategy: Work backwards.*

Before Chloe divides the number N, it is 14 times as large as her final answer, 5. So, N is equal to $14 \times 5 = 70$. When Mia accidentally adds the 14 to the 70, **Mia gets an answer of 84.**

4B METHOD 1: *Strategy: Make a table and look for a pattern.*

Since the constant difference of Kevin's numbers is 7, the table compares his sequence to the first 24 nonzero multiples of 7.

	1st	2nd	3rd	4th	5th	...	24th
Kevin's sequence	9	16	23	30	37	...	?
Counting by 7s	7	14	21	28	35	...	168

Each number in Kevin's sequence is 2 more than the corresponding multiple of 7. Therefore the 24th number in his sequence is 2 more than $24 \times 7 = 168$. **The twenty-fourth number in Kevin's sequence is 170.**

METHOD 2: *Strategy: Continue to add 7s.*

If you list the numbers in sets of 10, it will be easier to spot both patterns and addition errors.

9	16	23	30	37	44	51	58	65	72
79	86	93	100	107	114	121	128	135	142
149	156	163	170						

The twenty-fourth number in Kevin's sequence is 170.

4C *Strategy: List prime numbers starting with the least.*

2, 3, 5, 7, 11, 13, 17, 19, 23, 29, 31, ...

Note that 2 is the only even prime. If 2 is added to two odd primes, the sum is even and therefore not prime. Thus all three primes are odd. The least sum is $3 + 5 + 7 = 15$, which is not prime. The next smallest sum of primes is $3 + 5 + 11 = 19$. **Therefore, the least prime number that is the sum of 3 different prime numbers is 19.**

> **FOLLOW-UP:** *What is the least prime number that can be written as the sum of 3 different nonzero perfect square numbers? [29]*

4D   <u>*Strategy*</u>: *Compare the area of one piece to that of the screen.*

The area of the checkerboard is $8 \times 8 = 64$ sq units. Each piece has an area of 5 sq units. Because $64 \div 5 = 12$ R4, no more than 12 pieces can be placed on the checkerboard. To see whether 12 pieces can actually fit, place them as compactly as possible. For example, the figure at the right uses one of each kind of piece to cover 15 of the 16 squares in a 4×4 screen.

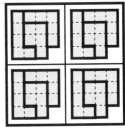

The 8×8 checkerboard can be divided into four 4×4 regions and this arrangement can be placed in each of them as shown at the right. Other arrangements are also possible.

The greatest number of pieces Jen can place on the checkerboard is 12.

4E   **METHOD 1:**   <u>*Strategy*</u>: *Draw a diagram to show each action Larry takes.*

Larry climbs exactly $\frac{2}{3}$ of the steps. [Action A in method 2]

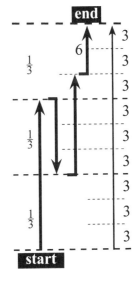

Then he goes back down exactly $\frac{1}{2}$ of the steps he just climbed: $\frac{1}{2}$ of $\frac{2}{3} = \frac{1}{3}$. [Action B]

From that spot, he climbs exactly $\frac{2}{3}$ of the steps above him: $\frac{2}{3}$ of $\frac{2}{3} = \frac{4}{9}$. [Action C]

From there, he climbs 6 stairs to reach the top.
Those 6 steps equal $\frac{2}{9}$ of the staircase.

Therefore, $\frac{1}{9}$ of the staircase = 3 steps and $\frac{9}{9}$ (the whole staircase) = 27 steps.

There are 27 stairs in the staircase.

METHOD 2:   <u>*Strategy*</u>: *Guess and check; make a table.*

The total number of steps has to be divisible by 3 and 9, and greater than 9. Start with a total of 18, 27, 36, …, steps, until the number in the last column equals the starting number.

Guess	After A	After B	Steps remaining	After C	6 more steps
18	step 12	step 6	12	14	20 (too much)
27	step 18	step 9	18	21	**27**

The staircase has 27 steps.

SET 8 SOLUTIONS

Olympiad 5

5A **METHOD 1:** *Strategy: Multiply all of the fractions together first.*
$\frac{1}{2}$ of $\frac{1}{3}$ of $\frac{1}{4}$ = $\frac{1}{2} \times \frac{1}{3} \times \frac{1}{4}$ = $\frac{1}{24}$, and then $\frac{1}{24} \times 240 = \mathbf{10}$

METHOD 2: *Strategy: Perform the multiplications one at a time.*
Work from right to left: First, $\frac{1}{4}$ of 240 = 60. Then $\frac{1}{3}$ of 60 is 20. Then $\frac{1}{2}$ of 20 is 10.

> ***FOLLOW-UP:*** *$900 is divided in half. Each half is divided into three equal piles, and each pile is divided equally among five people. How much money will each person receive?* [$30]

5B *Strategy: Start where there is only one possible choice.*
The square between 3 and 5 must contain 4. There is then only one possible location for 2 that lies adjacent to 1 and 3.

3	2		
4	1		
5	*		*
		16	

It seems there are two possible locations for 6. If 6 is placed to the right of 5, however, the lower left corner will be a dead end. So 6 is placed in the lower left corner. The other squares may now be filled in. **The sum of the numbers in the starred boxes is** $8 + 14 = \mathbf{22}$.

3	2	*11*	*12*
4	1	*10*	*13*
5	*8*	*9*	*14*
6	*7*	16	*15*

5C *Strategy: Use the definition of average.*
The average of a group of numbers is their total divided by the number of numbers, so the product of the number of numbers in the group and their average is equal to their total.

Group	Quantity × Average	= Total in group
A	10 × 10 =	100
B	20 × 20 =	400
C	30 × 30 =	900
D	40 × 40 =	1600
Total of all groups =		**3000**

The average of the combined group is $3000 \div 100 = \mathbf{30}$.

> ***FOLLOW-UP:*** *Jimmy bikes to a park, a distance of 30 miles, at 10 miles per hour. He bikes home along the same path at 6 miles per hour. What is Jimmy's average speed for the entire trip?* [7.5 miles per hour]

5D _Strategy: Organize the data in two tables._

In table 1 the first row shows the number of brothers that Judy could have. Because Judy has 2 more sisters than brothers, the second row shows the family with 3 more girls than boys.

Table 1:

# of boys in Judy's family	0	1	2	3	4	5
# of girls in the family	3	4	5	6	7	8

In table 2 the second row shows the number of brothers Mark has. This is 1 less than the number of boys on line 1 of table 1. Mark has twice as many sisters as brothers.

Table 2:

# of boys in Mark's family	0	1	2	3	4	5
# of brothers Mark has	–	0	1	2	3	4
# of girls in the family	–	0	2	4	6	8

Comparing the total numbers of boys and of girls, there are 5 boys and 8 girls. **13 children are in the family.**

5E _Strategy: Place the least number of blocks of each color._

The red block (R) is in a corner, so 3 faces are visible. To hide those 3 faces, 3 green (G) blocks are required.

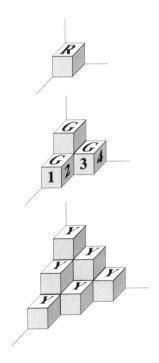

Now there are 4 blocks, 3 on the lower level and one on top of the hidden block.

On the new bottom level, there are four green faces visible (1, 2, 3, 4), but only three yellow blocks are necessary to cover them, for one yellow block can cover faces 2 and 3 both.

On the second tier, two yellow blocks (Y) will cover the tops of the bottom green blocks as well as the sides of the top green block. Then, one yellow block will cover the top of the uppermost green block. A total of 6 yellow blocks are needed.

At this point, there are $1 + 3 + 6 = $ **10 blocks in the box.**

SOLUTIONS, STRATEGIES, & FOLLOW-UPS

DIVISION M
SETS 9-16

Set 9   Olympiad 1

1A   *Strategy: Examine the possible sets that contain the number 17.*
The five possible sets are {13, 14, 15, 16, **17**}, {14, 15, 16, **17**, 18}, {15, 16, **17**, 18, 19}, {16, **17**, 18, 19, 20} and {**17**, 18, 19, 20, 21}.

In each set of numbers, there is a multiple of 5 and at least one multiple of 2. Then each product is a multiple of 10. In every case, **the ones digit of the product is 0**.

> ***Follow-Ups:*** *(1) The integers from 1 through 50 are multiplied together. How many terminal zeros are in the product?* [12; 25 and 50 each have **two** factors of 5] *(2) Find the largest number which must be a factor of the product of any five consecutive numbers.* [120]

1B   **METHOD 1:** *Strategy: Find the time required to travel one mile.*
At 45 mph, the train can travel 1 mile in $\frac{1}{45}$ of an hour and therefore, 12 miles in $\frac{12}{45}$ of an hour. This is $\frac{4}{15}$ of an hour = 16 minutes. Therefore **the train reaches Smalltown at 7:16 PM.**

METHOD 2: *Strategy: Simplify the time and distance.*
The train travels 45 miles in 60 minutes and therefore, 3 miles in 4 minutes. Since 12 = 3 × 4, the train travels 12 miles in 4 × 4 = 16 minutes. (This could also be done by dividing 12 by $\frac{3}{4}$.) The train reaches Smalltown at 7:16 PM.

> ***Follow-Up:*** *Two trains, 100 miles apart, move toward one another, each at 25 mph. At the same time, a fly travels back and forth between the trains at 35 mph without stopping. It touches one train, then the other, then the first again, etc. How many miles will the fly have flown by the time the two trains meet?* [70 miles; the trains will meet in 2 hours.]

1C   *Strategy: Find the number of true statements for each set of values.*
The three given numbers partition the autographs into four possible sets. The table states which of the three statements are true for each possibility.

Since exactly one statement is true, the number is between 45 and 61 inclusive. **The greatest number of autographs Noelle can own is 61.**

# of autographs	True statements
1 through 44	none
45 through 61	#3, only
62 through 76	#2 & #3, only
77 and up	#1, #2, and #3

> ***Follow-Up:*** *Suppose exactly one of the statements is false. What is the least number of autographs Noelle can own?* [62]

1D *Strategy: Do the division and look for a pattern.*

Perform the following long division: $37 \overline{\smash{)}9.000\,000\,000\,\ldots} = 0.243\,243\,243\,\ldots$

The decimal repeats every three digits. 2004 is a multiple of 3 because the sum of the digits in 2004 is a multiple of 3. Then the 2004th digit is the same as the third digit, 3. **The next digit, the 2005th, is 2.**

1E *Strategy: Use the symmetry of the rectangle.*

A rectangle is symmetric about its center. Rotate rectangle *ABCD* 180° about point *E* as shown in *figure 1*. Triangle **I** will be in the same place originally occupied by triangle **II**. These two triangles are congruent and have the same area.

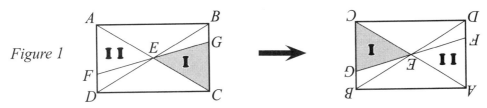

Figure 1

Notice that triangle *DEA* can be partitioned into triangles *DEF* and *FEA*, as shown in *figure 2*. Thus the sum of the areas of the two required triangles *FED* and *GEC* is the same as the area of triangle *DEA*.

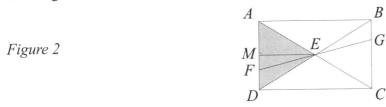

Figure 2

Triangle *DEA* has a base ($\overline{AD}$) of 12 cm and a height ($\overline{EM}$) of 9 cm. The area of triangle *DEA*, and thus **the total area of the** original **shaded regions, is** $\frac{1}{2} \times 12 \times 9 =$ **54 sq cm.**

> **FOLLOW-UPS:** *(1) How many capital letters are symmetric about their center (can be rotated 180° without changing their appearance)?* [7: H I N O S X Z]   *(2) Diagonals $\overline{AC}$ and $\overline{BD}$ of parallelogram ABCD meet at point E. Base $\overline{BC}$ is 20 cm long. Altitude $\overline{AF}$ is drawn to base $\overline{BC}$ and is 12 cm long. What are the areas of triangles ABE, BCE, CDE, and DAE?* [60 sq cm in each case.]

Olympiad 2

2A **METHOD 1:** _Strategy: Start with the units column._

In the units column, B + A = 2 or 12. But B + A cannot equal 2, because A would be no more than 2 and the final sum could not have three digits. Thus, B + A = 12. In the tens column, (A + A) plus a "carry" of 1 is an odd number, so B is odd. The organized table below tests the values of A and B for which AB + AA equals 1B2.

$$
\begin{array}{r}
A\,B \\
+\ A\,A \\
\hline
1\,B\,2
\end{array}
$$

A	B	AB	AA	AB + AA	1B2	Does AB + AA = 1B2?
3	9	39	33	72	192	no
5	7	57	55	112	172	no
7	**5**	**75**	**77**	**152**	**152**	**YES**
9	3	93	99	192	132	no

The value of A is 7.

METHOD 2: _Strategy: Start with the tens column._

In the tens column, A + A is at least 10, so the digit A is at least 5. Test (A,B) for (5,7), (7,5), (8,4), and (9,3). A represents 7 and B represents 5.

> ***Follow-Up:*** *Many other cryptarithms like this and more appear in section 7.1 of George Lenchner's book,* Creative Problem Solving in School Mathematics.

2B _Strategy: Make an organized list._

The possibilities are:

1, 1, 19	3, 3, 15	5, 5, 11	7, 7, 7
1, 3, 17	3, 5, 13	5, 7, 9	
1, 5, 15	3, 7, 11		
1, 7, 13	3, 9, 9		
1, 9, 11			

Emily can make the piles in 12 ways.

> ***Follow-Up:*** *Bianca arranged pencils on her desk. Groups of 9 pencils left 2 over. Groups of 6 pencils left 2 over. Groups of 4 left none over. What is the smallest number of pencils Bianca could have on her desk?* [20] *The next three smallest?* [56, 92, 128]

2C **METHOD 1:** _Strategy: Determine when Amy or Bill could claim to lie the previous day._

To make the statement, "I lied yesterday", one of two situations must exist:

    (1) Today they must tell the truth and yesterday they could lie, or

    (2) Today they could lie and yesterday they had to tell the truth.

The table summarizes the information given.

	Sun	Mon	Tue	Wed	Thur	Fri	Sat
Amy		truth	truth	truth	truth		
Bill	truth	truth				truth	truth

For Amy (1) exists only on Monday and (2) only on Friday. For Bill (1) exists only on Friday and (2) only on Tuesday. **The only day they both can say "I lied yesterday" is Friday.**

METHOD 2: _Strategy: List the days on which the statement could NOT be made._

Neither Amy nor Bill can make the statement "I lied yesterday" on a day on which the truth must be told if the previous day was _also_ one on which the truth must be told.

According to the chart in method 1, Amy cannot make the statement on Tuesday, Wednesday, or Thursday.

Bill cannot make the statement on Saturday, Sunday, or Monday. That eliminates every day but Friday.

2D METHOD 1: _Strategy: Examine the possible prime factors of N._

N is composite, so it is the product of two or more (not necessarily different) primes. None of the prime factors can be 2, 3, or 5, for then at least one of the fractions given would not be in lowest terms. The possible prime factors of N are 7, 11, 13, 17, etc. The composites using these factors are 7×7, 7×11, 7×13, 11×11, etc. Because only the first two composites are between 20 and 80, **the only possible values of N are 49 and 77.**

METHOD 2: _Strategy: Eliminate the whole numbers between 20 and 80 that don't work._ Start with the numbers 21, 22, 23, …, 79.

Since $\frac{2}{N}$, $\frac{3}{N}$, and $\frac{5}{N}$ are in lowest terms, eliminate all the multiples of 2, 3, and 5. This leaves 23, 29, 31, 37, 41, 43, 47, 49, 53, 59, 61, 67, 71, 73, 77, and 79. From this list, only 49 and 77 are composite. The rest are prime numbers. The possible values of N are 49 and 77.

> **_FOLLOW-UPS:_** _(1) Change the problem so that the interval for N is from 20 to 200. What composite numbers would be listed?_ [49, 77, 91, 119, 121, 133, 143, 161, 169, 187] _(2) What is the smallest composite number that has none of the factors 2, 3, 5, or 7?_ [121] _2, 3, 5, 7, or 11?_ [169] _Can you identify a pattern?_ [the square of the next prime]

2E _Strategy: Do the operations (subtractions) within parentheses._

$1 - \frac{1}{1980} = \frac{1980}{1980} - \frac{1}{1980} = \frac{1980 - 1}{1980} = \frac{1979}{1980}$

Proceed in like manner with each of the other factors. The expression becomes:

$$\frac{1979}{1980} \times \frac{1980}{1981} \times \frac{1981}{1982} \times \cdots \times \frac{2003}{2004} \times \frac{2004}{2005}$$

After cancellation, only the numerator 1979 and the denominator 2005 remain, and **the resulting product is $\frac{1979}{2005}$.** Because 1979 is prime, this is in lowest terms.

Olympiad 3

3A   **METHOD 1:** _Strategy: Split the $2.00 up into travel cost and start-up cost._
Think of the initial $2 as 40¢ for that first fifth-mile and $1.60 just to turn on the meter. Then Dan can afford $9.60 − 1.60 = $8.00 for the actual distance covered by the taxi. At 40¢ per fifth-mile, $8.00 can pay for 20 fifths of a mile. **The longest ride Dan can afford is 4 miles.**

METHOD 2: _Strategy: Make a table that compares each distance traveled to its cost._

Cost in cents	200	240	280	320	...	960
Fifths of a mile	1	2	3	4	...	20

The cost increases by 40¢ for each fifth of a mile traveled. When $9.60 is reached, the taxi will have traveled a length of 20 fifths, which is 4 miles.

METHOD 3: _Strategy: Use algebra._
Let N = the number of fifths of a mile after the first fifth mile that Dan can ride
$2 + the cost for the additional fifths costs $9.60: $2.00 + .40N = 9.60$

Subtract 2.00 from each side of the equation: $.40N = 7.60$
Divide each side of the equation by .40: $N = 19$

Add the first fifth of a mile, bringing the length of the ride to 20 fifths = 4 miles.

3B   _Strategy: Find the sum of the whole numbers from 1 through 12._
To find the sum quickly, add "from the outside in." $(1+12) + (2+11) + (3+10) + \ldots + (6+7) =$ $6 \times 13 = 78$, Sean's answer. This is only 3 less than the perfect square 81, so Allie's answer is 3 more than 81, namely 84. Since 84 is 6 more than 78, **Allie added 6 to Sean's answer.**

We should also check the next choice. Three more than the next largest square, 100, is 103. This is impossible because Allie cannot add 25 to Sean's 78.

3C   **METHOD 1:** _Strategy: Compare the two lists from which a number is chosen._
Compare a list of numbers in the set which are 1 more than a multiple of 4 against a list of numbers 1 more than a multiple of 5.

1 more than a multiple of 5:   ④①, 46, 51, 56, ⑥①, 66

1 more than a multiple of 4:   ④①, 45, 49, 53, 57, ⑥①, 65

Of the 27 numbers in the set, 11 different numbers can be chosen. **The probability is $\frac{11}{27}$.**

METHOD 2: *Strategy: Work with the multiples by subtracting 1 from each number in the set.* The question is equivalent to asking for the probability of choosing a multiple of 4 or 5 from the interval from 40 to 66 inclusive. Of the 27 members of the set, there are 7 multiples of 4 and 6 multiples of 5. However, these 13 multiples include 2 multiples of 20, the LCM of 4 and 5. Both multiples, 40 and 60, were counted twice. Thus, there are 11 numbers in the original set which are one more than a multiple of 4 or 5, and the probability is $\frac{11}{27}$.

> **FOLLOW-UP:** *A number is chosen at random from the set {1, 2, 3, ..., 99}. Find the probability that the number is one more than a multiple of 5 or of 6.* [$\frac{33}{99}$; In accordance with prevailing definitions, "What Every Young Mathlete Should Know" (our contest bible) defines 0 as a multiple of both 5 and 6. Have your students research it on the Internet.]

3D   **METHOD 1:** *Strategy: Find the percentage that does NOT exit at C.*
The only traffic that exits at B is the traffic that heads east at the two intersections on the north edge of town. At the first intersection, 70% (0.7) of the traffic heads east and at the second intersection 70% of that 70% (0.7 × 0.7) heads east to exit at B. 49% exits at B, and the *remaining* **51% of the traffic exits at C.**

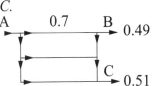

METHOD 2: *Strategy: Find the percentage that travels along each road.*
When two roads leave an intersection, multiply by 0.7 to get the percent heading east and by 0.3 to get the percent heading south. When two roads enter an intersection, add the percents to get the percent leaving. The diagram shows the results. 51% of the traffic exits at C.

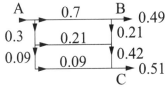

> **FOLLOW-UP:** *In the diagram at the right, how many different paths are there from A to B? Each move must be to the right or downward.* [126]

3E   *Strategy: Draw a useful line segment.*
To find the circumference of the circle, first find the radius.

METHOD 1: *Draw radius OD.*
Since the diameters are perpendicular and *ABCD* is a rectangle, *ADMO* is also a rectangle. Therefore, diagonals *OD* and *AM* are congruent. Then the length of radius *OD* is 20 cm, and the circumference of the circle must be 2 × 3.14 × 20 ≈ 125.6. **To the nearest centimeter, the circumference of the circle is 126 cm.**

METHOD 2: *Draw radius OC.*

Rectangle *ADMO* is congruent to rectangle *OMCB*, so diagonal *OC* is congruent to diagonal *AM*. Then *OC* = 20 cm, and, as in method 1, the circumference of the circle is approximately 126 cm.

FOLLOW-UP: *As shown at the right, AM = 10 cm and MP = 4 cm. What is the area of rectangle ABCD?* [96 sq cm; solution requires use of the Pythagorean Theorem.)

Olympiad 4

4A   *Strategy: Work backwards.*

To have the fewest hamsters, David must have only one hamster in the fourth cage (we assume all hamsters are whole). If there is one in the fourth cage, there are two in the third, four in the second, and eight in the first. **The fewest hamsters David can have is** $8 + 4 + 2 + 1$, or **15.**

4B   *Strategy: Write out all the numbers included in the problem and simplify.*

$\boxed{12} = 5 + 7 + 8 + 9 + 10 + 11.$

$\boxed{10} = 3 + 4 + 6 + 7 + 8 + 9.$

$\boxed{12} - \boxed{10} = (5 + \boxed{7 + 8 + 9} + \text{⑩} + 11) - (3 + \boxed{4 + 6} + \boxed{7 + 8 + 9}).$

$\boxed{12} - \boxed{10} = (5 + 11) - (3).$

$\boxed{12} - \boxed{10} = 13.$ **The simplified value is 13.**

4C   **METHOD 1:** *Strategy: Average the sums.*

Because more numbers average 43 than average 18, the average will be closer to 43 than 18. Thus, a simple average of 43 and 18 is incorrect; the overall average is said to be weighted.

The average of P and Q is 18, so $P + Q = 36$.
The average of R, S, and T is 43, so $R + S + T = 129$.

The average of P, Q, R, S, and T is $\frac{P + Q + R + S + T}{5} = \frac{36 + 129}{5} = \textbf{33}.$

METHOD 2: *Strategy: Place the overall average proportionally.*

As in method 1, the mean (average) is closer to 43 than 18. With three of the five numbers averaging 43, the overall average is $\frac{3}{5}$ of the interval from 18 to 43. $\frac{3}{5}$ of 25 is 15. The overall average is 15 more than 18, which is 33.

METHOD 3: _Strategy: Calculate the average deviation from an assumed "trial average"._ Suppose the numbers are 43, 43, 43, 18, and 18. Assume a trial average of 30. Then each of the first 3 numbers are 13 above this "average" and each of the last two numbers are 12 below the "average". Divide (13 + 13 + 13 + $^-$12 + $^-$12) by 5; the true average is 15 ÷ 5 = 3 above the trial average, 30. It is 33.

> **FOLLOW-UP:** _After four tests, Al has a test average of 88. Al needs a test average of 90 or above to receive an A in his class. What is the minimum he needs to score on the fifth test to receive an A?_ [98]

4D   _Strategy: Split the quarter-circle into more familiar figures._
If we remove the given triangle from the quarter-circle, we are left with the shaded region, called a _segment of a circle._

Area of the quarter-circle
  $\frac{1}{4} \times \pi r^2$ ≈ .25 × 3.14 × 4² = 12.56 sq cm (to the nearest hundredth)

Area of the triangle
  $\frac{1}{2} \times 4 \times 4$ = 8 sq cm

Area of the segment of the circle
  12.56 – 8 = 4.56 sq cm
  To the nearest tenth it is 4.6.

The area of the shaded region is 4.6 sq cm.

> **FOLLOW-UP:** _A square landing area is cut into quarters as shown. If a sky-diver lands inside the square, what is the probability she lands inside the target circle?_ [$\frac{\pi}{16}$ or approximately 0.196]

4E   _Strategy: Minimize the overlap in two flavors._
Suppose that those who said they liked strawberry and those who said they liked chocolate were all different students. That would require 65 + 75 = 140 students. There are only 100 in the survey. Therefore, 40 or more said they liked both strawberry and chocolate.

Repeat the process, treating those who like vanilla as one group and those who like both strawberry and chocolate as a second group. For these to be all different students, the survey would need to have included 85 + (at least 40) = at least 125 people. Since only 100 were surveyed, 25 (or more) students said they liked all three flavors. **The least number is 25.**

Note: This answer will be found regardless of which two flavors you start with.

> **FOLLOW-UPS:** _(1) What is the greatest number that could have said they liked all three flavors?_ [65]   _(2) What is the least number that could have said they liked chocolate and vanilla but not strawberry?_ [0]

Olympiad 5

5A   METHOD 1: _Strategy: Start with a simpler case and look for a pattern._
2 posts result in a fence 1 × 6 = 6 m long, 3 posts result in a fence 2 × 6 = 12 m long, and so on. Then **10 posts result in a fence** 9 × 6 or **54 m long.**

METHOD 2: _Strategy: Draw a picture._

There are ten posts and nine sections of fence between them. The fence is 6 × 9 or 54 m long.

> **FOLLOW-UP:** _How many fence posts are required to enclose a rectangular garden that is 12 m by 16 m if the posts are placed 4 m apart?_ [14]

5B   METHOD 1: _Strategy: Examine the prime factors._
The prime factors of 15,600 are 2 × 2 × 2 × 2 × 3 × 5 × 5 × 13. Of three consecutive numbers, no more than one can be a multiple of 5. Since there are two 5s in the list of prime factors, one number is a multiple of 25. One of the numbers is a multiple of 13, which suggests 26. Rearrange the prime factors as (2×13) × (5×5) × (2×2×2×3) = 26 × 25 × 24 = 15,600. **The least of the three numbers is 24.**

METHOD 2: _Strategy: Use the fact that the three factors are nearly equal._
Since $10^3 = 1000$, $20^3 = 8000$, and $30^3 = 27,000$, the numbers are between 20 and 30. One of the numbers must be a multiple of 5, so try 25^3, which is 15,625. Therefore, one possible answer could be 24 × 25 × 26. Since that gives us the correct product of 15,600, the least of the three numbers is 24.

5C   METHOD 1: _Strategy: Find the percent represented by the given amount._
Since 60% of the students are female, then 40% are male. The number of females exceeds the number of males by (60 – 40) = 20% of the total number of students. Then 72 is 20%, or one-fifth, of the total. The total number of students is 5 × 72 = 360. Thus 40% of 360 = **144 male students are enrolled.**

METHOD 2: _Strategy: Try simpler related cases and look for a pattern._
Assuming a total of 100, 200, and 300 students, this table shows in each case the subtraction of the number of males from the number of females.

# of students	# of females	# of males	Difference
100	60	40	20
200	120	80	40
300	180	120	60

Notice that in each case the number of males (column 3) is twice the difference (column 4). Since the actual difference is 72, the number of male students is 144.

METHOD 3: _Strategy: Use algebra._

Let x = the number of males.

Then $x + 72$ = the number of females and $2x + 72$ = the total number of students.

Set up a proportion: $\qquad \qquad \dfrac{x + 72}{2x + 72} = \dfrac{60}{100}$

Now cross-multiply: $\qquad \qquad \qquad 60(2x + 72) = 100\,(x + 72)$

Multiply out on each side of the equation: $\quad 120x + 4320 = 100x + 7200$

Subtract $100x + 4320$ from each side of the equation: $\quad 20x \qquad = \qquad 2880$

Divide each side of the equation by 20: $\qquad \quad x \qquad = \qquad 144$

Thus, 144 male students are enrolled.

5D _Strategy: Split the region into more familiar shapes._

Draw two lines as shown to divide the square into four congruent smaller squares.

METHOD 1: _Strategy: Find the area of each shaded region separately._

Square **A**, fully shaded, has an area of 16 sq m. In squares **B** and **C**, each shaded region is found by removing the quarter circle from the square. Each of those areas is then about $16 - (\frac{1}{4} \times 3.14 \times 4^2)$, which then simplifies to 3.44 sq m. Adding 16, 3.44, and 3.44 and then rounding off, **the area of the shaded region is then 22.9 sq m.**

METHOD 2: _Strategy: Find the area of the unshaded region._

METHOD 2A: The unshaded area is the sum of the areas of regions **D**, **C**, and **B**. The area of square **D** is 16 sq m. The area of one quarter-circle is $\frac{1}{4} \times 3.14 \times 4^2 \approx 12.56$, sq m. The area of the unshaded region is about $16 + 2 \times 12.56 = 41.12$ sq m. The area of the shaded region is then about $64 - 41.12 = 22.88$, which rounds to 22.9 sq m.

METHOD 2B: Think of the complete unshaded region as the sum of two semicircles of radius 4 meters minus the "overlap". The overlap, divided into 2 parts by the dotted line in the diagram, consists of two regions congruent to the region considered in problem 4D. Its area was computed as approximately 4.56, so the area of the unshaded region is about 2×4.56 less than $2 \times (\frac{1}{2} \times 3.14 \times 4^2)$. As above, the area of the shaded region is $64 - 41.12$ = about 22.9 sq m.

**FOLLOW-UP:** A semicircle with area 18π is inscribed in an isosceles right triangle as shown. Find the area of this triangle.[72]

5E   **METHOD 1:** _Strategy_: List all possible values for the tens digit.

Consider the second condition first. The possible two-digit numbers are 13, 25, 37, and 49. The table compares the results of the first condition against those of the second condition.

Tens digit	1	2	3	**4**
Units digit	3	5	7	**9**
Number	13	25	37	**49**
3 × Sum of digits	12	21	30	**39**
Difference = 10?	_no_	_no_	_no_	**_YES_**

The two-digit number is 49.

METHOD 2: _Strategy_: Use algebra.

Let t = the tens digit and u = the units digit.

Then $10t + u$ = the two-digit number and $t + u$ = the sum of the digits.

English: "The number is equal to 10 more than 3 times the sum of the digits."
  Equation 1: $10t + u = 3(t + u) + 10$

English: "The units digit is 1 more than twice the tens digit."
  Equation 2: $u = 2t + 1$

Substituting $\underline{2t + 1}$ for u in both places in equation 1, we get:

$$10t + \underline{2t + 1} = 3(t + \underline{2t + 1}) + 10$$

Combine like terms on each side of the equation: $12t + 1 = 3(3t + 1) + 10$

Multiply $3t + 1$ by 3: $12t + 1 = 9t + 3 \quad + 10$

Add 3 and 10: $12t + 1 = 9t + 13$

Subtract 1 from each side of the equation: $12t = 9t + 12$

Subtract $9t$ from each side of the equation: $3t = 12$

Divide each side of the equation by 3: $t = 4$

Because $u = 2t + 1$, $u = 2(4) + 1$, so that $u = 9$. The two-digit number is 49.

Set 10   Olympiad 1

1A   **METHOD 1:** _Strategy_: Use the alternating signs to group terms.

$(40 - 36) + (32 - 28) + (24 - 20) + (16 - 12) + (8 - 4) = 5 \times (4) = 20$.
The value is 20.

METHOD 2: _Strategy_: Combine positive and negative terms separately.

Rewrite as $40 + {}^-36 + {}^+32 + {}^-28 + {}^+24 + {}^-20 + {}^+16 + {}^-12 + {}^+8 + {}^-4$

$= (40 + 32 + 24 + 16 + 8) + ({}^-36 + {}^-28 + {}^-20 + {}^-12 + {}^-4)$

$= \quad\quad (120) \quad\quad + \quad\quad\quad ({}^-100)$

$= \quad\quad\quad\quad 20$

The value is 20.   _Note: Many students may just subtract and add, left to right._

1B   METHOD 1: _Strategy: Consider one restriction on N at a time._
N satisfies two conditions: (1) N is a factor of 14; and (2) $N > 4$, because a remainder is less than the divisor. The factors of 14 are 1, 2, 7, and 14. Of these only 7 and 14 are greater than 4. Therefore, **there are 2 values of** N.

METHOD 2: _Strategy: Divide 18 by each counting number less than 18._

Divisor N	1	2	3	4	5	6	7	8	9	10	11	12	13	14	15	16	17
Quotient	18	9	6	4	3	3	2	2	2	1	1	1	1	1	1	1	1
Remainder	0	0	0	2	3	0	4	2	0	8	7	6	5	4	3	2	1

The remainder is 4 for only 2 values of N, 7 and 14.

> _FOLLOW-UP: Suppose 50 is divided by each counting number less than 50. What is the least remainder that occurs only once?_ [3; the divisor is 47.]

1C   METHOD 1: _Strategy: Create a convenient unit of currency._
Pair each dime with a quarter to make one "quime" worth $.35. The total value of the four unpaired quarters is $1.00 and of the quimes, $4.20. At 35¢ each, there are 12 quimes. **Amy has 12 dimes** (and 16 quarters).

METHOD 2: _Strategy: Examine the smallest numbers to find a pattern._

Number of coins		1	2	3	...	12
	Dimes	1	2	3	...	12
	Quarters	5	6	7	...	16
Value of coins	Dimes	$0.10	$0.20	$0.30	...	$1.20
	Quarters	$1.25	$1.50	$1.75	...	$4.00
Total value		$1.35	$1.70	$2.05	...	$5.20

For every additional dime, the total value increases by 35¢. This can shorten the number of trials needed to conclude that Amy has 12 dimes.

METHOD 3: _Strategy: Use algebra._
Let D = the number of dimes and $10D$ = their value in cents.
Then $D + 4$ = the number of quarters and $25(D + 4)$ = their value in cents.

The value of all the dimes and quarters is 520 cents: $\quad 10D + 25(D + 4) \quad = 520$

Multiply $D + 4$ by 25: $\qquad\qquad\qquad\qquad 10D + 25D + 100 \quad = 520$
Combine $10D$ and $25D$: $\qquad\qquad\qquad\qquad\quad 35D + 100 \quad = 520$
Subtract 100 from each side of the equation: $\qquad 35D \qquad\qquad = 420$
Divide each side of the equation by 35: $\qquad\qquad D \qquad\qquad = 12$
Amy has 12 dimes.

> _FOLLOW-UPS: (1) Lew has $6 more in quarters than in dimes. He has twice as many quarters as dimes. What is the total value of Lew's quarters and dimes?_ [$9.00]   _(2) Michelle has 50 coins, all dimes and quarters. The total value of the coins is $8.15. How many dimes are there?_ [29]

1D   METHOD 1: _Strategy: Compare each interior line segment to a side of the large square._
The diagram shows four vertical and four horizontal segments, each equal
in length to a side of the large square, which is 10 cm. They also are all the
sides of the four smaller figures, so **the sum of the perimeters of A, B, C,
and D is** 8×10 cm = **80 cm.**

METHOD 2: _Strategy: Trace the perimeter of each of the small regions._
Each of the four exterior segments of the original square is traced once, while
each of the two interior segments is traced twice. The sum of the perimeters of
A, B, C, and **D** is equal to the perimeter of the original square plus twice the
length of each of the two interior line segments. Since the area of the original
square is 100 sq cm, the length of each side and each interior segment is 10
cm. **The sum of the perimeters is** $(2 \times 10) + (2 \times 10) + 40 =$ **80 cm.**

METHOD 3: _Strategy: Pick a convenient value for the length of a side of one small region._
The problem seems to suggest that the answer doesn't depend on the dimensions of the
individual regions. Suppose one side of square B measures 7 cm. Then each side of each
region measures either 7 or 3 cm. The sum of the perimeters of the regions **A, B, C,** and **D**
is $20 + 28 + 12 + 20 = 80$ cm, respectively. To check correctness, also test at least two more
values other than 7 cm for the side-length of B.

1E   _Strategy: First determine the denominators._
The fractions are in lowest terms, so each denominator is a factor of 56. The factors of 56 are
1, 2, 4, 7, 8, 14, 28, and 56. Only 7 and 8 are consecutive so those are the denominators.

Denote the numerators as A and B. Then $\frac{A}{7} + \frac{B}{8} = \frac{51}{56}$. The fractions are in lowest terms, so the
value of B is 1, 3, 5, or 7. Subtract $\frac{1}{8}, \frac{3}{8}, \frac{5}{8}$, and $\frac{7}{8}$ in turn from $\frac{51}{56}$. Only $\frac{51}{56} - \frac{5}{8}$ (which equals
$\frac{51}{56} - \frac{35}{56}$) gives a result, $\frac{16}{56}$, that can be reduced to a fraction that has a denominator of 7, namely
$\frac{2}{7}$. **The greater of the two fractions,** $\frac{2}{7}$ **and** $\frac{5}{8}$, **is** $\frac{5}{8}$.
   [_Note:_ $\frac{51}{56} + \frac{0}{56}$ (_or_ $\frac{0}{56} + \frac{51}{56}$) _is not acceptable because_ $\frac{0}{56}$ _is not in lowest terms._]

   FOLLOW-UPS: _(1) If_ $\frac{2}{C} + \frac{3}{D} = \frac{E}{24}$ _and each fraction is in lowest terms, find the values of C,
   D, and E._ [One set of values is $C = 3$, $D = 8$, $E = 25$].   _(2) There are another two sets of
   values for C, D, and E. Can you find them?_ [Hint: Look at $E = 25$.]

SET 10   SOLUTIONS

2A *Strategy: Start with the least possible number for Jo.*
The more CDs Jo has, the more CDs Ken and Maisie have. Suppose Jo has 11 Compact Discs, the least number possible. Then Ken has 22 CDs and Maisie has 66 CDs. **The least number of CDs that Maisie can have is 66.**

> **FOLLOW-UP:** *What is the greatest number of CDs that Maisie could have if the sum of Jo's, Ken's, and Maisie's CDs is less than 500?* [330]

2B **METHOD 1:** *Strategy: Find the car opposite car number 1.*
Start at car 14 and count up to car 30, as shown; there are 15 cars in between them. Then there must be 15 more cars on the other semicircle. **There are** $15 + 15 + 2$ or **32 cars on the Ferris wheel.**

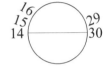

METHOD 2: *Strategy: Determine the number of pairs of cars.*
The numbers of any two cars opposite each other differ by 16. Then the Ferris wheel has 16 pairs of cars. There are 32 cars.

METHOD 3: *Strategy: Invent a fictional car "0".*
The numbers of any two cars opposite each other differ by 16. Then car 16 is opposite either car 32 or car "0". Since the least car number is 1, the Ferris wheel has 32 cars.

2C **METHOD 1:** *Strategy: Find the problem-solving rate for all 8 mathletes.*
Eight mathletes work at a rate of 2 problems per minute (ppm) when they solve 20 problems in 10 minutes. However, n mathletes must work at a rate of 6 ppm in order to solve 30 problems in 5 minutes. This requires three times as many mathletes. **24 mathletes are needed.**

METHOD 2: *Strategy: Find the problem-solving rate for one mathlete.*
Eight mathletes need 10 minutes to solve 20 problems. Then to solve 20 problems, one mathlete working alone needs 80 minutes. To solve 30 problems, one mathlete needs 120 minutes. To complete the task in just 5 minutes, $120 \div 5 = 24$ mathletes are needed.

SET 10 SOLUTIONS

2D METHOD 1: _Strategy: Count in an organized way._
One vertex is on one line and the other two are on the other line.
Suppose one vertex is on line 1 and two vertices are on line 2.
There are 6 such triangles using vertex P: PST, PSU, PSV, PTU,
PTV, and PUV. Likewise, there are 6 such triangles using vertex
Q and 6 more using vertex R, for a total of 18.

line 1 P Q R

line 2 S T U V

Now suppose one vertex is on line 2 and two vertices are on line 1. There are 3 such triangles
using vertex S (SPQ, SPR, and SQR), 3 more triangles using vertex T, 3 more using vertex U,
and 3 more using vertex V, for a total of 12. In all, **30 triangles can be formed using any
three of the points as vertices.**

METHOD 2: _Strategy (for more advanced students): Use combinatorics._
For each of the 3 points on line 1, there are $_4C_2 = 6$ pairs of points on line 2. This gives us 18
triangles. For each of the 4 points on line 2, there are $_3C_2 = 3$ pairs of points on line 1. This
gives us 12 more triangles. Thus, a total of 30 triangles can be formed.

> **FOLLOW-UPS:** _(1) Suppose all 7 points are on a circle. How many triangles can be formed_
> _using any 3 of the points as vertices?_ [35]   _(2) See pages 111-114 in_ Creative Problem
> Solving in School Mathematics, _2nd Edition._

2E METHOD 1: _Strategy: Find the greatest common factor (GCF) of the differences._
Since the remainder is the same when each of 17, 25, and 41 is divided by the counting number
D, the difference between any two of the numbers is a multiple of D (see *example below).
The differences between each pair of numbers are $41 - 25 = 16$, $41 - 17 = 24$, and $25 - 17 = 8$.
The GCF of 16, 24, and 8 is 8, so **the greatest counting number is 8.**

  *Example: $41 = 8 \times 5 + \blacksquare$; $25 = 8 \times 3 + \blacksquare$

$41 - 25 = (8 \times 5 + \blacksquare) - (8 \times 3 + \blacksquare)$
$41 - 25 = 8 \times 5 - 8 \times 3$ [Notice that the common remainder of 1 drops out.]
$41 - 25 = 8 \times (5 - 3)$ [Thus $41 - 25$ is a multiple of 8.]

METHOD 2: _Strategy: Make a table of remainders._
Since 17 is not a factor of 25 or 41, the greatest divisor to test is 16. The table shows the
remainders when each of 17, 25, and 41 is divided by every counting number less than 17.
From the table, the greatest divisor that results in all equal remainders is 8. (Others are the
factors of 8: 4, 2, and 1.)

Divisors

	16	15	14	13	12	11	10	9	8
17	1	2	3	4	5	6	7	8	**1**
25	9	10	11	12	1	3	5	7	**1**
41	9	11	13	2	5	8	1	5	**1**

> **FOLLOW-UP:** _When each of the numbers 123, 135, 165, and 183 is divided by the same_
> _whole number N, the remainder is the same. Find the greatest possible value of N._ [6]

SET 10   SOLUTIONS

Olympiad 3

3A *Strategy: Start the month with a day off.*
Choose a month with 31 days, and let him work the last 4 days of the previous month. Then he starts the month with a day off. Then Bill's other days off are all one day more than the multiples of 5: 6, 11, 16, 21, 26, 31. **The greatest number of days off that Bill can get in one month is 7.**

> **FOLLOW-UP:** *What is the least number of days off Bill could have in any one month?* [5]

3B *Strategy: Place the largest digits in the tens places.*
The multiplication is either (83)(61) or (81)(63). Their products are, respectively, 5063 and 5103. **The greatest product that can be obtained is 5103.**

> **FOLLOW UPS:** *(1) What is the least product that can be obtained?* [608]   *(2) The perimeter of a rectangle is 48 cm. What is the greatest area it may have?* [144 sq cm] *What do you notice about the dimensions and the area?* [The closer to equal the dimensions are, the greater the area is.]

3C *Strategy: Take the conditions one at a time.*
Denote the 5 test scores as A, B, C, D, and E, in increasing order.

(I) The mean is 80, so $A + B + C + D + E = 400$ since $5 \times 80 = 400$.
(II) The median is 81, so C is 81. Also $B \le 81$ and $D \ge 81$.
(III) The mode is 88, so two or more scores are 88. Since $C = 81$, *exactly* two scores, D and E, are 88. Also B is not 81, because the mode is unique. The numbers now are A, B, 81, 88, and 88.

The sum of all five numbers is 400, so $A + B = 143$. The least value of A occurs when B is greatest. Since the greatest possible value for B is 80, **the least possible score Miguel could receive is** $143 - 80 = 63.$

> **FOLLOW-UPS:** *(1) What is the greatest possible integral score for Miguel's worst test?* [71]   *(2) What would Miguel have to score on a sixth test to raise his mean to 82?* [92] *(3) Exploration: Suppose the mode is increased one point at a time. How does this affect the least score?   (4) Exploration: How would increasing each score by 6 points affect the mean, median, and mode?*

3D **METHOD 1:** <u>Strategy</u>: *Convert the percent into a ratio.*
A 20% increase means that for every 5¢ that a candy bar used to cost, it now costs 6¢. This cost is $\frac{6}{5}$ of what it had been. The same amount of money now buys $\frac{5}{6}$ as many candy bars as before. Because $\frac{5}{6}$ of 42 is 35, **the same amount of money can now buy 35 candy bars.**

METHOD 2: <u>Strategy</u>: *Pick a convenient value for the original cost.*
Suppose each candy bar originally cost $1. Then 42 bars cost $42. If the price of a candy bar rises 20%, each bar now costs $1.20. Now $42 buys $42 ÷ $1.20 = 35 candy bars. Check by assuming at least two other original costs.

3E **METHOD 1:** <u>Strategy</u>: *Use the intuitive concept of slope.*
As line *m* moves from point *E* to point *A*, it moves right 4 cm and up 2 cm. That is, for every 2 cm it runs right, it rises 1 cm. As it moves from point *A* to point *C*, it runs right 6 cm. Thus, it rises 3 cm. **The length of one side of the largest square is** 3 + 6 = **9 cm.**

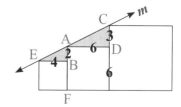

METHOD 2: <u>Strategy</u>: *Use similar triangles.*
Triangles *EAB* and *ACD* are similar, so their sides are in proportion: $\frac{AB}{EB} = \frac{CD}{AD}$. Because *BF* = 4 cm and *AD* = 6 cm, *AB* = 2 cm. The proportion becomes $\frac{2}{4} = \frac{CD}{6}$. Then *CD* = 3 cm. Therefore, the length of one side of the largest square is 3 + 6 = 9 cm.

> ***FOLLOW-UPS:*** *(1) Suppose the next two larger squares are drawn. What are the lengths of their sides?* [13.5 cm, 20.25 cm]   *(2) Suppose line m intersects the line formed by the bases of the squares. What is the area of the triangle formed by the two lines and the left side of the square of side 4?* [16 sq cm]

Olympiad 4

4A <u>Strategy</u>: *Substitute and simplify.*
$(3^2 + 1) - (2^1 + 3) = (9 + 1) - (2 + 3) = 10 - 5 = $ **5**

> ***FOLLOW-UPS:*** *(1) If N ★ N ⬭ N = 10 × N for a positive integer N, find N.* [3]   *(2) For what values of c and a is a ★ b + c = a ★ b − c?* [c = 0; *a* can be any number.]

4B   *Strategy: Convert all times to London time.*

From the first sentence, London time (LT) is 5 hours later than New York time (NYT). The first plane departs at 12 noon LT and arrives at 11 am NYT, which is 4 pm LT, so the travel time is 4 hours. The second plane leaves New York at noon NYT, which is 5 pm LT. The travel time is 4 hours, so **it is 9 pm in London when the second plane arrives.**

4C   *Strategy: Find the total cost and total distance traveled.*

The cost for the first 75 miles is $10 \times 75 = 750$ cents. The cost for the remaining 45 miles is $18 \times 45 = 810$ cents. The total cost for the trip is 1560 cents. The total distance is 120 miles. **The average cost per mile for the entire trip is** $1560 \div 120 = $ **13 cents.**

> *FOLLOW-UPS: (1) Jar M contains 3 liters of a mixture that is 10% oil. Jar N contains 6 liters of a mixture that is 40% oil. The contents of the jars are blended together. What percent of the resulting mixture is oil?* [30 or 30%]   *(2) Sara has averaged 80 on her first 3 math tests. What must she average on her next two tests to raise her average to 86?* [95]

4D   **METHOD 1:** *Strategy: Convert the percent to a fraction.*

40% of a number is $\frac{2}{5}$ of that number. Bert has $\frac{2}{5}$ *more* jelly beans than Vicki. That is, for every 5 jelly beans that Vicki has, Bert has $5 + 2 = 7$ of them. So of every 7 jelly beans that Bert has, he must give 1 to Vicki in order for them to have the same number. **Bert must give $\frac{1}{7}$ of his jelly beans to Vicki.**

METHOD 2: *Strategy: Pick a convenient starting number.*

Suppose Vicki has 100 jelly beans. Then Bert has 40% more, or 140 jelly beans. If Bert gives 20 jelly beans to Vicki, they will each have 120. Bert has to give $\frac{20}{140} = \frac{1}{7}$ of his jelly beans to Vicki. To verify, assign at least two other numbers to Vicki to start with.

> *FOLLOW-UPS: (1) A store decreases the price of a coat by 40%, and then increases the price by 40%. What percent of the original price is the final price of the coat?* [84 or 84%] *(2) Why is the final price less than the original price?* [The original price is higher than the discounted price, so 40% of the higher price will be greater than 40% of the lower price. That is, more money was subtracted during the first transaction than was added during the second transaction.]

4E **METHOD 1:** _Strategy: Rearrange the parts of the figure into more familiar shapes._

From the first diagram above to the last diagram, no region has a change in area. The shaded area is the region inside the square of side 6 cm but outside the circle of radius 3 cm. $36 - (3.14 \times 3^2) \approx 7.74$. **The area of the shaded region is 8 sq cm**, to the nearest sq cm.

METHOD 2: _Strategy: Use the symmetry of the figure._

The area of the shaded region inside square $ABCD$, which is $\frac{1}{4}$ of the entire shaded region, is the difference between the area of the square and the area of a quarter-circle. The circle has a radius of 3 cm, so the area of the shaded region inside square $ABCD$ is about $9 - (\frac{1}{4} \times 3.14 \times 3^2) = 1.935$. The area of the entire shaded region is approximately $4 \times 1.935 = 7.74$. To the nearest sq cm, the area is 8 sq cm.

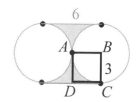

Olympiad 5

5A _Strategy: Determine the production rate per hour._

A rate of 10 widgets per second is equivalent to 600 widgets per minute. This in turn is equivalent to 36,000 widgets per hour. At that rate, **it will take the factory** $90,000 \div 36,000 = 2\frac{1}{2}$ **hours to produce 90,000 widgets.**

5B _Strategy: Factor the number into prime numbers._

$45 = 3 \times 3 \times 5$. A perfect square can be expressed as the product of two equal factors. $45 \times A = 3 \times 3 \times 5 \times A$. **The least positive integral value of A is 5.**

    FOLLOW-UPS: _(1) What is the next least integer A for which $45 \times A$ is a perfect square?_ [20] _(2) What is the least positive integer A for which $45 \times A$ is a perfect cube?_ [75] _(3) What two years in the eleventh century (1001 to 1100) are perfect squares?_ [1024,1089]

5C METHOD 1: *Strategy: Start with the first few days; look for a pattern.*

Day Number	1	2	3	4	5	6	...	30
Quantity eaten this day	1	3	5	7	9	11	...	
Total eaten to date	1	4	9	16	25	36	...	900

The total Lou eats for the first N days is N^2. September has 30 days, so **Lou eats 900 jelly beans in September.**

METHOD 2: *Strategy: First find the number eaten on the last day.*
We must add the first 30 odd counting numbers. The 30th even number is 60, so the 30th odd number is 59. In September, Lou eats $1 + 3 + 5 + ... + 59$ jelly beans. To find this sum efficiently, add in an organized way.

METHOD 2a:
$$01 + 03 + 05 + 07 + 09 = 5 \times 0 + 25 = 25$$
$$11 + 13 + 15 + 17 + 19 = 5 \times 10 + 25 = 75$$
$$21 + 23 + 25 + 27 + 29 = 5 \times 20 + 25 = 125 \quad ...and\ so\ on.$$

The total is $25 + 75 + 125 + 175 + 225 + 275 = 900$. Lou eats 900 jelly beans in September.

METHOD 2b: Group the numbers to get a constant sum (Gaussian method).
$$1 + 3 + 5 + ... + 55 + 57 + 59 = (1 + 59) + (3 + 57) + (5 + 55) + ...$$
There are fifteen pairs, each with a sum of 60. Thus Lou eats 900 jelly beans in September. See pages 49-51 of *Creative Problem Solving in School Mathematics, 2nd Edition* for further discussion.

Follow-Ups: *(1) Suppose that Lou begins each month by eating 1 jelly bean on the first day of the month, 3 on the second day, and continuing in a fashion similar to that of September. How many more jelly beans does Lou eat in October than in September? [61] How many more in 2008 than in 2007? [57]   (2) Juana and Mike start work on the same day. Juana is paid $1 today, $2 tomorrow, $3 the next day, and so on. Mike is paid $25 every day. At the end of how many days have both people earned the same total amounts? How much? [49 days; $1225. They earn the same on day 25. Pair the 24 days before that with the 24 days afterwards.]*

5D *Strategy: Draw some useful line segments.*
The area of the shaded region is the difference between the areas of the circle and the square. Draw the diagonals of the square. The diagonals split the square into four congruent isosceles right triangles. The area of each triangle is $18 \div 4 = 4.5$. The diagonals are also diameters of the circle, so the base and height of each of the small right triangles is a radius of the circle. The area of each triangle, $\frac{1}{2} \times r \times r$, is 4.5, so $r = 3$ cm. The area of the circle is approximately $3.14 \times 3^2 = 28.26$. The difference between the areas of the circle and square is $28.26 - 18 = 10.26$. Rounding off, **the area of the shaded region is 10 sq cm.**

5E <u>*Strategy*</u>: *Work backwards from the end of the sentence.*

What number exceeds 23 by 4 more than twice **the amount by which 15 exceeds –3**?

What number exceeds 23 by 4 more than <u>twice</u> **18** ?

What number exceeds 23 by <u>4 more than</u> **36** ?

What number <u>exceeds 23 by</u> **40** ?

The number is 63.

Set 11   Olympiad 1

1A <u>*Strategy*</u>: *Rearrange the numbers in a more convenient order.*

Rewrite $40 \times 30 \times 20 \times 10 \div 20 \div 40 \div 6$ as $40 \times 30 \times 20 \times 10 \times \frac{1}{20} \times \frac{1}{40} \times \frac{1}{6}$. Then rearrange terms: $(40 \times \frac{1}{40}) \times (20 \times \frac{1}{20}) \times (30 \times \frac{1}{6}) \times 10 = 5 \times 10$. **The value is 50.**

1B <u>*Strategy*</u>: *Make an organized list.*

One way is to list the paths by the number of towns she visits. A tree diagram may also prove useful.

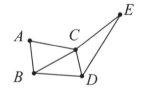

3 towns:	*ACE*		
4 towns:	*ABCE*	*ABDE*	*ACDE*
5 towns:	*ABCDE*	*ABDCE*	*ACBDE*

There are 7 ways the traveler can travel from *A* to *E*.

> **FOLLOW-UPS:** *(1) Connect a sixth town, F to towns D and E. How many paths are there from A to F in which no town is visited more than once?* [13]   *(2) Exploration: Connect more towns, one at a time, to each of the two towns most recently added to the diagram. [(So far: 2, 4, 7, 13), then 24, 44, 81, ...]   Can you find a pattern in the number of paths from A to the newest town added?*

1C *Strategy*: *Examine possible arrangements of the squares.*

30 congruent squares can form any of four rectangles: 1 square wide by 30 squares long; or 2 by 15 squares; 3 by 10 squares; or 5 by 6 squares.

1 by 30 rectangle:	perimeter	= 62 squares	= 124 cm
2 by 15 rectangle:	perimeter	= 34 squares	= 68 cm
3 by 10 rectangle:	perimeter	= 26 squares	= 52 cm
5 by 6 rectangle:	perimeter	= 22 squares	= 44 cm

The least possible perimeter is 44 cm.

1D *Strategy*: *Pick a convenient arbitrary distance.*

The wording of the question implies that the distances traveled don't affect the requested speed, so choose a convenient distance. Later, verify that the distance does not affect the final answer by testing other arbitrarily chosen distances. By algebra we can prove that distance is irrelevant; the variable representing the distance will be divided out and its disappearance indicates its irrelevance.

To keep calculations easy, choose 360 km, the LCM of 60 and 72, as the round trip distance. Then each one-way distance is 180 km. The round trip requires 360 km ÷ 72 kph = 5 hours. Since traveling to work requires 180 ÷ 60 = 3 hours, the return trip of 180 km takes 2 hours. **Mrs. Allen's speed from work to home is** 180 ÷ 2 = **90 kph.**

The chart below shows a concise way to use the formula "rate × time = distance" to solve this problem.

	Rate	Time	Distance
To work	60	3	180
To home	90	2	180
Round trip	72	5	360

The problem concerned 3 average rates of speed: the whole trip (72 kph), going (60 kph), and returning. This is a *weighted average* problem, but appears as a simple average problem to those not experienced with weighted averages.

Why is 84 wrong? A *rate* of speed is an average and you can't average averages. You can only average actual measurements. The distances coming and going are the same, but, since their rates are different, their times are different. The overall rate, 72 kph, results from ***total*** distance (twice the one-way distance) ÷ ***total*** time (the sum of two unequal times).

To check that 84 kph is incorrect: test the 84 and the 60. Pick some different one-way distances and divide by both 84 and 60 to get the times, and then divide total distance by total time. Regardless of the distance, the average speed of the round trip will be 70 kph and never 72 kph.

1E   METHOD 1: _Strategy: Use the divisibility tests for 5, 4, and 3._

The number B is a multiple of 5 and ends in 0 or 5. Since the numbers on either side of B are even, B ends in 5. So A ends in 4 and C in 6. The number formed by the last two digits of any multiple of 4 is divisible by 4, so A ends in 04, 24, 44, 64, or 84. Any multiple of 6 is also a multiple of 3 and its digit-sum is divisible by 3.

Starting at 2000, the possibilities are:

A	B	C	Is C a multiple of 3?
2004,	2005,	2006	no
2024,	2025,	2026	no
2044,	2045,	2046	YES

The smallest possible value of A is 2044.

METHOD 2: _Strategy: Use the least common multiples._
Find a number near A, B, and C that is a multiple of 4, 5, and 6.

Consider $A - 4$:
   A is a multiple of 4, so $A - 4$ is also a multiple of 4.
   B is a multiple of 5 and $A - 4$ is 5 less than B, so $A - 4$ is also a multiple of 5.
   C is a multiple of 6 and $A - 4$ is 6 less than C, so $A - 4$ is also a multiple of 6.

$A - 4$ is then a multiple of the LCM of 4, 5, and 6, which is 60.

Since $2000 \div 60$ is between 33 and 34, the smallest multiple of 60 greater than 2000 is $60 \times 34 =$ 2040. Since 2040 is represented by A – 4, A = 2044. The smallest possible value of A is 2044.

Olympiad 2

**2A   ** _Strategy: Find the sum of the numbers on all the faces._
The sum of the six numbers on one die is 21, so the sum of the numbers on all three dice is 63. The sum of the visible numbers is 26, so **the sum of the numbers on all the faces that are _not_ visible is 37.**

2B   METHOD 1: _Strategy: Represent Ava's money visually._

The top line segment represents Ava's money. The second segment shows the relation to Dan's money. The third segment "removes" the $5, thus representing $18. The fourth segment adds the last third of Dan's money. **Dan has $27.**

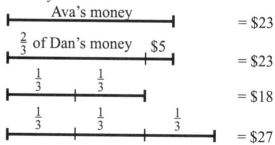

METHOD 2: *Strategy: Use algebra.*

Let d represent Dan's money in dollars. Then Ava has $\frac{2}{3}d + 5$ dollars.

The equation is:	$\frac{2}{3}d + 5 = 23$
Subtract 5 from each side of the equation:	$\frac{2}{3}d = 18$
Divide each side of the equation by 2:	$\frac{1}{3}d = 9$
Multiply each side of the equation by 3:	$d = 27.$ Thus, Dan has \$27.

> **FOLLOW-UP:** *Mark put aside some money in order to purchase a new outfit. He plans to spend half of this money on a jacket, and a third of the remaining money on socks. This will leave him $50 to buy pants. How much money has Mark put aside? [$150]*

2C *Strategy: Use the divisibility rule for 11.*

Represent the number by A6B8, where A and B are digits, not necessarily different. For this number to be a multiple of 11, the difference $(6 + 8) - (A + B)$ must be a multiple of 11. Then A + B is either 3 or 14. All the possible pairs (A,B) are shown below.

A + B	Possible values of (A,B)	Number of possibilities
3	(1,2), (2,1), (3,0)	3
14	(9,5), (8,6), (7,7), (6,8), (5,9)	5
	Total	**8**

> **FOLLOW-UP:** *For what values of (A,B) is 3AB13 a multiple of 99? [A=8, B = 3]*

2D METHOD 1: *Strategy: Find the length of each side of ABCD.*
Width AD of rectangle $ABCD$: Suppose $AM = 1$ cm. Then $AF = 1$ cm and $AQ = 3$ cm. Thus $MP = MD = 3$ cm and $AD = 4$ cm.

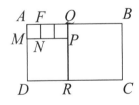

Length AB of rectangle $ABCD$: Since $QB = QR = AD$, $QB = 4$ cm and $AB = 3 + 4 = 7$ cm. Then the area of $ABCD$ is 28 sq cm.

However, the area is given as greater than 100 sq cm. Try $AM = 2$ cm. Then using the reasoning above, AD would be 8 cm, AB would be 14 cm, and the area of $ABCD$ would be 112 sq cm. **The smallest possible area of rectangle $ABCD$ is 112 sq cm.**

METHOD 2: *Strategy: Choosing a convenient unit, compute the areas of all squares.*
Call AM 1 unit, a counting number of cm. Then the areas of $AFNM$, $MPRD$, $QBCR$, and $ABCD$ are 1, 9, 16, and 28 sq units, respectively. Consider the ratios of their areas. The area of $ABCD$ is 28 times the area of square $AFNM$. If $AM = 1$ cm, the area of $ABCD = 28$ sq cm, which is less than 100 sq units. If $AM = 2$ cm, the area of $AFNM = 4$ sq cm and the area of $ABCD = 4 \times 28 = 112$ sq cm The smallest possible area of rectangle $ABCD$ is 112 sq cm.

2E   *Strategy: Count in an organized way.*

Either 6 is the hundreds digit or the tens digit. It can't be both. Consider each case separately.

Case 1: Suppose 6 is the hundreds digit: ☐6☐☐. There are 5 possible values for the thousands digits: 1, 2, 3, 4, or 5. A tens digit of 5 produces 5 possible ones digits (4, 3, 2, 1, 0). A tens digit of 4 produces 4 possible ones digits, and so on. There are then $5 + 4 + 3 + 2 + 1 = 15$ possible ways to fill in the tens and units digits. Each of these 15 possibilities may be used with each of the 5 possible thousands digits, making $15 \times 5 = 75$ up-and-down numbers.

Case 2: Now suppose 6 is the tens digit: ☐☐6☐. There are 6 possible ones digits (5, 4, 3, 2, 1, 0). The thousands digit can be 1, 2, 3, or 4, but not 0. If the thousands digit is 1, there are 4 possible hundreds digits (2, 3, 4, 5). As above, there are $4 + 3 + 2 + 1 = 10$ possible ways to fill in the thousands and hundreds digits. Each of these 10 possibilities may be used with any of the 6 possible ones digits, making $10 \times 6 = 60$ up-and-down numbers. In all, **there are** $75 + 60$ **= 135 up-and-down numbers in which the largest digit is 6.**

> ***FOLLOW-UPS:*** *(1) How many four-digit up-and-down numbers have no digit which is smaller than 6?* [22]   *(2) How many four-digit up-and-down numbers are there in which the maximum digit is 6 and at least one of the digits is a 3?* [65]

◄ Olympiad 3 ►

3A   **METHOD 1:** *Strategy: Pair each of Jake's CDs with one of Emily's.*

After pairing, there are 2 CDs left over, the 2 extra that Emily has. Then 18 CDs are paired, 9 each of Jake's and Emily's. **Jake has 9 CDs.**

METHOD 2: *Strategy: Start in the middle and adjust.*

Suppose each person has 10 CDs. For every CD that Jake gives up and Emily takes, the difference in their numbers increases by 2. To make the difference equal to 2, Jake gives 1 CD to Emily and so, Jake has 9 CDs.

METHOD 3: *Strategy: Use algebra.*

Let J = the number of CDs that Jake has. Then J + 2 = the number of CDs Emily has. The equation is $J + J + 2 = 20$. Solving, $J = 9$. Jake has 9 CDs.

> ***FOLLOW-UP:*** *Neil and Karen have a total of 36 DVDs. Karen has 40% more DVDs than Neil. How many DVDs does Karen have?* [21]

3B   *Strategy: Count steps from the starting point.*

When Austin returns toward Taylor, his first 10 steps bring him back to the starting point. His remaining 14 steps cover the same ground as Taylor's 10 steps. Therefore, **7 of Austin's steps equal the length of 5 of Taylor's steps.**

3C _Strategy: Consider the number of even factors._
The sum of three odd numbers is also odd, so one of the three prime numbers is even, namely 2. Then the sum of the other two primes is 48. The table below lists all primes between 2 and 24 and the corresponding subtractions from 48 in order to find the third prime in each triple.

Prime = p	3	5	7	11	13	17	19	23
48 − p	45	43	41	37	35	31	29	25
Is (48 − p) also prime?	_no_	**YES**	**YES**	**YES**	_no_	**YES**	**YES**	_no_

The sets of three primes are {2, 5, 43}, {2, 7, 41}, {2, 11, 37}, {2, 17, 31}, and {2, 19, 29}.

Therefore, **50 can be expressed as the sum of three different prime numbers in 5 ways.**

> **FOLLOW-UPS:** _(1) In how many ways can 70 be expressed as the sum of two different prime numbers?_ [5]   _(2) In how many ways can 50 be expressed as the sum of four different prime numbers?_ [8]

3D METHOD 1: _Strategy: Split the figure into more convenient pieces._
Wrap triangle _PQR_ in the shaded rectangle _QRTS_ as shown. The area of _QRTS_ is twice the area of triangle _PQR_ because they share the same base and height. Since the area of _PQR_ is 6.4, the area of _QRTS_ is 12.8 sq cm.

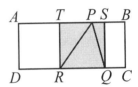

Rectangle _QRTS_ has the same height as rectangle _ABCD_ but its base _RQ_ is $\frac{2}{5}$ of _DC_, the base of _ABCD_. The area of _QRTS_ is then $\frac{2}{5}$ of the area of _ABCD_. **The area of rectangle _ABCD_ is** $12.8 \div \frac{2}{5}$ **= 32 sq cm.**

METHOD 2: _Strategy: Assign a convenient number._
Since _RQ_ is $\frac{2}{5}$ of _DC_, assume that _RQ_ = 2 cm and _DC_ = 5 cm. Then in triangle _PQR_ the area 6.4 is equal to $\frac{1}{2} \times 2 \times$ (the altitude to side $\overline{RQ}$), so the altitude is 6.4 cm. Thus _AD_ = 6.4 cm also. Therefore, the area of rectangle _ABCD_ is _DC_ × _AD_ = 32 sq cm.

3E METHOD 1: _Strategy: Use simpler cases to look for a pattern._
Start at the beginning of the series and find partial sums.
$$1 = 1^2 \qquad 1 + 3 = 4 \text{ or } 2^2 \qquad 1 + 3 + 5 = 9 \text{ or } 3^2 \qquad 1 + 3 + 5 + 7 = 16 \text{ or } 4^2$$
In each case, the sum is the square of the number of terms being added.

To find 1 + 3 + 5 + ... + 2007, determine the number of terms in the sum. One way is to add 1 to each term to produce the series 2 + 4 + 6 + ... + 2008, which contains 1004 even numbers. Thus, the original series contained 1004 odd numbers.

Then $1 + 3 + 5 + ... + 2003 + 2005 + 2007 = 1004^2$, and **the whole number _N_ is 1004.**

METHOD 2: _Strategy_: _Use the pattern in the numbers being added._
Add the numbers "from the outside inward": $(1 + 2007) + (3 + 2005) + (5 + 2003) + \ldots + (1003 + 1005)$. Each pair sums to 2008. Proceed as in Method 1 to determine that there are 1004 numbers. (Or you can use the fact that the value of the kth odd number is $2k - 1$.) With 1004 numbers, there are 502 pairs. The sum is $502 \times 2008 = 502 \times (2 \times 1004) = (502 \times 2) \times 1004$, which is 1004^2. The whole number N is 1004.

> **FOLLOW-UP:** _How much greater is the sum "$1 + 2 + 3 + \ldots + 75$" than the sum "$1 + 3 + 5 + \ldots + 75$"? [1406]. How many different ways can you find the difference? [Results will vary.]_

Olympiad 4

4A METHOD 1: _Strategy_: _Change to an addition problem._
The resulting problem is shown at the right. $8 + Y$ ends in 4, so $Y = 6$. Next, $1 + 7 + 7$ ends in X so $X = 5$. Then $1 + Z + 3 = 8$, so $Z = 4$. **The sum $X + Y + Z$ is 15.**

$$\begin{array}{r} Z\,7\,8 \\ +\ 3\,7\,Y \\ \hline 8\,X\,4 \end{array}$$

METHOD 2: _Strategy_: _Reason from right to left._
For $4 - Y = 8$, Y must be 6 after regrouping. In the tens place the subtraction must be $14 - 7 = 7$. Thus, after regrouping, $X = 5$. Because of regrouping, the digits in the hundreds place now read $7 - 3 = Z$. Thus, $Z = 4$, and $X + Y + Z = 15$.

$$\begin{array}{r} 8\,X\,4 \\ -\ 3\,7\,Y \\ \hline Z\,7\,8 \end{array}$$

4B METHOD 1: _Strategy_: _Draw a picture._
Draw a square 1005 units on a side and inside it draw square A 1003 units on a side as shown. Then $N = 1005^2 - 1003^2$, which equals the sum of the areas of square B and rectangles C and D, which is $(2 \times 2) + (2 \times 1003) + (1003 \times 2)$. **The value of N is 4016.**

METHOD 2: _Strategy_: _Write the squares as sums of consecutive odd numbers._
As shown in the solution of problem 3E, $1005^2 = 1 + 3 + 5 + \ldots + (2\times1005 - 1)$.
Then: $1005^2 = 1 + 3 + 5 + \ldots + 2005 + 2007 + 2009$.
$1003^2 = 1 + 3 + 5 + \ldots + 2005$.
Subtracting, all terms drop out except for 2007 and 2009:
$$1005^2 - 1003^2 = 2007 + 2009 = 4016.$$

> **FOLLOW-UP:** _If the sum $(20 \times 1) + (19 \times 3) + (18 \times 5) + \ldots + (1 \times 39)$ is equal to the sum $1^2 + 2^2 + 3^2 + \ldots + N^2$, find the value of N. [20]_

4C **METHOD 1:** _Strategy:_ _Use reasoning._

Liam drove $\frac{2}{3}$ of the distance, so Jessica drove the remaining $\frac{1}{3}$ of the distance. When Liam awoke, 20% or $\frac{1}{5}$ of Jessica's distance was left to drive, so Liam slept for $\frac{4}{5}$ of the distance that Jessica drove. Since $\frac{4}{5}$ of Jessica's $\frac{1}{3}$ is $\frac{4}{15}$, **Liam slept for $\frac{4}{15}$ of the whole trip.**

METHOD 2: _Strategy:_ _Draw a picture and label the parts._

The problem involves both thirds and fifths, so mark a number line in fifteenths.

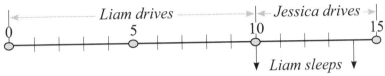

After Liam drove for $\frac{10}{15}$ of the trip, he slept for $\frac{4}{15}$ of the whole trip.

METHOD 3: _Strategy:_ _Choose an arbitrary distance._

Since all information is given as fractional parts of the whole, the exact distance is irrelevant. Suppose the trip is 300 km, a multiple of both 3 and 5. Liam drove $\frac{2}{3}$ of the way, 200 km, and that left 100 km for Jessica to drive. After Liam wakes, 20% of Jessica's 100 km, or 20 km, remain. Then Liam slept for her first 80 km. The fractional part of the trip that Liam slept is $\frac{80}{300} = \frac{4}{15}$.

4D **METHOD 1:** _Strategy:_ _Use the definition of average._

In a set of numbers the total doesn't change if every number is replaced by their average. Assume every student scored 73 on the exam. Marcia's score was fourteen points above the average and raised the average a half point. If the fourteen "extra" points were distributed equally so that each student "received" a half point, there would be 28 total students. Then **28 students, including Marcia, took the test.**

METHOD 2: _Strategy:_ _Use algebra._

Let N = the number of students, including Marcia, who took the test.

The total score of the students other than Marcia is $73(N-1)$.
The total score of all the students, including Marcia, is $73.5N$.

Then the equation is: $\qquad\qquad\qquad 73.5N = 73(N-1)+87$
Multiply $N-1$ by 73: $\qquad\qquad\quad 73.5N = 73N - 73 + 87$
Combine -73 and 87: $\qquad\qquad 73.5N = 73N + 14$
Subtract $73N$ from each side: $\qquad\ 0.5N = 14$
Double each side of the equation $\qquad N = 28$

Including Marcia, 28 students took the test.

FOLLOW-UPS: _Suppose the average of the first 27 students' scores was 73, rounded to the nearest whole number. (1) What is the smallest score Marcia might get that could raise the class average to exactly 73.5? [74] (2) What is the highest score she might get and still not raise the average to exactly 73.5 or more? [99]_

4E **METHOD 1:** *Strategy: Redraw the diagram in a more convenient form.*
Rotate the inner square to touch the outer square in the same four points as
the circle. Draw the two diameters as shown to divide the outer square into
4 small squares. Each side of the inner square is a diagonal of each small
square and so, cuts its area in half. Thus the area of the inner square is then
half the area of the outer square, which is 100 sq cm. **The area of the inner
square is 50 sq cm.**

METHOD 2: *Strategy: Draw some useful line segments.*
Draw the two diameters as shown at the right. The horizontal diameter is
equal to a side of the outer square, 10 cm. The other diameter, also 10 cm
in length, is a diagonal of the inner square. If s represents a side of the inner
square, $s^2 + s^2 = 100$ (Pythagorean Theorem) and $s^2 = 50$. The area of the
inner square is also given by s^2, so the area of the inner square is 50 sq cm.

Olympiad 5

5A *Strategy: Find Sara's number first.*
Sara's number is $\frac{1}{2} \times (\frac{1}{2} + \frac{1}{3}) = \frac{1}{2} \times (\frac{5}{6}) = \frac{5}{12}$.

Ali's number is $\frac{1}{2} \times (\frac{1}{2} + \frac{5}{12}) = \frac{1}{2} \times (\frac{11}{12}) = \frac{11}{24}$.   **Ali's number is $\frac{11}{24}$.**

> **FOLLOW-UP:** *Jacob's number, which is $\frac{3}{4}$, is the average of Ali's number and another number.
> What is that other number?* $[\frac{25}{24}]$

5B *Strategy: Limit the possible areas for the largest square.*
If the side of a square is a counting number, then the area is a perfect square number. Also, with
three squares, the largest area is more than one-third of the given total of 65. Therefore, the
area of the largest square is a perfect square number between 22 and 65: 25, 36, 49, or 64. The
sum of all three areas is 65, so the sum of the two smaller areas is 40, 29, 16 or 1, respectively.
Of these, only 29 is the sum of two square counting numbers: 25 and 4. Thus, the area of the
largest square is 36 sq cm, each side is 6 and, therefore, **the perimeter of the square with the
greatest area is 24 cm.**

> **FOLLOW-UP:** *Express 65 as the sum of two perfect squares two different ways.* [64 and 1;
> 49 and 16]

5C METHOD 1: _Strategy:_ _Use probability directly._

If the series lasts exactly 2 games, then either Team A won both games or Team B won both games. The probability of Team A winning both games is 70% × 70%, or 49%. Likewise, the probability of Team B winning both games is 30% × 30%, or 9%. Then **the probability that they play exactly 2 games is 58%**, the sum of 49% and 9%.

METHOD 2: _Strategy:_ _Find the probability of the complementary event._

If the series does not end in exactly 2 games, then each team wins 1 of the first 2 games. The probability that A wins the first and B wins the second is 70% × 30%, or 21%. Likewise, the probability that B wins the first and A the second is also 21%. Therefore, the probability that the first two games are won by different teams is 42%. Then the probability of the first two games being won by the same team is 58%.

> **FOLLOW-UP:** _Team C plays the winner of the series between A and B in a series of games until one team has won two games. The probability that Team C beats Team A in any single game is 40% and the probability that Team C beats Team B in any single game is 80%. What is the probability that the two series will last exactly four games?_ [31.6%]

5D METHOD 1: _Strategy:_ _Draw a diagram showing time._

Mark the opposite shores in minutes, 0 to 35. The slower boat touches alternating shores at 7, 14, 21, 28, and 35 minutes. The faster boat touches alternating shores at 5, 10, 15, 20, 25, 30, and 35 minutes. Where the paths cross, the boats are passing. From the diagram, **the faster boat passes the slower boat 7 times.**

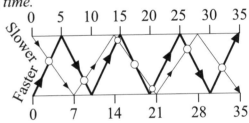

METHOD 2: _Strategy:_ _Examine the distances covered at each passing._

The first time the boats pass each other, the sum of the distance covered by both boats is 1 lake-width (LW). Each boat covers a fraction of a LW.

The second time the boats pass, going in _opposite_ directions, the sum of the distances covered is 3 LWs. Each covers one-and-a-fraction LWs.

Similarly, the boats pass each other going in _opposite_ directions when the sum of the distances is 5, 7, 9, … LWs. In 35 minutes the fast boat crosses the lake 7 times and the slow boat 5 times; they travel a total of 12 LWs. The boats pass going in opposite directions at 1, 3, 5, 7, 9, and 11 LWs, a total of 6 times.

PASS IN OPPOSITE DIRECTIONS.

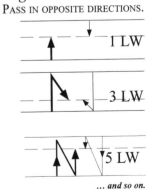

... and so on.

When the faster boat passes the slower boat while headed in the <u>same direction</u>, the *difference* in LWs traveled by the two boats is 1. As above, the faster boat passes the slower boat when the difference in LWs is 1, 3, 5, … Over the entire 35 minute span, the difference in LWs is only 2, so the faster boat passes the slower boat while going in the same direction only once.

PASS IN SAME DIRECTION

In total, the faster boat passes the slower boat 7 times.

METHOD 3: *Strategy: Consider the path of the faster boat.*
Both boats need an odd number of minutes to cross the lake. They never meet at a shore, because one of the boats, crossing an odd number of times, would need an odd number of minutes, while the other boat, crossing an even number of times, would need an even number of minutes. The faster boat, which crosses the lake 7 times, passes the slower boat just once on each crossing. Therefore the faster boat passes the slower boat 7 times.

> *FOLLOW-UPS:* *(1) How many minutes have elapsed when the two boats first pass each other?* $[2\frac{11}{12}]$ *(2) How many minutes have elapsed when the faster boat passes the slower boat while headed in the same direction?*$[17.5]$

5E *Strategy: Begin with any number and build the arrangement.*
Choose any of the given numbers: for example, 3. Of the given numbers, only 6 and 13 can be added to 3 to get a perfect square, so place one of them on each side of 3. Next to the 13 can only be the 12. However, no other number can go next to the 6, so it is placed either first or last. Next to the 12, place the 4. Next to the 4, place the 5. The arrangement is either 5, 4, 12, 13, 3, 6 or it is 6, 3, 13, 12, 4, 5. In both cases, **the sum of the two middle numbers is 25.**

Set 12   Olympiad 1

1A *Strategy: Consider the statements one at a time.*
The greatest distance between any two of the points is *BD*:

$$\overset{\text{B} \qquad \text{D}}{\longleftrightarrow} \quad or \quad \overset{\text{D} \qquad \text{B}}{\longleftrightarrow}$$

A is the midpoint of $\overline{CD}$:

$$\overset{\text{B} \quad \text{C A D}}{\longleftrightarrow} \quad or \quad \overset{\text{D A C} \quad \text{B}}{\longleftrightarrow}$$

Points *B* and *C* are to the right of *A*:

$$\overset{\text{D A C} \quad \text{B}}{\longleftrightarrow}$$

From left to right, the points are *D, A, C, B*.

1B **METHOD 1:** _Strategy: Make a list._

List the primes and count to the 24th digit. Since there are 4 one-digit primes, the 24th digit is the ones digit of the 10th two-digit prime. The two-digit primes are 11, 13, 17, 19, 23, 29, 31, 37, 41, and 43. Therefore, **the 24th term in the sequence is 3.**

> ***FOLLOW-UP:*** _The first time that two 9s appear consecutively in Sequence B are as the 44th and 45th terms. What is the 43rd term?[8] The 46th term? [7]_

1C **METHOD 1:** _Strategy: Use the Least Common Multiple of the given numbers._

METHOD 1a: Any number divisible by 3, 4, 6, and 8 is a multiple of their LCM, which is 24. Divide 1100 by 24; the remainder is 20. Then $1100 - 20 = 1080$ is a multiple of 24. **The greatest number less than 1100 that is also divisible by 3, 4, 6, and 8 is 1080.**

METHOD 1b: Any number divisible by 3, 4, 6, and 8 is a multiple of their LCM, which is 24. It is given that 1008 is a multiple of 24. To get other multiples of 24 less than 1100, repeatedly add 24 to 1008 to get 1032, 1056, 1080, 1104. The greatest number less than 1100 that is also divisible by 3, 4, 6, and 8 is 1080.

METHOD 2: _Strategy: List separately the multiples of each of 3, 4, 6, and 8._

Only 2 lists are needed because any number divisible by 8 is also divisible by 4 and any number divisible by 6 is also divisible by 3:

> Divisible by 8:   1008, 1016, 1024, …, 1080, 1088, 1096
> Divisible by 6:   1008, 1014, 1020, …, 1080, 1086, 1092, 1098.

The greatest number common to the 2 lists and therefore greatest number less than 1100 that is divisible by 3, 4, 6, and 8 is 1080.

> ***FOLLOW-UP:*** _How many numbers between 1000 and 2000 are divisible by each of 3, 5 and 7? [10]_

1D **METHOD 1:** _Strategy: Use the Distributive Property to simplify the computation._

If each value is multiplied by 3.6 and the products are added, the sum is the same as 3.6 times the sum of the original values. If 4 is added to each product and the results are added, the sum is the same as the sum of the products and 6×4. **The mean of the new set of data values is**
$$\frac{3.6(\,1 + 2 + 7 + 15 + 17 + 18) + 6(4)}{6} = \frac{3.6(\,60) + 6(4)}{6} = 36 + 4 = \mathbf{40.}$$

METHOD 2: _Strategy: Do the indicated computation._

Multiply each number by 3.6 and then add 4. The results are 7.6, 11.2, 29.2, 58, 65.2, and 68.8. The sum of the six new numbers is 240 and their mean is 40.

SET 12 SOLUTIONS

1E *Strategy: Count in an organized way.*
Label each single region separately. Then count the triangles which enclose only 1 region, then those that enclose 2 regions, and so on. Thus:

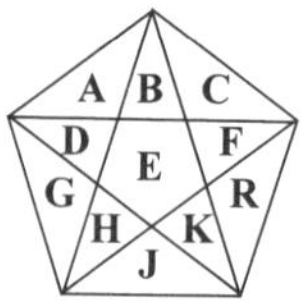

# of regions	List of triangles by named regions	Subtotals
1	A, B. C, F, R, K, J, H, G, D	10 triangles
2	AB, BC, CF, FR, RK, KJ, JH, HG, GD, DA	10 triangles
3	ABC, CFR, RKJ, JHG, GDA, DEF, BEK, FEH, KED, HEB	10 triangles
5	BEHKJ, FEDHG, KEBDA, HEBFC, DEFKR	5 triangles
	Total	35

There are 35 triangles of all sizes in the diagram.

> **FOLLOW-UPS:** *(1) A large square is marked off into 9 smaller congruent squares. How many squares of all sizes are shown in this diagram?* [14] *(2) How many squares of all sizes are there on a standard 8 × 8 checkerboard?* [204] *(3) How many rectangles of all sizes are shown in this diagram?* [36] *(4) How many rectangles of all sizes are there on a standard 8 × 8 checkerboard?* [1296]

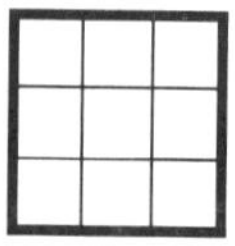

Olympiad 2

2A METHOD 1: *Strategy: Simplify the expression, using common fractions:*
$2.375 = 2\frac{3}{8}$ and $2 \times 2\frac{3}{8} = 4\frac{3}{4}$. Then $12\frac{3}{4} - 4\frac{3}{4} = 8$ and $8 = 2^3$ **The value of N is 2.**

METHOD 2: *Strategy: Simplify the expression, using decimal form.*
$12\frac{3}{4} - 2 \times 2.375 = 12.75 - 4.75 = 8 = 2^3$. The value of N is 2.

2B METHOD 1: *Strategy: Find the total number of points scored.*
From the graph, the 12 mathletes scored a total of 31 points. Then the mean is $31 \div 12 \approx 2.58$. To the nearest tenth, **the mean number of points scored per mathlete is 2.6.**

METHOD 2: *Strategy: Measure the deviation from an assumed mean.*
Suppose the mean is 2. Three students scored 1 point above the mean, one scored 2 above, two scored 3 above, two scored 1 below, and one scored 2 below. The total deviation from 2 is $1 + 1 + 1 + 2 + 3 + 3 - 1 - 1 - 2 = 7$ for the 12 mathletes. The true mean is then $2 + \frac{7}{12}$, or to the nearest tenth, 2.6.

> **FOLLOW-UP:** *The coach had forgotten to include one mathlete's score. When she did so, the average of the 13 scores was 2.7, to the nearest tenth. How many points did the 13th mathlete score?* [4]

2C METHOD 1: *Strategy: Group the numbers in fours.*
$(100 + 99 - 98 - 97) + (96 + 95 - 94 - 93) + \ldots + (4 + 3 - 2 - 1) = 4 + 4 + 4 + \ldots + 4$. There are twenty-five groups of four numbers, each with a value of 4. **The expression simplifies to 100.**

METHOD 2: *Strategy: Rearrange the numbers in a more convenient order.*
The given expression can be written as $(100 - 98) + (99 - 97) + (96 - 94) + (95 - 93) + (92 - 90) + (91 - 89) + \ldots + (4 - 2) + (3 - 1)$. Each indicated difference is 2, and there are 50 indicated differences. The expression simplifies to 100.

> ***FOLLOW-UPS:*** *(1) Simplify $100 + 99 + 98 - 97 + 96 + 95 + 94 - 93 + \ldots + 4 + 3 + 2 - 1$, where every fourth term is subtracted.* [200 + 12(200) = 2600]   *(2) Exploration: How many other thought-filled methods of solution can you find for Problem 2C?*

2D *Strategy: List the paths from A to C*

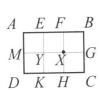

Paths with X	Paths without X
AMYXHC	AMDKHC
AMYXGC	AMYKHC
AEFXHC	AEFBGC
AEFXGC	AEYKHC
AEYXHC	
AEYXGC	

There are 10 five-cm paths from A to C, 6 of which pass through X. **The probability that the chosen path passes through point X is $\frac{6}{10}$ or $\frac{3}{5}$ or .6 or 60%.**

> ***FOLLOW-UP:*** *Investigation: Research the topic of Taxicab Geometry.*

2E *Strategy: Find the length of the wire.*
A square of area 225 sq cm has a side of length 15 cm. Then the length of the wire is 60 cm. The frame of the cube consists of its 12 edges, so the length of each edge is 5 cm. **The volume enclosed by the cube is 125 cubic centimeters.**

15 cm

5 cm

> ***FOLLOW-UP:*** *Suppose all faces of the cube are solid. What is its surface area?* [150 sq cm]

Olympiad 3

3A   METHOD 1: _Strategy: Find the Greatest Common Factor of the numbers._
Any number that is a factor of both 36 and 60 is a factor of their GCF, 12. The factors of 12 are 1, 2, 3, 4, 6, and 12. There are **6 positive integers that are factors of both 36 and 60.**

METHOD 2: _Strategy: Find the Common Prime Factors of the numbers._
$36 = 2^2 \times 3^2$ and $60 = 2^2 \times 3^1 \times 5^1$.
Their greatest common factor is $12 = 2^2 \times 3^1$.
The table shows all six factors of $2^2 \times 3^1$.
Each is a factor of both 36 and 60.

×	2^0	2^1	2^2
3^0	1	2	4
3^1	3	6	12

METHOD 3: _Strategy: List the factors of each number._
Factors of 36: **1**, **2**, **3**, **4**, **6**, 9, **12**, 18, 36
Factors of 60: **1**, **2**, **3**, **4**, 5, **6**, 10, **12**, 15, 20, 30, 60
There are 6 **[boldfaced]** positive integers that are factors of both 36 and 60.

**FOLLOW-UP:** How many positive integers are factors of all of 144, 288, and 540? [9]

3B   METHOD 1: _Strategy: Regroup the factors to simplify the computation._
$2^7 \times 5^3 = (2^4 \times 2^3) \times 5^3 = 2^4 \times (2^3 \times 5^3) = 2^4 \times 10^3 = 16 \times 1000 = 16{,}000$.
The sum of the digits is 7.

METHOD 2: _Strategy: Do the computation._
$2^7 = 128$ and $5^3 = 125$. The product of 128 and 125 is 16,000. The sum of the digits is 7.

3C   METHOD 1: _Strategy: Work backwards._
Ben ended with twice as many of the 36 CDs as Ali, so Ben ended with 24 and Ali with 12. Ali had given Ben 40%, or $\frac{2}{5}$ of her original number, so the 12 she ended with was $\frac{3}{5}$ of the number she started with. Then $\frac{1}{5}$ of her original number was 4, and **Ali had 20 CDs originally.**

METHOD 2: _Strategy: Make a table._
Ali gave Ben 40% of her CDs, so she started with a multiple of 5. The top row of the table assumes those multiples and computes the resulting numbers. Only in the last column does Ben end with twice as many CDs as Ali, so Ali originally had 20 CDs.

If Ali began with:	5	10	15	**20**
Then Ben began with:	31	26	21	16
Ali gave Ben:	2	4	6	8
Ali ended with:	3	6	9	**12**
Ben ended with	33	30	27	**24**

METHOD 3: _Strategy:_ _Use algebra._
Let a = the number of CDs Ali started with. Then Ben started with $36 - a$ CDs.
Ali gives Ben $0.4a$ CDs, so Ben ends with $(36 - a) + 0.4a$ CDs, and Ali with $a - 0.4a$ CDs.

At the end Ben has twice as many CDs as Ali:	$2(a - 0.4a) = (36 - a) + 0.4a$
Simplify each side of the equation:	$2(0.6a) = 36 - 0.6a$
Simplify the left side of the equation further:	$1.2a = 36 - 0.6a$
Add $0.6a$ to each side of the equation:	$1.8a = 36$
Divide each side of the equation by 1.8:	$a = 20$

Ali had 20 CDs originally.

> _**Follow-Up:**_ _Together Amy, Ben and Zoe have 90 marbles. Ben has twice as many marbles as Amy. Zoe has three times as many marbles as Amy. How many marbles must Amy lose to the others so that the ratio of marbles held by Amy, Ben and Zoe, respectively, is 1:3:5?_
> [5] _How many marbles does each of the others gain? [none to Ben, 5 to Zoe]_

3D _Strategy:_ _Use the definition of reciprocal._
N and $\frac{1}{N}$ are reciprocals (multiplicative inverses) of each other.
If $N = \frac{1}{101}$, then $\frac{1}{N} = 101$. Since $11(101-1) + 9(101) = 1100 + 909$, **the value is 2009.**

3E _Strategy:_ _Maximize the "contact area"._
The surface areas of the three cubes, when separated, are 6×1^2, 6×2^2, and 6×3^2 sq cm for a total of 84 sq cm. When they are glued together, the 3 pairs of surfaces glued together are no longer included in the total. To maximize the glued area, place the 2 larger cubes as shown and then place the smallest cube so that it has one face in contact with each of the others. Then the 84 sq cm must be decreased by 2×1, 2×1, and $2 \times 4 = 12$ sq cm, and **the least possible surface of the solid is 72 sq cm.**

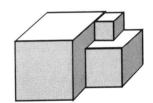

Olympiad 4

4A _Strategy:_ _Use the property of additive inverses (opposites)._
Write the sum as $(^-2007 + {}^-2006 + \cdots + {}^+2006 + {}^+2007) + {}^+2008 + {}^+2009$. The sum in parentheses is 0. Thus **the sum of all the integers from $^-2007$ through 2009 is** $^+2008 + {}^+2009 = \mathbf{4017.}$

4B *Strategy : Draw a picture and examine the possibilities.*
There are two possible cases. Either ⊔ or ⊏ is 55 cm.

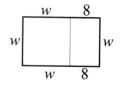

The first case ⊔ is not possible. If the sum of 8 and three widths is 55 cm, then the width is not an integer.

The second case ⊏ is possible. If the sum of 16 and three widths is 55 cm, then the width is 13 cm. This makes the length 21 cm, and **the perimeter of the rectangle 68 cm.**

> **FOLLOW-UPS:** *(1) Find a value to replace the 55 so that the first case results in an integer value but the second does not. [Any of the numbers 11, 14, 17, and so on.] (2) Can you find a value that satisfies both situations? Explain.* [No]

4C *Strategy: Use the definition of average speed.*
The average speed is the total distance traveled divided by the total time elapsed. The graph shows that Jen traveled 10 miles from home before she rested and then traveled 10 miles back. The total time was 4 hours, so **her average speed was** 20 mi ÷ 4 hrs = **5 mph.**

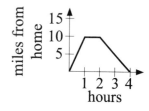

> **FOLLOW-UP:** *Describe a situation that could be represented by each of these graphs:*

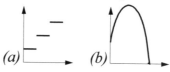

> (a)   (b)

[Many situations are possible. For example: The step graph, (a), might represent the number of buses needed for a large group of people. The parabola, (b), might represent the height over time of a ball tossed upwards.]

4D *Strategy: Count in an organized way.*

METHOD 1: *Strategy: Examine all the ones and tens digits separately.*
The ones digit of 8: It occurs 1 time in every set of 10 consecutive numbers. From 1 through 384, there are 38 complete sets of 10 and therefore the digit 8 appears 38 times as a ones digit.

The tens digits of 8: It occurs 10 times in every set of 100 consecutive numbers. From 1 through 384, there are 3 complete sets of 100 (1-100, 101-199, 200-299); the digit 8 appears 30 times as a tens digit. In addition, the numbers 380-384 contain 5 more tens digits of 8. In all, **the digit 8 appears a total of 73 times.**

METHOD 2: *Strategy:* *Count by intervals, treating the 80s as a special case.*

Interval	1-79	80-89	90-179	180-189	190-279	280-289	290-379	380-384
# of 8s	8	11	9	11	9	11	9	5

Add the numbers in the second row. The digit 8 appears a total of 73 times.

4E *Strategy:* *Examine the prime factors.*
Since $180 \times N$ is a perfect cube, it is the product of three equal factors. Each of these factors is prime or is the product of prime numbers. Because $180 = 2 \times 2 \times 3 \times 3 \times 5$, the perfect cube, $180 \times N$, must represent the product of 2^3, 3^3, and 5^3. N must represent the missing additional factors 2, 3, 5, and 5. **The least possible value of N is $2 \times 3 \times 5 \times 5 = 150$.** As a check, $180 \times 150 = 27{,}000$, which is 30^3.

Alternately, $(2^3 \times 3^3 \times 5^3) \div 180 = 27{,}000 \div 180 = 150$.

> **FOLLOW-UPS:** *(1) What is the least N greater than 150 for which the product of 180 and N is a perfect cube?* [1200] *(2) What is the least positive integer N for which the product of 12 and N is a perfect fourth power?* [108] *(3) What are the three least integers which are both perfect squares and perfect cubes?* [0, 1, 64; they are actually sixth powers.]

Olympiad 5

5A **METHOD 1:** *Strategy:* *Find the cost of an equal number of each item.*
Suppose you purchased 2 pens and 3 erasers and then 3 pens and 2 erasers. The total of 5 pens and 5 erasers would cost you $40 + 55 = 95¢$. Then **the total cost of 1 pen and 1 eraser is $95¢ \div 5 = 19¢$.**

METHOD 2: *Strategy:* *Find the cost of 1 eraser and of 1 pencil.*
Suppose you purchased 2 pens and 3 erasers for 40¢. Replacing one of the erasers by a pen, which gives 3 pens and 2 erasers, increases the cost by 15¢. That is, a pen costs 15¢ more than an eraser. Then, if in another purchase you replace 2 erasers by 2 pens, you would have bought 5 pens and increased the cost by 30¢. So 5 pens cost 85¢ and one pen costs 17¢. One eraser costs 2¢, and the total cost of 1 pen and 1 eraser is 19¢.

> **FOLLOW-UPS:** *(1) Solve the problem algebraically following each method above. (2) Suppose instead 3 pens and 2 erasers cost a total of 84 cents. If each pen costs 4 cents more than 2 erasers, how much does an eraser cost?* [9 cents]

5B   *Strategy*: Count in an organized way.
If the product of two different odd prime numbers is less than 100, at least one of the primes is less than 10 (namely 3, 5, or 7). Then 3 can be paired with nine different primes (5, 7, 11, 13, 17, 19, 23, 29, and 31); 5 can be paired with five different primes (7, 11, 13, 17, and 19); and 7 can be paired with two different primes (11 and 13). In all, **there are 16 positive integers less than 100 which can be expressed as the product of two different odd primes.**

> **FOLLOW-UP:** *How many odd positive integers less than 500 can be expressed as the product of three different primes? [16]   Any three primes? [42]*

5C   *Strategy*: Find the x- and y-coordinates separately.
The horizontal distance from *A* to *B* is 10 − 4 = 6, and one-third of that distance is 2. The vertical distance from *A* to *B* is 15 − 6 = 9, and one-third of that distance is 3. **The coordinates of point *T* are** (4 + 2,15 − 3) = **(6,12).**

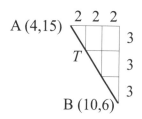

> **FOLLOW-UP:** *Point C is on line segment AB and is $\frac{1}{3}$ of the way from A to B. If the coordinates of C are (4, 16) and B are (10, 6), find the coordinates of A. [(1, 21)]*

5D   **METHOD 1:** *Strategy*: Draw a picture.
Figure 1 shows the original array of pennies, a square formation. Separate it into rectangular sections A, B, and C, where B and C are the bottom two rows.

Figure 1

In figure 2, row C is moved to a new position, column C'. Note that each row in section A now contains one more penny and that there is one less row (row C).

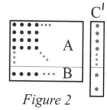

Figure 2

In figure 3, row B and the bottom 2 pennies in column C' are removed (shown by the dashed gray rectangles). In all, 10 pennies are removed and the new rectangle is produced. Thus row B contained 8 pennies and **there were 8 × 8 = 64 pennies originally.**

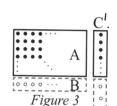

Figure 3

METHOD 2: *Strategy: Build a table.*

Assume the original configuration had 5, 6, 7, 8, … pennies per row and build a table to compare the new number of pennies with the original. The second column shows 2 fewer rows and 1 more penny per row. Only in the bottom row is the new number of pennies 10 less than the original number. There were 64 pennies originally.

Original # of pennies	New # of pennies
$5 \times 5 = 25$	$3 \times 6 = 18$
$6 \times 6 = 36$	$4 \times 7 = 28$
$7 \times 7 = 49$	$5 \times 8 = 40$
$8 \times 8 = 64$	**$6 \times 9 = 54$**

METHOD 3: *Strategy: Use algebra.*

Let N = the number of pennies in each row.

Originally, the number of rows equals the number of pennies in each row.

$N^2 - 10$ = the number of pennies after 10 are removed.

$N - 2$ = the number of rows after rearranging.

$N + 1$ = the number of pennies in each row after rearranging.

Pennies per row × the # of rows = total # of pennies:	$(N + 1)(N - 2) = N^2 - 10$
Multiply $N - 2$ by $N + 1$:	$N^2 - N - 2 = N^2 - 10$
Subtract N^2 from each side of the equation:	$-N - 2 = -10$
Multiply each side of the equation by -1:	$N + 2 = 10$
Subtract 2 from each side of the equation:	$N = 8$

With 8 rows of 8 pennies each originally, there were 64 pennies.

5E *Strategy: Find the sum of the numbers in each row and column.*

$2 + 4 + … + 18 = 90$, so the sum of the numbers in each row, each column, and each diagonal is 30. Then the middle number in column 2 is 10, so the remaining number in row 2 is 14.

In the top row, $A + x = 28$. Of the remaining numbers, only 12 and 16 have that sum. If $x = 16$, the sum in the last column is more than 30. **Then x represents 12**.

The completed magic square is at the right.

A	2	x
6	**10**	**14**
	18	

16	2	**12**
6	10	14
8	18	4

Set 13   Olympiad 1

1A   _Strategy: Rearrange the factors in a more convenient order._
$$125 \times 25 \times 5 \times 2 \times 4 \times 8$$
$$= (5 \times 2) \times (25 \times 4) \times (125 \times 8)$$
$$= 10 \times 100 \times 1000$$
$$= \mathbf{1{,}000{,}000}.$$

1B   _Strategy: Look for perfect squares near the given number._
Since $11^2 = 121$ and $12^2 = 144$, the least whole number value for N is the value for which $123 + N = 144$. **The least whole number N is 21.**

1C   **METHOD 1:** _Strategy: Use the definition of even number._
Because each of the two even numbers has a factor of 2, their product is a multiple of 4. Conversely, every multiple of 4 can be written as the product of two even numbers. There are 19 positive multiples of 4 that are less than 80, but we must exclude the 4 multiples that are 18 or less. **Thus, 15 numbers between 19 and 79 are the product of two even numbers.**

METHOD 2: _Factor every even number between 19 and 79._
List the even numbers in the interval: 20, 22, 24, …, 74, 76, 78. Try factoring each into the product of 2 even numbers. Eliminate those that cannot be so factored. The remaining numbers are 20, 24, 28, 32, 36, 40, 44, 48, 52, 56, 60, 64, 68, 72, and 76. In all, there are 15 possible products between 19 and 79.

> **FOLLOW-UP:** _How many multiples of 3 are less than 500 and are not the product of two multiples of 3? [111]_

1D   **METHOD 1:** _Strategy: First find the length AB._
As shown, $AB + BC = 25$ cm and $BC + CD = 46$ cm. With BC common to both lengths, CD is 21 cm longer than AB. But $CD = 2.5 \times AB$. Then $(2.5 \times AB) - AB = 21$. Therefore, $1.5 \times AB = 21$ and the length $AB = 21 \div 1.5 = 14$. Finally, **the length of $\overline{BC}$ is $25 - 14 = \mathbf{11}$ cm.**

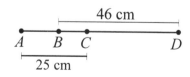

METHOD 2: _Strategy: Use possible lengths AB and CD to find BC._

The table shows possible lengths CD and AB. Each pair is in the ratio of 5:2 and calculates the length BC in two ways. Only when CD is 35 and AB is 14 do both computations give the same value of BC. The length of $\overline{BC}$ is 11 cm.

CD	20	25	30	**35**	40
AB	8	10	12	**14**	16
BC = 46 − CD	26	21	16	**11**	6
BC = 25 − CD	17	15	13	**11**	9

METHOD 3: _Strategy: Use algebra._

Because $CD{:}AB = 5{:}2$, represent the length CD by $5x$ and the length AB by $2x$. Then the length BC can be represented two ways, by $25 - 2x$ and by $46 - 5x$, as shown below.

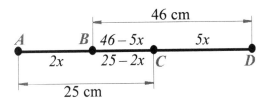

From the diagram represent BC two ways: $\qquad 25 - 2x = 46 - 5x$

Add $5x$ to each side of the equation: $\qquad 25 + 3x = 46$

Subtract 25 from each side of the equation: $\qquad 3x = 21$

Divide each side of the equation by 3: $\qquad x = 7$

Then $BC = 46 - 5(7) = 11$. Checking, $BC = 25 - 2(7) = 11$.

> **FOLLOW-UP:** _Points A, B, C, D, and E lie on a straight line in the given order. The ratios of lengths are as follows — BC:AB = 4:3 and BC:CD = 2:1. If AE is 48 units and DE = BA, what is BC?_   [16 units]

1E METHOD 1: _Strategy: Use counting principles._

Emma buys a German novel and a Spanish novel, or a German novel and a French novel, or a Spanish novel and a French novel. She has 4 choices for the German novel and 5 for the Spanish novel, so she can buy novels in those two languages in $4 \times 5 = 20$ ways. Likewise, she can buy a German novel and a French novel in $4 \times 6 = 24$ ways, and she can buy a Spanish novel and a French novel in $5 \times 6 = 30$ ways. In all **Emma can purchase two novels in two languages in** $20 + 24 + 30 =$ **74 ways.**

METHOD 2: *Strategy: Make an organized list.*

Denote the 4 German novels as G_1, G_2, G_3, G_4, and similarly for the others.

If G_1 is one of the books, the other book can be S_1, S_2, S_3, S_4, S_5, *or* F_1, F_2, F_3, F_4, F_5, F_6 — that is 11 ways. Likewise, there are 11 ways if G_2 is chosen, 11 with G_3, and 11 with G_4 for a total of 44 ways.

If no German novel is chosen, one book must be in Spanish and one in French.

If S_1 is one book, F_1, F_2, …, F_6 is the other: 6 ways. Continuing, there are 6 with S_2, etc., for a total of 30 ways. In all Emma can purchase the two novels in $44 + 30 = 74$ ways.

> *FOLLOW-UP:* *(1) In how many ways can Emma purchase, in any order, two novels in the same language? [31]   (2) In how many ways can she purchase, in any order, two novels in one language and one in each of the other two languages?[720]*

Olympiad 2

2A METHOD 1: *Strategy: First find* $m\angle COD$.

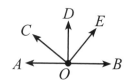

(1) $\begin{aligned} m\angle COB &= 130 \\ - m\angle DOB &= \underline{\ 90} \\ m\angle COD &= 40 \end{aligned}$ (2) $\begin{aligned} m\angle COE &= 90 \\ - m\angle COD &= \underline{\ 40} \\ \mathbf{m\angle DOE} &= \mathbf{50} \end{aligned}$

METHOD 2: *Strategy: First find* $m\angle AOC$.

(1) $\begin{aligned} m\angle AOB &= 180 \\ - m\angle COB &= \underline{130} \\ m\angle AOC &= 50 \end{aligned}$ (2) $\begin{aligned} m\angle AOD &= 90 \\ - m\angle AOC &= \underline{50} \\ m\angle COD &= 40 \end{aligned}$ (3) $\begin{aligned} m\angle COE &= 90 \\ - m\angle COD &= \underline{40} \\ m\angle DOE &= 50 \end{aligned}$

2B *Strategy: Use the distributive property.*

$$\frac{2.3 \times 2.01 + 3.7 \times 2.01}{0.3 \times 4.02} = \frac{(2.3 + 3.7) \times 2.01}{0.3 \times 4.02} = \frac{6.0 \times 2.01}{0.3 \times 4.02} = \frac{6.0}{0.3} \times \frac{2.01}{4.02} = 20 \times \tfrac{1}{2} = \mathbf{10}.$$

Variation: Notice that 4.02 is twice 2.01. Rewrite the denominator as 0.6×2.01. Then $\frac{6.0 \times 2.01}{0.3 \times 4.02} = \frac{6.0 \times \cancel{2.01}}{0.6 \times \cancel{2.01}} = \frac{6.0}{0.6} = \frac{60}{6} = 10$.

2C METHOD 1: *Strategy: Combine the two cases.*

Suppose 2 students are absent and Mr. Alvarez still gives each student 4 sheets. He will have the original 16 sheets left over and in addition the 4 sheets that he would have given to each of the absentees. This total of 24 sheets is enough to give each of the students who are present 1 additional sheet, with 3 left over. Then there are $24 - 3 = 21$ students present. **Mr. Alvarez has** $5 \times 21 + 3 = \mathbf{108\ sheets\ of\ paper.}$

METHOD 2: *Strategy: Use algebra.*

The class has N students registered and $N-2$ students present when 2 students are absent.

Then $4N + 16 =$ four sheets per student, with 16 sheets left over.

And $5(N-2) + 3 =$ five sheets per student when 2 students are absent with 3 sheets left over.

The number of sheets is the same whether or not the 2 students are absent:

$$5(N-2) + 3 = 4N + 16$$

Multiply $N - 2$ by 5: $\quad 5N - 10 + 3 = 4N + 16$

Add -10 and 3: $\quad 5N - 7 = 4N + 16$

Add 7 to each side of the equation: $\quad 5N = 4N + 23$

Subtract $4N$ from each side of the equation: $\quad N = 23$

Then Mr. Alvarez started with $4 \times 23 + 16 = 108$ sheets of paper.

> **FOLLOW-UP:** *Find the least whole number* N *such that* N *is 1 more than a multiple of 3,* N $- 3$ *is 2 more than a multiple of 5, and* N $- 6$ *is 3 more than a multiple of 7.* [100; Hint: Find a number near N that is divisible by 3, 5, and 7.]

2D METHOD 1: *Strategy: Compare terms.*

The terms in Series A increase by 2. The terms in Series B increase by 4. If Series A is multiplied by 2 (row 2), its terms will also increase by 4.

Series A: $\quad 1 + 3 + 5 + 7 + \ldots + 21 + 23 + 25 = 169$

2 × Series A: $\quad 2 + 6 + 10 + 14 + \cdots + 42 + 46 + 50 = 338$

Series B: $\quad 1 + 5 + 9 + 13 + \cdots + 41 + 45 + 49 = \ ?$

Each of the 13 terms in row 2 is 1 greater than the corresponding term in row 3. Therefore **the sum $1 + 5 + 9 + \cdots + 41 + 45 + 49 = 338 - 13$ is 325.**

METHOD 2: *Strategy: Use "Gaussian Addition".*

In the series $1 + 5 + \cdots + 49$, we get from 1 to 49 by adding 4 twelve times, so the series has 13 terms. Pair these terms as follows, working from the outside inward.

$(1 + 49) + (5 + 45) + (9 + 41)$, and so on. The sum of each pair is 50 and there are 6 pairs. The unpaired number is 25, the middle number. The sum is then $6 \times 50 + 25 = 325$.

METHOD 3: *Strategy: Look for a pattern in the partial sums.*

The table at the right examines the sums of the first few terms. In each case, the sum is the product of the number of terms and the middle term (or the average of the 2 middle terms). Since the series has 13 terms, the sum we are looking for is $1 + 5 + 9 + \ldots + 41 + 45 + 49 = 13 \times 25 = 325$.

Series	Sum	Sum, Factored
1	1	1×1
$1 + 5$	6	2×3
$1 + 5 + 9$	15	3×5
$1 + 5 + 9 + 13$	28	4×7
$\vdots$	$\vdots$	$\vdots$

Other approaches are possible.
How many can you find?

SET 13   SOLUTIONS

FOLLOW-UPS: *(1) In the series 1 + 5 + 9 + ..., find the formula for the value of the nth term.* [4n – 3]   *(2) What is the formula for calculating the sum of this series?* [n(2n – 1); see table]   *(3) If $x^3 = 3 \times 6 \times 12 \times 24 \times 48 \times 96$, what is the value of x?* [288]

2E   METHOD 1: *Strategy: Use a frequency definition of probability.*
Consider a large and convenient number of days, say 100. Rain is expected for 40 days and fair weather for 60 days. Jess would expect to earn a total of (40 × $1500) + (60 × $400) = $84,000. During the 100 day period, **Jess expects to earn** $84,000, which is **an average of $840 daily.**

METHOD 2: *Strategy: Pretend the average weather actually happens one day.*
Consider an "average" day. Assume it rains 40% of that day. During that time Jess earns 40% of $1500, which is $600 that day. It is fair the other 60% of that day, so Jess earns 60% of $400, which is another $240. Thus, on that "average" day, Jess expects to earn $840.

Olympiad 3

3A   METHOD 1: *Strategy: Write the numbers in standard form.*
500,000,000 ÷ 170,000 = 50,000 ÷ 17, which is between 2000 and 3000. **There are 4 digits to the left of the decimal point.**

METHOD 2: *Strategy: Use scientific notation.*
500,000,000 ÷ 170.000 = $(5 \times 10^8) \div (1.7 \times 10^5)$ = 2.□□ × 10^3. Multiplying a one-digit number by 1000 produces 4 digits to the left of the decimal point.

3B   *Strategy: Count the number of multiples of 7.*
Only multiples of 7 contain factors of 7. There are four multiples of 7 less than 30 and each contains 7 as a factor exactly once. Thus, **7 appears as a factor of the product 4 times.**

FOLLOW-UPS: *The product is often written as 30! ("30 factorial"). (1) How many factors of 3 does 30! have?* [14]   *(2) In part 1, why is the answer 14 instead of 10 or 13?* [9 and 18 each contain 3^2 and 27 contains 3^3.]   *(3) 30! has how many factors of 10?* [7]   *(4) In part 3, why is the answer 7 instead of 3?* [10 is not prime. Look for the number of times 5 appears as a factor.]   *(5) In part 5, why do we use the factor 5 instead of the factor 2?*

3C *Strategy: Consider all three games.*

To win for the first time in the third game, Chloe must lose the first two games and then win the third. Since the probability that Chloe wins a game is $\frac{3}{5}$, then the probability that she does *not* win a game is $\frac{2}{5}$. By the multiplication principle, **the probability that Chloe loses the first two games and then wins the third is** $\frac{2}{5} \times \frac{2}{5} \times \frac{3}{5} = \frac{12}{125}$.

> ***FOLLOW-UPS:*** *(1) Using the same information, what is the probability that Chloe wins for the second time in the third game?* $\left[\frac{36}{125}\right]$ *(2) What is the probability that Chloe wins at least 2 games?* $\left[\frac{81}{125}\right]$

3D **METHOD 1:** *Strategy: Rearrange the regions more conveniently.*

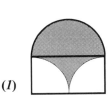 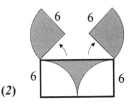 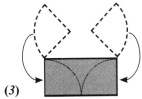

(1)   *(2)*   *(3)*

The area of the shaded region is the same as the area of the rectangle, which is $6 \times 12 = $ **72 sq cm.**

METHOD 2: *Strategy: Add and subtract areas.*

The radius of the given semicircle is 6 cm.

From the sum of the areas of the given semicircle and the rectangle, subtract the areas of the two quarter circles:

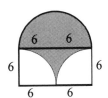

The area of the given semicircle:

$[\pi 6^2 \div 2]$ sq cm $+ [12 \times 6]$ sq cm $- [(\pi 6^2 \div 4) \times 2]$ sq cm $=$
18π sq cm $+$ 72 sq cm $-$ 18π sq cm $=$
72 sq cm.

The area of the shaded region is 72 sq cm.

3E *Strategy: Write the fraction as a mixed number.*

$$\frac{45}{7} = 6 + \frac{3}{7} = a + \frac{1}{b + \frac{1}{c}}, \text{ so } a = 6.$$

Now write $\frac{3}{7}$ so that its numerator is 1: $\frac{3}{7} = \frac{1}{\frac{7}{3}} = \frac{1}{b + \frac{1}{c}}$

Next examine b and c: $\frac{7}{3} = 2 + \frac{1}{3} = b + \frac{1}{c}$, so $b = 2$ and $c = 3$.

Thus, $a = 6$, $b = 2$, and $c = 3$.

SET 13 SOLUTIONS

Olympiad 4

4A METHOD 1: _Strategy: Express each side as the product of factors._
Rewrite each side of the equation as the product of common factors.

$$52 \times 50 \times N = 40 \times 13 \times 35$$
$$4 \times 13 \times 5 \times 10 \times N = 4 \times 10 \times 13 \times 5 \times 7$$
$$4 \times 13 \times 5 \times 10 \times N = 4 \times 13 \times 5 \times 10 \times 7$$

Notice the common factors of 4, 13, 5 and 10 on each side. **N is 7.**

METHOD 2: _Strategy: Use algebra._
Do the multiplication to get $2600N = 18{,}200$. Divide both sides of the equation by 2600. $N = 7$.

> **FOLLOW-UP:** _Find the least common multiple of 520 and 280._ [3640]

4B _Strategy: List the multiples of each._
Write two lists of multiples between 0 and 100, as shown below.

Multiples of 17:   17, 34, 51, 68, **85**, …
Multiples of 21:   21, 42, 63, **84**, …

The only pair of consecutive integers is 84 and 85. Therefore, **the greater of the two consecutive integers is 85.**

> **FOLLOW-UPS:** _(1) Without continuing the lists, how could you find other pairs of consecutive integers such that one is a multiple of 17 and the other of 21?_ [Add 17×21 to both 84 and 85 as often as desired.]   _(2) Is it possible for two multiples of 15 and 21 to be consecutive integers? Explain._ [No. With a common factor of 3, every pair must differ by a multiple of 3.]

4C _Strategy: Find the radii of the circles._
The area of a circle is given by the formula $A = \pi r^2$, so circles with areas of 9π, 25π, and 100π have radii of 3, 5, and 10 respectively. The lengths of the sides of the triangle are found by adding pairs of radii together. Therefore, AB = 8 cm, BC = 15 cm, and CA = 13 cm. **The perimeter of the triangle is** $8 + 15 + 13 = $ **36 cm.**

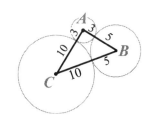

4D **METHOD 1:** _Strategy: Use the multiplication algorithm._
Start with the multiplication on the left. Each partial product contains only 2 digits. First, q is 1, so <u>C = 7</u> and <u>pq</u> represents 91. In the tens column, (9 + s) ends in 1. Then <u>s is 2</u>, so <u>B = 4</u> and <u>rs</u> represents 52. This yields the multiplication on the right.

$$
\begin{array}{r}
1\ 3 \\
\times\ \text{A B C} \\
\hline
p\ q \\
r\ s \\
t\ u \\
\hline
3\ \square\ 1\ 1
\end{array}
\qquad
\begin{array}{r}
1\ 3 \\
\times\ \text{A 4 7} \\
\hline
9\ 1 \\
5\ 2 \\
t\ u \\
\hline
3\ \square\ 1\ 1
\end{array}
$$

Since the thousands digit of the product is 3, <u>t</u> is 2 or 3 and A is 2 or 3. If A is 3, <u>tu</u> represents 39 and the final product is <u>4</u>511, not 3□11. Thus <u>A is 2</u>, <u>tu</u> represents 26 and the final product is 3211. **The missing digit is 2**.

METHOD 2: _Strategy: Start with an arbitrary value._
Divide 3011 by 13 to get a quotient of 231 and a remainder of 8. Since 100 divided by 13 leaves a remainder of 9, each time we increase 3011 by 100, we add 9 to that remainder value of 8: 8, 17, 26, … and look for a multiple of 13. Since 26 is a multiple of 13 and is obtained by adding 2 nines to 8, then 3011 + 200 = 3211 will be a multiple of 13. The number is 3211 and the missing digit is 2.

Dividend	Remainder
3011	8
3111	8 + 9 = 17
3211	8 + 18 = 26

METHOD 3: _Strategy: Use a divisibility test._
There are several tests for divisibility by 13. Here are two:

1. Start at the right and split the digits into groups of 3. Alternately add and subtract the groups until a 3 digit number remains. The original number is divisible by 13 if and only if the final 3 digit number is. Here, 3□11 is divisible by 13 only if □11 – 3 = □08 is. Use Method 2 to find that the missing digit is 2.

2. Multiply the units digit by 4 and add it to the original number without the units digit. Continue in this fashion until a 2 digit number remains. The original number is divisible by 13 if and only if the final 2 digit number is. Here 3□11 → 3□1 +4(1) = 3□5. 3□ + 4(5) = 5□. Only if the missing digit is 2 is 5□ a multiple of 13.

4E _Strategy: Wrap the square in a box._
Draw △DEC congruent to right △AOD as shown. ∠r ≅ ∠s and ∠O ≅ ∠ADC, so the sum of the three angles at D equals the sum of the three angles in △AOD (180°). Thus $\overline{ODE}$ is a straight line segment and E is on the x-axis. Construct 2 more right triangles congruent to △AOD, as shown, to produce square OEFG.

Because C is at (7,4), OE = 7 and CE = 4. Then OD = 4 and DE = 3. Since the four triangles are congruent, the legs in each triangle have lengths of 3 and 4.

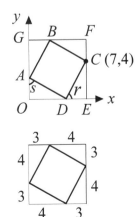

METHOD 1: *Strategy: Use known areas.*
OEFG is a square of side 7, so its area is 49. The area of each of the four right triangles is
½(3)(4) = 6. **The area of the square *ABCD* is** then 49 – 4 × 6 = **25.**

METHOD 2: *Strategy: Use the Pythagorean Theorem.*
In right $\triangle CDE$, $CD^2 = 3^2 + 4^2$. So $CD = 5$, and the area of the square $ADCB = 5^2 = 25$.

> ***FOLLOW-UP:*** *(1) Find the area of the shaded square in the center of the largest square in this picture.* [49] *(2) Find the area of a triangle whose vertices are A(0,0), B (4,5) and C(2,6).* [7 sq units; wrap the triangle in a rectangle and subtract areas.]

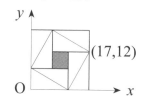

Olympiad 5

5A *Strategy: Use the definition of the operation.*
$2 \maltese 6 = 2 + 3 \times 6 = 20$ and $N \maltese 4 = N + 3 \times 4 = N + 12$
Then $20 = N + 12$ and **the value of *N* is 8.**

5B **METHOD 1:** *Strategy: Extend the process of "cancellation".*
"Cancel" identical numerators and denominators with each other (that is, divide out each identical common factor greater than 1). This can be done 6 times. Then we are left with $\frac{2}{90}$.
In simplest terms, the product is $\frac{1}{45}$.

METHOD 2: *Strategy: Multiply all fractions and then simplify.*
The product of all the numerators is 40,320.
The product of all the denominators is 1,814,400.
$1,814,400 \div 40,320 = 45$. In simplest terms, the product is $\frac{1}{45}$.

5C *Strategy: Simplify the sum.*
Start with a sum of zero: The sum $^-10 + {^-9} + {^-8} + \cdots + 8 + 9 + 10 = 0$. Continue to add integers starting with 11 until the desired sum is obtained. Because $11 + 12 + 13 + 14 = 50$, ***N* = 14.**

5D   **METHOD 1a:**   _Strategy: Consider the number of wins._

The following table shows that the Pumas won 2 of their first 9 games and then 3 of every 4 games on average. They ended with 2 wins in every 3 games.

Games won	2	5	8	...	35	**38**
Games played	9	13	17	...	53	**57**

Since only $\frac{38}{57}$ simplifies to $\frac{2}{3}$, **the Pumas won 38 games in all.**

METHOD 1b: _Strategy: Consider the number of losses._

The following table shows that the Pumas lost 7 of their first 9 games and then lost 1 of every 4 games on average. They ended with 19 losses in 57 games, which is 1 loss in every 3 games.

Games lost	7	8	9	...	18	**19**
Games played	9	13	17	...	53	**57**

Since they lost a total of 19 games, the Pumas won 38 games in all.

METHOD 2: _Strategy: Use algebra._

Let w = ratio factor. Then they won $3w$ and lost $4w$ of the remaining games.
In all the Pumas won $2 + 3w$ games and played $9 + 4w$ games.

$$\frac{2 + 3w}{9 + 4w} = \frac{2}{3}$$

Cross-multiply:	$3(2 + 3w) = 2(9 + 4w)$
Multiply out on each side of the equation:	$6 + 9w = 18 + 8w$
Subtract $8w$ from each side of the equation:	$6 + w = 18$
Subtract 6 from each side of the equation:	$w = 12$
Now find the value of $2 + 3w$:	$2 + 3w = 38$

The Pumas won 38 games in all.

5E   **METHOD 1:** _Strategy: Split the figure into more familiar shapes and add._

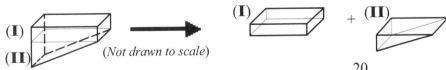

(I)   Volume of **I** = $6 \times 20 \times 1 = 120$ cu m:

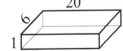

(II)   Volume of **II** = $\frac{1}{2} \times 6 \times 20 \times 3 = 180$ cu m:

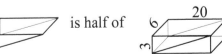

The pool can hold $120 + 180 = $ **300 cubic meters of water.**

METHOD 2: _Strategy: Embed the figure in a more familiar shape and subtract._

Box in the pool and compute the volume of the resulting rectangular solid. Next, find and subtract the volume of the extra "wedge" you added.

 = minus half of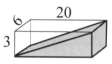

The volume of water in the pool = $(4 \times 6 \times 20) - \frac{1}{2} \times (3 \times 6 \times 20)$

= $480 - 180$

= 300 cu m

METHOD 3: _Strategy: Use formulas._

In the diagram, consider the shaded side of the pool as the base of a prism. The volume of the prism is $V = Bh$, where B is the area of the base and h is the height of the prism.

The base is a trapezoid, and its area is given by $\frac{1}{2} h (b_1 + b_2)$, where h is the height of the trapezoid and b_1 and b_2 are the lengths of its bases. The area of this trapezoid is $B = \frac{1}{2}(20)(4 + 1) = 50$ sq m, and the volume of the pool is $Bh = 50 \times 6$. The pool can hold 300 cu m of water.

Set 14   Olympiad 1

1A   **METHOD 1:** _Strategy: Count the number of times each digit appears._

Multiply each value by the number of times it appears. Add those products.
$(10 \times 2) + (9 \times 4) + (6 \times 6) = 92$. **The sum is 92.**

METHOD 2: _Strategy: Separate into a rectangle of 2s and a triangle of 4s._

```
2  2  2  2        2  2  2  2              
2  2  6  2        2  2  2  2                    4
2  6  6  2   =    2  2  2  2     +       4   4
6  6  6  2        2  2  2  2          4  4  4
  4  4  4  4         2  2  2  2       4  4  4  4
4  4  4  4  4                      4  4  4  4  4
```

The sum is $(16 \times 2) + (15 \times 4) = 92$.

1B   **METHOD 1:** _Strategy: Compare each coin to the average value._

Each nickel is worth 5 cents less than the average; each quarter is worth 15 cents more. Combine each quarter with 3 nickels for an average value of 10 cents. There are 12 nickels, so **4 quarters must be added to the collection.**

METHOD 2: _Strategy: Use algebra._
Let Q represent the number of quarters to be added. The total value of the coins is 25Q + 60.
The total number of coins is Q + 12. Divide to obtain the average value of the coins.

$$\frac{25Q + 60}{Q + 12} = 10$$

Multiply both sides of the equation by $Q + 12$: $\quad\quad 25Q + 60 = 10Q + 120$
Subtract $10Q + 60$ from each side of the equation: $\quad 15Q \quad = \quad\quad 60$
Divide both sides of the equation by 15: $\quad\quad\quad\quad Q \quad = \quad\quad 4$

Thus, 4 quarters must be added.

> **FOLLOW-UP:** _How many $5 bills must be added to twenty $100 bills so that the average value of all the bills is $10?_ [360]

1C _Strategy: Find the least and greatest possible sums._
The least possible sum is obtained by adding –12 and –11. The greatest possible sum is obtained by adding 7 and 8. Every integer between these extremes is also a possible sum. By examining a number line from –23 to +15 inclusive, you should see 23 negative sums, 15 positive sums, and zero. **There are 39 different sums that can be obtained.**

> **FOLLOW-UP:** _How many distinct sums can be obtained by adding two different integers chosen from the consecutive even integers from –12 to +8, inclusive?_ [19]

1D **METHOD 1:** _Strategy: Use the divisibility rules to find factors of 561._
The sum of the digits of 561 is 12, so 3 is a factor and 561 ÷ 3 = 187. Next, 187 satisfies the test of divisibility for multiples of 11 (that is, 1 – 8 + 7 = 0), so 11 is also a factor and 187 ÷ 11 = 17. Thus 561 factors into 3 × 11 × 17. The table shows that there are 4 factor pairs of 561. Of these 8 factors, 3 are prime. Therefore, **there are 5 factors of 561 which are not prime.**

$$\frac{561}{\begin{array}{l} 1 \times 561 \\ 3 \times 187 \\ 11 \times 51 \\ 17 \times 33 \end{array}}$$

METHOD 2: _Strategy: Find the total number of factors without factoring._
Call the three prime factors P, Q, and R. Their product is PQR and the table shows all its factor pairs. In all, there are 8 factors, of which 3 are prime. Thus, there are 5 factors of 561 which are not prime.

$$\frac{PQR}{\begin{array}{l} 1 \times PQR \\ P \times QR \\ Q \times PR \\ R \times PQ \end{array}}$$

> **FOLLOW-UPS:** _(1) N is the product of 4 different prime numbers. How many factors of N are not prime?_ [12] _(2) N is the product of 5 different prime numbers. How many factors does it have altogether?_ [32] _(3) What is the least number with exactly 8 factors?_ [30] _(4) Why is 1 neither prime nor composite?_ [A prime has exactly 2 factors and a composite has at least 3 factors. 1 has only one factor.]

1E _Strategy:_ Find the unshaded area.

METHOD 1: _Strategy:_ Assign convenient numerical lengths to the sides.

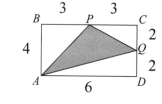

Suppose for example that $BC = 6$ and $CD = 4$. Then BP and PC each are 3, and CQ and QD each are 2, and the area of rectangle $ABCD$ is 24.

The area of $\triangle ABP$ is $\frac{1}{2}(4)(3) = 6$, of $\triangle PCQ$ is $\frac{1}{2}(3)(2) = 3$, and of $\triangle QDA$ is $\frac{1}{2}(6)(2) = 6$. The total unshaded area is $6 + 3 + 6 = 15$, and the area of $\triangle APQ$ is 9. **The area of $\triangle APQ$ is $\frac{9}{24} = \frac{3}{8}$ of the area of rectangle $ABCD$.**

METHOD 2: _Strategy:_ Split the figure into more convenient shapes.

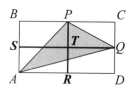

Draw $\overline{PR}$ and $\overline{QS}$ parallel to the sides of the rectangle as shown.

The area of $\triangle ABP$ is $\frac{1}{2}$ the area of rectangle $ABPR$, which is $\frac{1}{2}$ the area of $ABCD$. Then $\triangle ABP$ is $\frac{1}{4}$ the the area of ABCD.

The area of $\triangle QDA$ is $\frac{1}{2}$ the area of rectangle $SQDA$ which is $\frac{1}{2}$ the area of $ABCD$. So $\triangle QDA$ is $\frac{1}{4}$ the area of $ABCD$.

The area of $\triangle PCQ$ is $\frac{1}{2}$ the area of rectangle $PCQT$ which is $\frac{1}{4}$ the area of $ABCD$. So $\triangle PCQ$ is $\frac{1}{8}$ the area of $ABCD$.

The unshaded area then is $\frac{1}{4} + \frac{1}{4} + \frac{1}{8} = \frac{5}{8}$ of the area of $ABCD$.

Thus, the area of the shaded region is $\frac{3}{8}$ of the area of rectangle $ABCD$.

Olympiad 2

2A **METHOD 1:** _Strategy:_ Add decimals in a convenient order.

Rewrite each term as a decimal and then combine terms of the same sign.

$$\begin{aligned}
1 - \tfrac{2}{10} + \tfrac{3}{100} - \tfrac{4}{1000} &= 1 - .2 + .03 - .004 \\
&= (1.00 + .03) - (.200 + .004) \\
&= \quad 1.030 \quad - \quad .204 \\
&= \quad\quad\quad \mathbf{.826}
\end{aligned}$$

METHOD 2: _Strategy:_ Eliminate the denominators (temporarily).

Multiply each term by 1000 and simplify. Later, divide by 1000 to undo step 1.

$$\begin{aligned}
1000 &- \tfrac{2000}{10} + \tfrac{3000}{100} - \tfrac{4000}{1000} \\
&= 1000 - 200 + 30 - 4 \\
&= \quad\quad 826
\end{aligned}$$

Now divide by 1000 to undo the first step. The result is 0.826.

2B   *Strategy: Work backwards.*

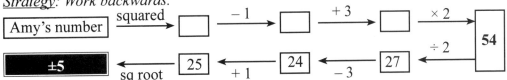

Amy picked a whole number, so **she started with 5.**

2C   METHOD 1: *Strategy: Use the symmetry of the given information.*
27, 35, and 32 are each the sum of a different pair of sides of the triangle.

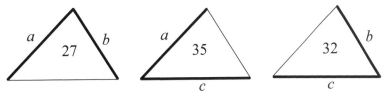

Then $27 + 35 + 32$ is the sum of the three sides, each counted twice. Thus 94 is twice the perimeter and **the perimeter of the triangle is 47 cm.**

METHOD 2: *Strategy: Use algebra to find the length of each side.*

Let a, b, and c represent the sides of the triangle. Then the three equations are:

(1) $a + b = 27$,   (2) $a + c = 35$, and   (3) $b + c = 32$.

One way to solve this system is to add equations (1) and (2), and then subtract (3) from the result.

(1)	$a + b$	$= 27$
(2)	$a\ \ \ \ + c$	$= 35$
	$2a + b + c$	$= 62$
(3)	$b + c$	$= 32$
	$2a$	$= 30$
(4)	a	$= 15$

Now add (4) and (3):

(4)	a	$= 15$
(3)	$b + c$	$= 32$
	$a + b + c$	$= 47$

The perimeter of the triangle is 47 cm.

> ***Follow-Ups:*** *(1) The area of 3 different faces of a box (rectangular solid) are 20, 28, and 35 sq cm. What is the volume of the box?* [140 cm³]   *(2) Suppose 51 cm, 63 cm, and 39 cm each are the sum of 2 sides of a parallelogram. What is the perimeter of the parallelogram?* [102 cm]

2D   *Strategy: Continue the sequence and look for a pattern.*
The sixth term is $-(3 + -6 + 1) = -(-2) = 2$. The sequence is **1, 2, 3, –6,** 1, 2, 3, –6, **1, 2, 3, –6,** and so on. The terms repeat in groups of four. Thus, every fourth term is – 6. Therefore the 100ᵗʰ term is –6, and so **the 99ᵗʰ term is 3.**

FOLLOW-UP: *A sequence begins 1, 2, 3, ... The fourth term is the third term minus the second term; the fifth term is the fourth minus the third, and so on. What is the 49th term?* [–1]

2E **METHOD 1:** <u>*Strategy*</u>: *Find the sum of the numbers.*
Each term of the series $1 + 3 + 5 ... + 49$ is obtained by adding 2 to the previous term. To go from 1 to 49, 2 is added twenty four times, so the series has 25 terms. Pair these terms as follows, working from the outside inward $(1 + 49) + (3 + 47) + (5 + 45)$, and so on. The sum of each pair is 50 and there are 12 pairs.

The number without a pair is the middle one, 25. The sum is then $(12 \times 50) + 25 = 625$. Then, $\sqrt{625}$ **is 25.**

METHOD 2: <u>*Strategy*</u>: *Look for a pattern in the partial sums.*
The table below examines the square root of the sums of the first few terms. In each case, the square root is equal to the number of terms added.

Number of terms	Sum of terms	Square root of the sum of terms
1	1	1
2	4	2
3	9	3
4	16	4
5	25	5

There are 25 odd numbers from 1 to 49 and therefore 25 terms in the given sequence. Thus the square root of the sum of the series is 25.

Olympiad 3

3A **METHOD 1:** <u>*Strategy*</u>: *Look for a perfect square near 420.*
The page numbers differ by 1, so the factors of 420 must be nearly equal. $20^2 = 400$, so try 20 as a factor. $420 = 20 \times 21$, and **the sum of the two page numbers is 41.**

METHOD 2: <u>*Strategy*</u>: *Combine the prime factors of 420.*
The prime factorization of 420 is $2 \times 2 \times 3 \times 5 \times 7$. Combining the factors into two products whose difference is 1, we get 20×21. Their sum is 41.

FOLLOW-UP: *The sum of the 6 page numbers in a chapter of the book is 153. What is the number on the first page of the chapter?* [23]

3B *Strategy: Minimize the number of acorns in each hole.*
Each hole requires a different number of acorns, so put 1 in the first hole, 2 in the second, and so on. Continue until the total number of acorns is near 80. $1 + 2 + 3 + \ldots + 11 + 12 = 78$, and $1 + 2 + 3 + \ldots + 13 = 91$. 13 holes require at least 91 acorns. The squirrel puts the first 78 acorns into 12 holes as indicated. The squirrel then can put the other two acorns into the 12th hole, making 14 acorns in that hole. **The greatest possible value of N is 12.**

> ***FOLLOW-UPS:*** *(1) Aside from 1,2,3, . . .,11,14 above, how many other sets of 12 different counting numbers have a sum of 80?* [1: the last 2 numbers are 12 and 13] *(2) In how many different ways can the squirrel bury 20 acorns in two holes if each hole has a different number of acorns and no hole is empty?* [9] *(3) 20 acorns in 3 holes?* [24]

3C *Strategy: List the possible numerators and denominators.*
Denote the fraction and its reciprocal by $\frac{A}{B}$ and $\frac{B}{A}$. Their sum has a denominator of 15, so A and B must be chosen from $\{1, 3, 5, 15\}$. Neither A nor B can be 15, for $\frac{15}{1}, \frac{15}{3}$, and $\frac{15}{5}$ are each larger than $2\frac{4}{15}$. Likewise, neither A nor B can be 1, for $\frac{5}{1}$ and $\frac{3}{1}$ are also larger than $2\frac{4}{15}$. The only possibility is that the fractions are $\frac{3}{5}$ and $\frac{5}{3}$. In fact, their sum is $\frac{34}{15} = 2\frac{4}{15}$. Of these two, **the proper fraction is $\frac{3}{5}$.**

> ***FOLLOW-UP:*** *What is the least possible sum of a positive fraction (not necessarily proper) and its reciprocal?* [2]

3D *Strategy: Look for a pattern.*
Consider the points where the path changes direction. Since (5,3) is in the first quadrant, find the path length to each of the upper right "corners": (2,1), (3,2), (4,3), (5,4), and so on.

Coordinates of corner point	Path length
(1,0)	1
(2,1)	$1 + 1 + 2 + 2 + 3 = 9$
(3,2)	$9 + 3 + 4 + 4 + 5 = 25$

The path lengths are consecutive odd squares. In fact, they are the squares of the sum of the coordinates of the corner points. The corner point closest to (5,3) is (5,4) and the path length to (5,4) is 81 units. Following the spiral, (5,3) is the next lattice point reached, so **the length of the path is 82 units.**

> ***FOLLOW-UP:*** *In the other 3 quadrants what patterns are formed by the path's lengths to the corners?*

3E **METHOD 1:** _Strategy: Find the speed of each hand in degrees per minute._
The minute hand rotates 360° in 1 hour and thus rotates 6° per minute. The
hour hand rotates $\frac{1}{12}$ as far as the minute hand every hour and therefore rotates
$\frac{1}{12}$ as far every minute, i.e. $\frac{1}{2}°$ per minute. At 8:00 the hour hand is 240° ahead
of the minute hand. In the next 24 minutes the hour hand rotates an additional
12° and the minute hand rotates 144°. **At 8:24 the angle between the hands
is** 240 + 12 − 144 = **108°.**

METHOD 2: _Strategy: Start at 12:00 and see how far each hand has rotated._
From 8:00 to 8:24, the minute hand has rotated $\frac{24}{60} = \frac{2}{5}$ of the way around the clock. That is,
it has rotated $\frac{2}{5}$ of 360° = 144°. Think of 12:00 as 0°, 3:00 at 90°, and 6:00 as 180°. Then the
minute hand is pointing to 144°.

Meanwhile, the hour hand, which needs 12 hours to rotate 360°, rotates 30° every hour. Thus,
at 8:00, it was pointing to 240°. At 8:24, it has rotated another $\frac{2}{5}$ of 30° = 12° and is pointing
to 252°. At 8:24 the angle between the hands is 252 − 144 = 108°.

Olympiad 4

4A **METHOD 1:** _Strategy: Start with Kayla, whose position is known._

Kayla is the third person.	——, ——, K , …
Kayla is 2 places in front of Eli.	——, ——, K , ——, E , …
Eli is 4 places behind Sara.	S , ——, K , ——, E , …
Sara is 3 places in front of Abby.	S , ——, K , A , E , …
Abby is in the center of the line.	S , ——, K , A , E , ——, ——

Abby is the 4th person in line. There are 3 people in front of her and 3 people behind her.
There are 7 students in the line.

METHOD 2: _Strategy: Create the line, keeping Abby in the center._

Sara is 3 places in front of Abby.	…, S , ——, ——, A , ——, ——, ——, …
Eli is 4 places behind Sara.	…, S , ——, ——, A , E , ——, ——, …
Kayla is 2 places in front of Eli.	…, S , ——, K , A , E , ——, ——, …

Kayla is the 3rd person in line, so no additional spaces are needed in front of Sara.
There are 7 students in the line.

4B _Strategy: Calculate the required values._
The median is $\frac{8+6}{2} = 7$. The mode is 6. The mean is $\frac{3+6+6+8+10+12}{6} = \frac{45}{6}$.
Then $\frac{3 \times (7) - (6)}{6 \times (\frac{45}{6})} = \frac{15}{45} = \frac{1}{3}$.

FOLLOW-UPS: *(1) The mean and median of a set of five different positive integers is 12. One number is 3 less than the median and another is half the mean. What is the greatest possible integer in the set?* [20]   *(2) The mean, median and mode of a set of five positive integers are all equal. Three of the numbers are 9, 13, and 41. Find the missing numbers that satisfy this condition. There are two different answers.* [21 and 21 is one answer; 41 and 101 is the other.]

4C **METHOD 1:** *Strategy: Count up from the lesser number.*
From –1 to 13 is an increase of 14. **Increasing –5 by 14 is 9.**

METHOD 2: *Strategy: Draw a number line.*
The upper line segment shows the amount by which 13 exceeds –1. The lower line segment shows the amount by which the desired number exceeds –5.

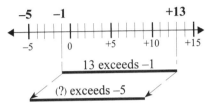

Sliding the upper segment into the lower position requires moving the left endpoint from –1 to –5, 4 units to the left. Then the right endpoint also slides 4 units to the left, from 13 to 9. The integer is 9.

4D **METHOD 1:** *Strategy: Find the unshaded area inside each circle.*
The areas inside the two circles are 25π and 9π respectively.

The unshaded area inside circle A is $25\pi - \frac{7\pi}{2} = \frac{43\pi}{2}$.

The unshaded area inside circle B is $9\pi - \frac{7\pi}{2} = \frac{11\pi}{2}$.

The total unshaded area is $\frac{43+11}{2}\pi = 27\pi$ sq cm.

METHOD 2: *Strategy: Start with the total area of the two circles.*
The sum of the areas of the circles is $25\pi + 9\pi = 34\pi$. This, however, counts the shaded area twice, once for each circle. The total unshaded area is $34\pi - 2(\frac{7\pi}{2}) = 27\pi$.

4E **METHOD 1:** *Strategy: Count in an organized way.*
To form a triangle, two points must be chosen from 1 row and one from the other. Suppose two points are chosen from the top row. Label the four points in the top row A, B, C, D. Two points may be chosen in 6 ways (AB, AC, AD, BC, BD, CD). For each of these 6 pairs of points, the third vertex may be any of the 4 points in the bottom row. There are then $6 \times 4 = 24$ triangles using 2 points from the top row and 1 from the bottom row.

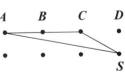

$\triangle ACS$ **is shown.**

Likewise, there are 24 triangles using 2 points from the bottom row and 1 from the top. In all, **48 triangles can be formed.**

METHOD 2: _Strategy: Make an organized list._

Label all 8 points, as shown. List all 18 triangles containing vertex A, all 14 triangles containing vertex B but not A, all 10 triangles containing vertex C but not A or B, and all 6 triangles containing vertex D but not A or B or C. A total of 48 triangles can be formed.

```
A   B   C   D
•   •   •   •

•   •   •   •
P   Q   R   S
```

$\triangle ABP$	$\triangle ACP$	$\triangle ADP$	$\triangle BCP$	$\triangle BDP$	$\triangle CDP$	$\triangle CPQ$	$\triangle DPQ$
$\triangle ABQ$	$\triangle ACQ$	$\triangle ADQ$	$\triangle BCQ$	$\triangle BDQ$	$\triangle CDQ$	$\triangle CPR$	$\triangle DPR$
$\triangle ABR$	$\triangle ACR$	$\triangle ADR$	$\triangle BCR$	$\triangle BDR$	$\triangle CDR$	$\triangle CPS$	$\triangle DPS$
$\triangle ABS$	$\triangle ACS$	$\triangle ADS$	$\triangle BCS$	$\triangle BDS$	$\triangle CDS$	$\triangle CQR$	$\triangle DQR$
$\triangle APQ$	$\triangle APR$	$\triangle APS$	$\triangle BPQ$	$\triangle BQR$	$\triangle CQS$	$\triangle CRS$	$\triangle DQS$
$\triangle AQR$	$\triangle AOS$	$\triangle ARS$	$\triangle BPR$	$\triangle BQS$			$\triangle DRS$
			$\triangle BPS$	$\triangle BRS$			

METHOD 3: _Strategy: Use combinations. Subtract the triples that don't work._

Given eight points, three points may be chosen in $_8C_3 = 56$ ways.

No triangle is formed if all three points are chosen from the same row. There are $_4C_3 = 4$ sets of three points in the top row and another 4 sets in the bottom row.

Thus $56 - 4 - 4 = 48$ triangles can be formed.

> **FOLLOW-UP:** _How many triangles can be formed with vertices chosen from a 3×3 array of points?_ [76]

Olympiad 5

5A   METHOD 1: _Strategy: Group the numbers by tens and look for a pattern._

Interval	Satisfactory numbers	Number of numbers
10-19	12, 13, 14, 15, …, 19	8
20-29	23, 24, 25, …, 29	7
30-39	34, 35, …, 39	6
⋮	⋮	⋮
80-89	89	1
	Total	**36**

There are **36 two-digit numbers in which the ones digit is greater than the tens digit.**

METHOD 2: _Strategy: Eliminate all unwanted numbers._

There are 90 two-digit counting numbers. Eliminate the 9 numbers with equal digits (11, 22, etc.). Then eliminate the 9 multiples of 10. The remaining 72 numbers have 2 unequal nonzero digits. In half of them the ones digit exceeds the tens digit. There are then 36 such numbers.

5B **METHOD 1:** *Strategy:* *Make a table.*

Number of checks	A: Flat Fee = $7.50	B: $3 + 20¢ per check
1	$7.50	$3.20
10	$7.50	$5.00
20	$7.50	$7.00
21	$7.50	$7.20
22	$7.50	$7.40
23	$7.50	$7.60

Therefore, **the least number of checks such that Plan A costs less than Plan B is 23.**

METHOD 2: *Strategy:* *Use Algebra.*
Let N represent the number of checks for which plan A is cheaper.
Then their cost would be $300¢ + 20N¢$. (Use cents to avoid decimals.)

Plan B must cost more than 750 cents: $\qquad\qquad\qquad$ $20N + 300 > 750$
Subtract 300 cents from each side of the inequality $\qquad$ $20N \qquad > 450$
Divide each side of the equation by 20: $\qquad\qquad\quad$ $N \qquad > \quad 22.5$

Checks come in whole numbers. At least 23 checks are needed for Plan A to cost less than Plan B.

5C **METHOD 1:** *Strategy:* *Assign arbitrary dimensions.*
In ratio problems, assigning convenient measures does not affect the answer. For ease of computation, let the base be 20 and the height 10 so that the area is $\frac{1}{2}(20)(10) = 100$ sq units. If the base is increased by 20%, the new base is 24. If the height is increased by 30%, the new height is 13. The area of the new triangle is $\frac{1}{2}(24)(13)=156$ square units. The increase over the original 100 is 56. Therefore, **the area is increased by** 56 compared to $100 = \mathbf{56\%.}$

METHOD 2: *Strategy:* *Compare areas using the area formula.*
The area of the original triangle is given by $A = \frac{1}{2}bh$. The area of the changed triangle is given by $\frac{1}{2}(1.20b)(1.30h) = \frac{1}{2}(1.56)bh$, which in turn equals 1.56 times $\frac{1}{2}bh$. Therefore the area of the new triangle is 1.56 times *as great as* the area of the original. This is 56% *greater than* the area of the original. The increase is 56%.

> **FOLLOW-UP:** *Suppose the base of a triangle is decreased by 20%, and its height is decreased by 30%. By what percent is the area of the triangle decreased?* [44]

5D *Strategy: Determine how many of the first 300 numbers can't be used.*

In each of the sets 1 through 100, 101 through 200, and 201 through 300, 10 numbers have a ones digit of 9, and 10 numbers have a tens digit of 9. However, in each set the number ending in 99 has been counted twice, so each set has 19 numbers that contain a digit of 9. In the overall list 1 through 300, 57 numbers must be eliminated. Refill the list with the next 57 numbers, 301 through 357. There are 5 numbers in this set that can't be used (309, 319, 329, 339, 349). Add on 5 more numbers, 358 through 362. One of these, 359, can't be used, so add on one more number. **The 300ᵗʰ number on Sara's list is 363.**

5E *Strategy: Draw possible paths.*

By drawing some paths, you may see two things: (1) the path can turn either left or right, and (2) each horizontal segment has an odd length while each vertical segment has an even length.

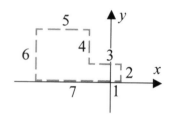

Consider first the horizontal segments that can end back at the starting point. Neither {1 unit and 3 units} nor {1, 3 and 5 units} can end at the origin, but {1, 3, 5, and 7 units} can. By traveling 1 and 7 units to the right, and 3 and 5 units to the left, the horizontal part of the path can end at zero.

The longest vertical segment is either 6 or 8 units, the even numbers on either side of 7. Since 2 + 4 = 6, if 2 and 4 are directed up and 6 is directed down, the vertical part of the path also ends at zero. **Thus the shortest possible path consists of 7 segments** and is shown above.

> **FOLLOW-UPS:** *(1) A path consisting of N line segments is drawn in the coordinate plane. The first segment starts at (0,0) and is drawn to (2,0). The second segment starts at (2,0) and is drawn to (2,4). Each of the N segments is drawn at a right angle to the segment before it and is 2 units longer than that segment. The Nᵗʰ segment ends at (0,0). What is the least possible value of N? [7] (2) What is the least possible value of N greater than 7? [8] (3) What are the next 2 possible values of N? [15, 16]*

Set 15   Olympiad 1

1A **METHOD 1:** *Strategy: Factor and regroup.*

$$2 \times 6 \times 10 \times 14 = (1 \times 3 \times 5 \times 7) \times (2 \times 2 \times 2 \times 2)$$
$$= (1 \times 3 \times 5 \times 7) \times N$$

Then $N = 2 \times 2 \times 2 \times 2$, so $N = $ **16.**

METHOD 2: *Strategy: Do the multiplication and solve the equation.*
Since $2 \times 6 \times 10 \times 14 = 1680$ and $1 \times 3 \times 5 \times 7 = 105$, the equation simplifies to $1680 = 105 \times N$.
Because $1680 \div 105 = 16$, $N = 16$.

FOLLOW-UP: *Find the whole number N if $2^2 \times 3^3 \times 4^4 = 27 \times 2^N$.* [10]

1B **METHOD 1:** *Strategy: Start with 1 person in each room.*
After placing 26 people, 1 per room, there are 14 people left over. Place these 14 people, 1 per room, so that there are 14 rooms with 2 people in each. That leaves **12 rooms occupied by exactly one person.**

METHOD 2: *Strategy: Start with 2 people in each room.*
Place the 40 people 2 per room. This fills 20 rooms, leaving 6 rooms empty. Take 1 person from each of 6 of the full rooms to occupy the empty rooms. There are then $6 + 6 = 12$ rooms each occupied by exactly one person.

METHOD 3: *Strategy: Suppose every room has 2 people.*
To fill all 26 rooms with 2 people in each room would require 52 people, There are only 40 people, so $52 - 40 = 12$ rooms will be occupied by just 1 person.

FOLLOW-UPS: *Suppose 60 people occupy the 26 rooms. There are 1, 2, or 3 people per room. (1) What is the least number of rooms with 3 people?* [8] *(2) What is the greatest number of rooms with 3 people?* [17]

1C *Strategy: Find the dimensions of the small rectangles.*
Represent BC by L and DC by $L + W$.

Then $DC - BC = W$.

$DC - BC = 6$, so $W = 6$ mm and $AD = 4W = 24$ mm.

The area of *ABCD* is $24 \times (24 + 6) =$ **720 sq mm.**

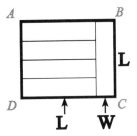

FOLLOW-UP: *Determine the difference in the lengths BC and CD given that the area of rectangle ABCD is 2000 square mm.* [10 mm]

1D *Strategy: Find the fractional part of the total each paid.*
Call the roommates A, B, and C. A pays half the amount that B and C together pay. That is, of every \$3 paid, A pays \$1 and B and C together pay \$2. A then pays $\frac{1}{3}$ of the total, or \$100. In a similar manner, since B pays $\frac{1}{3}$ the amount paid by A and C together, B pays $\frac{1}{4}$ of the total, or \$75. A and B together pay \$175, so **the third roommate C pays** $300 - 175 =$ **\$125.**

1E   _Strategy: List the arrangements systematically._

Denote the 6 girls, from shortest to tallest, by 1, 2, 3, 4, 5, and 6.

METHOD 1: _Strategy: Position the girls, working from both ends of the list._

1 must be in the front row at the far left. 6 must be in the back row at the far right.

2 can be in either row but must be at the far left of the available spaces.

    or

5 can be in either row but must be at the far right of the available spaces.

   or   or

3 and 4 go in the remaining spaces. If they are in the same row, 3 goes to the left. If one is directly behind the other, 3 goes in front. Otherwise, 3 and 4 may go in either available space.

   or   or   or   or

In all, 5 arrangements are possible.

METHOD 2: _Strategy: Fill in the front row first._

As above, 1 must be at the far left of the front row and 6 at the far right of the back row. It seems that the remaining 2 places in the front row can be filled in 6 ways by choosing any two of 2, 3, 4, and 5, namely 2 & 3, 2 & 4, 2 & 5, 3 & 4, 3 & 5, or 4 & 5. However, if 4 and 5 are both in the front row, the back row is 236, with 3 behind 4, which is not allowed by the given conditions. The remaining 5 choices lead to the 5 arrangements shown in Method 1. Five arrangements are possible.

> **FOLLOW-UP:** _Suppose 8 girls of different heights are lined up subject to the same conditions. How many arrangements are possible?_ [14]

Olympiad 2

2A   _Strategy: Consider the ones digits._

P × Q ends in a 1. The only different single-digit numbers whose product ends in 1 are 3 and 7. Therefore **PQ and QP are 37 and 73** (in either order).

> **FOLLOW-UPS:** _(1) Find a single digit number Q, such that P × Q + P + Q = PQ, where PQ is a two-digit number._ [9]   _(2) Why does this work?_

2B _Strategy: First determine the value of A; then use a common denominator._
Because $\frac{A}{6}$ is in lowest terms, A must be 1 or 5. But $\frac{5}{6} > \frac{3}{4}$, so $A = 1$.
Then $\frac{2}{12} + \frac{B}{12} = \frac{9}{12}$ and $B = 7$. **The sum of A and B is** $1 + 7 = \mathbf{8}$.

2C **METHOD 1:** _Strategy: Look for a pattern in the sum of each row._
Add the numbers in each row.

Row number	1	2	3	4	...	**10**
Sum of numbers	1	8	27	64	...	**?**

1
3 5
7 9 11
13 15 17 19
and so on ...

The sum of the numbers in each row is the cube of that row number.
Then **the sum of the numbers in the 10th row is** $10^3 = \mathbf{1000}$.

METHOD 2: _Strategy: Find a pattern in each row's first number._

Row number	1	2	3	4	5
1st entry in row	1	$3 = 2\times1 + 1$	$7 = 3\times2 + 1$	$13 = 4\times3 + 1$	$21 = 5\times4 + 1$

Based on this pattern, the first number in the tenth row is $10\times9 + 1 = 91$. The sum of the ten numbers in the tenth row is $91 + 93 + 95 + ... + 107 + 109 = (91+109) + (93+107) + (95+105) + (97+103) + (99+101) = 5 \times 200 = 1000$.

> **FOLLOW-UPS:** _(1) Can you find a pattern in the last number of each row?_ _(2) How is the average (mean) of each row related to the number of that row?_ _(3) How could **FOLLOW-UP** 2 be used to find the answer to contest problem 2C?_

2D **METHOD 1:** _Strategy: Count the cubes on each face; then adjust._
The greatest number of visible faces is 3. Count the number of cubes visible on each of the 3 faces of the solid. There are $(6 \times 8) + (6 \times 10) + (8 \times 10) = 188$ of them. However, this counts cubes along the 3 visible edges twice and the corner cube 3 times. Count the number of cubes along the edges. There are $10 + 8 + 6$ of them, but the corner cube is counted 3 times here as well, once on each edge. Then $188 - 24$ counts all visible cubes except the corner one.

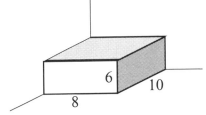

The greatest number of cubes you can see is $188 - 24 + 1 = \mathbf{165}$.

METHOD 2: _Strategy: Count and remove the cubes on each visible face._
As above, the greatest number of visible faces is three. Remove the 80 cubes on the top face to be left with a **5** × 8 × 10 solid. Next, remove the 40 cubes on the front face to be left with a 5 × 8 × **9** solid. The 45 cubes on the side face are the only ones remaining from the original visible cubes. Originally, a total of 80 + 40 + 45 = 165 cubes were visible.

> **FOLLOW-UP:** _Suppose you painted all the faces of the rectangular solid in the problem red. How many of the one-inch cubes would have 0 faces painted red? 1 face? 2 faces? 3? 4? 5? 6? [192, 208, 72, 8, 0, 0, 0]_

2E   **METHOD 1:** _Strategy: Consider terminating decimals in fractional form._
A one-place decimal can be written as a fraction with a denominator of 10, a two-place decimal can be written with a denominator of 100, three places with a denominator of 1000, and so on. Then any fraction that can be represented by a terminating decimal must be equivalent to one of these fractions. The only prime factors of 10 or 100 or 1000, ... , are 2 and 5. So the unit fractions that can be written as terminating decimals are those with denominators that have only 2s and 5s as prime factors.

- Denominators with only 2 as a factor: 2, 4, 8, 16, 32
- Denominators with only 5 as a factor: 5, 25
- Denominators with both 2 and 5 as factors: 10, 20, 40, 50

There are 11 fractions on the list that have decimal representations that terminate.

METHOD 2: _Strategy: Look for a pattern in the fractions with terminating decimals_
For the unit fractions from $\frac{1}{2}$ to $\frac{1}{10}$ inclusive, the only fractions that have terminating decimals are $\frac{1}{2}, \frac{1}{4}, \frac{1}{5}, \frac{1}{8}$, and $\frac{1}{10}$. Notice that the only factors in the denominators are 2 or 5. This is a requirement for the decimal to terminate because 2 and 5 are the only prime factors of 10, 100, 100, and so on. The remaining fractions that terminate in the original list are $\frac{1}{16}, \frac{1}{20}, \frac{1}{25}, \frac{1}{32}, \frac{1}{40}$, and $\frac{1}{50}$. This is a total of 11 fractions.

Olympiad 3

3A   _Strategy: Write the problem as an addition._
In the ones place, 3 + 8 ends in 1 so p is 1; 1 is carried.
In the tens place, 1 + r + 6 ends in 4, so r is 7; 1 is carried.
In the hundreds place, 1 + 4 + q = 8, so q = 3.

Then **p + q + r = 11.**

$$\begin{array}{r} 4\ r\ 3 \\ +\ q\ 6\ 8 \\ \hline 8\ 4\ p \end{array}$$

> **FOLLOW-UP:** _Find w + y + z, if 4z × y7 = 1w02. (Note: 4z and y7 are 2-digit numbers and 1w02 is a 4-digit number.) [16]_

3B _Strategy: Determine possible values of the radicand._
If $\sqrt{50-x}$ is a positive integer and x is positive, $(50-x)$ must be a perfect square less than 50. So $(50-x)$ can be any of 49, 36, 25, 16, 9, 4, or 1, leading to $x = 1, 14, 25, 34, 41, 46,$ or 49, respectively. **There are 7 positive integer values of x for which $\sqrt{50-x}$ is a whole number.**

> _**FOLLOW-UP:** For how many whole number values of x is $\sqrt{108-3x}$ a whole number?_ [3]

3C _Strategy: List values of the prime, P, in increasing order._
The first row lists prime numbers. The second row lists the difference between 98 and the prime. The third row states if the entry in the second row is prime and identifies a simple factor if the entry is composite.

P	2	3	5	7	11	13	17	**19**
$98 - P$	96	95	93	91	87	85	81	**79**
Is $98 - P$ prime?	no ($\div 2$)	no ($\div 5$)	no ($\div 3$)	no ($\div 7$)	no ($\div 3$)	no ($\div 5$)	no ($\div 3$)	**PRIME**

Therefore, **the least value of P is 19.**

> _**FOLLOW-UP:** Find a whole number value for N such that the value of $N^2 + N + 41$ is not prime._ [The least is 40; the most readily found is 41.]

3D **METHOD 1:** _Strategy: Determine the x- and y-coordinates separately._
C is $\frac{2}{3}$ of the way from A to B. Then the x-coordinate of C is $\frac{2}{3}$ of the way from the x-coordinate of A to the x-coordinate of B. The x (horizontal) distance from A to B is $7 - (-5) = 12$ and $\frac{2}{3}$ of $12 = 8$. The x-coordinate of C is $(-5) + 8 = 3$.

Similarly, the y-coordinate of C is $4 + \frac{2}{3} \times (13 - 4) = 10$.

The coordinates of point C are (3,10).

METHOD 2: _Strategy: Show the $\frac{2}{3}$ visually._
Replace the horizontal and vertical distances of 12 and 9 in _method 1_ by three 4 by 3 "steps" as shown. To go from A to C, start at $(-5,4)$, move to the right 4 and 4 again, and move up 3 and 3 again. Then $(-5 + 4 + 4, 4 + 3 + 3)$ yields $(3,10)$.

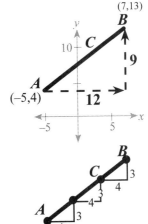

> _**FOLLOW-UP:** Suppose point C is $\frac{3}{5}$ of the way from A to B, the coordinates of A are (7,21) and the coordinates of C are (13,9). What are the coordinates of B?_ [(17,1)]

3E **METHOD 1:** _Strategy: Factor the given expression._

$7! = 1 \times 2 \times 3 \times 4 \times 5 \times 6 \times 7$
$ = 5! \times (6 \times 7).$

Then $5! + 7! = 5! + (5! \times 6 \times 7)$
$ = (5! \times 1) + (5! \times 6 \times 7)$
$ = 5! \times (1 + 6 \times 7)$ \hspace{2em} [by the distributive property]
$ = (1 \times 2 \times 3 \times 4 \times 5) \times 43.$

43 is larger than any prime factor of 5!.

The largest prime factor of 5! + 7! is 43.

METHOD 2: _Strategy: Perform the indicated operations and then factor._
$5! + 7! = 120 + 5{,}040 = 5{,}160.$
Factor out as many small primes as you can: $5{,}160 = 2^3 \times 3 \times 5 \times 43.$
The largest prime factor of 5! + 7! is 43.

> **FOLLOW-UP:** _Find the value of N for which N! $\times$ 4! = (N+1)!_ [23]

Olympiad 4

4A _Strategy: Use reasoning._

First fill in the boxes labeled A and B which must contain the numbers
3 and 4. A is not 4, so A must be 3 and B must be 4. Next fill in box
D with a 2. Then C is 1 or 4. Since C cannot be 4, C is 1 and **the box
marked with an X contains a 4.**

	4	1	A
		B	2
3	C	D	X
		3	

> **FOLLOW-UP:** _Create your own 4 × 4 Sudoku-type puzzle by filling in the answers and then
> erasing some of the numbers. Make sure that the numbers you leave allow only 1 solution._

4B **METHOD 1:** _Strategy: Factor the numerator and denominator._

Factor out the common factor in both the numerator and denominator and then cancel to get
the following.

$$\frac{5 \, (1 - 2 + 3 - 4 + \ldots - 98 + 99 - 100)}{7 \, (1 - 2 + 3 - 4 + \ldots - 98 + 99 - 100)} = \frac{5}{7}$$

METHOD 2: _Strategy: Pair numbers in both numerator and denominator._

Numerator: $(5 - 10) + (15 - 20) + \ldots + (495 - 500) = (-5) + (-5) + (-5) + \ldots + (-5) = -250$
Denominator: $(7 - 14) + (21 - 28) + \ldots + (693 - 700) = (-7) + (-7) + (-7) + \ldots + (-7) = -350$
Then $\frac{-250}{-350} = \frac{5}{7}$

METHOD 3: *Strategy: Look for a pattern in the partial sums.*
Start with $\frac{5}{7}$, next $\frac{5-10}{7-14}$, then $\frac{5-10+15}{7-14+21}$, and so on. In each case the fraction equals $\frac{5}{7}$. In the given fraction both the numerator and denominator contain the same number of terms, 100, so the value remains at $\frac{5}{7}$.

> **FOLLOW-UP:** *Explain why the successive fractions listed in Method 3 are equivalent.*

4C *Strategy: Set up and solve possible equations.*
C is 10 more than A. Also, B. is 3 away from one number and 7 away from the other number. Then $A < B < C$. Moreover, either $B = A + 3$ or $B = A + 7$ as shown below.

Substitute $C = A + 10$ and each possibility for B into $A + B + C = 32$. The result will be two equations: $A + (A + 3) + (A + 10) = 32$ and $A + (A + 7) + (A + 10) = 32$. The first equation results in $A = \frac{19}{3}$ and the second equation results in $A = 5$. A is a whole number so $A = 5$ and **$B = 12$.**

4D *Strategy: Remove the label from the can.*
Cut open the cylinder along the dotted line and unroll it to get a rectangle with A along the top edge and B along the bottom edge. This makes it easier to see the shortest distance from A to B. Then connect A and B with a straight line segment. Place C as shown to form right triangle ACB. Since C is opposite B on the cylinder, BC is one-half the circumference. Then $AC = 8$ cm and $BC = 6$ cm. Apply the Pythagorean Theorem or recognize the Pythagorean triple 6-8-10 to get $AB = 10$ cm. **The shortest distance from A to B is 10 cm.**

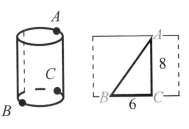

4E *Strategy: List the primes and subtract each prime from 30.*
The probability is the ratio of the number of pairs of primes whose sum is 30 to the total number of all pairs of primes.

Sum is 30: The first nine prime numbers are: 2, 3, 5, 7, 11, 13, 17, 19, and 23. Begin with the greatest prime. $30 - 23 = 7$, also a prime. $30 - 19 = 11$, a prime. $30 - 17 = 13$, a prime. The next prime is 13 which is accounted for; There's no need to test further. Only 3 pairs of primes have a sum of 30: {7, 23}, {11, 19}, and {13, 17}.

All pairs of primes: There are several ways to count all 36 possible pairs of primes. Three methods are offered.

1. Pair each prime with the greater primes: thus 2 is paired with each of the 8 other primes greater than 2, 3 with each of the 7 primes greater than 3, 5 with each of the 6 primes greater than 5, and so on. In all there are $8 + 7 + 6 + 5 + 4 + 3 + 2 + 1 = 36$ pairs of primes.

2. There are 9 possible values for the first of the two primes. Pair each of these with any of the 8 remaining primes, a total of $9 \times 8 = 72$. This, however, counts each pair twice (e. g. 2 paired with 3 and 3 paired with 2). The total number of pairs is $72 \div 2 = 36$.

3. List all pairs of primes in an orderly manner.

The probability that the sum of the 2 primes 30 is $\frac{3}{36} = \frac{1}{12}$.

> ***FOLLOW-UPS:*** *(1) Two different primes are selected from the first 9 prime numbers. What is the probability that their sum is odd? [$\frac{16}{72}$ or $\frac{2}{9}$]   (2) Two primes, not necessarily different, are selected from the first 9 prime numbers. What is the probability that their sum is odd? [$\frac{16}{81}$]   (3) Two different primes are selected from the first 20 prime numbers. What is the probability that their sum is 30? [$\frac{3}{190}$]*

Olympiad 5

5A *Strategy: Maximize the digits, working from the left.*
The largest possible value for A is 9. Since $A = B \times C$, the values of B and C are either 3 and 3, or 9 and 1. Of these, the largest possible value of B is 9. Then C is 1. Thus $B = C \times D$ becomes $9 = 1 \times D$ and D is 9. **The greatest 4-digit number ABCD is 9919.**

> ***FOLLOW-UP:*** *Find the largest 4-digit number, ABCD, so that $A \times B = C$ and $A \times C = D$.*
> [3139]

5B **METHOD 1:** *Strategy: Use algebra and the definition of mean.*
Rewrite $23 - x = y - 71$ as $x + y = 23 + 71 = 94$.

The mean of x and y is $\frac{1}{2}(x + y) = \frac{1}{2}(94) = $ 47.

METHOD 2: *Strategy: Assign values to x.*
The wording of the question implies that there is a single answer no matter what value is assigned for x. Therefore assign any value to find the mean: suppose $x = 1$. Then $y = 93$ and the mean is $\frac{1}{2}(1 + 93) = 47$.

To check, assign at least two very different values to $23 - x = y - 71$: If $x = 80$, then $y = 14$ and again the mean is 47. And if $x = -7$, then $y = 101$ and still the mean is 47.

5C *Strategy: Find a pattern in the successive powers of 2 and of 3.*

$2^1 = \mathbf{\underline{2}}$, $2^2 = \mathbf{\underline{4}}$, $2^3 = \mathbf{\underline{8}}$, $2^4 = 1\underline{6}$, $2^5 = 3\underline{2}$, $2^6 = 6\underline{4}$, $2^7 = 12\underline{8}$, $2^8 = 25\underline{6}$, and so on. The ones digits repeat in the pattern 2, 4, 8, 6 and then 2, 4, 8, 6, and so on. Then 2^4, 2^8, 2^{12}, and 2^{16} all have the same ones digit, 6. Similarly, 2^3, 2^7, 2^{11}, and 2^{15} all have the same ones digit, 8.

Repeat the process on powers of 3. The successive ones digits are 3, 9, 7, 1 and then 3, 9, 7, 1 again, and so on. Then 3^{10} has the same as the ones digit as 3^2, namely 9. Thus **the ones digit in $2^{15} + 3^{10}$** is the same as that of $8 + 9$, which **is 7.**

> ***FOLLOW-UPS:*** *(1) What is the ones digit in the product of $2^{2012} \times 3^{2013} \times 5^{2014}$?* [0]　*(2) How many consecutive zeros appear at the end of the product?* [2012]

5D *Strategy: Draw a picture.*

The angle through which the boat turns is $\angle BOF$. $m\angle BOE = 90 - 41 = 49$ and $m\angle WOF = 90 - 59 = 31$. To begin at a heading of B and finish at a heading of F, the boat must turn either $41 + 90 + 31 = 162°$ counterclockwise, or $49 + 90 + 59 = 198°$ clockwise. The lesser angle requires less time, and at $3°$ per second, **the least time required is** $162 \div 3 = \mathbf{54\ seconds.}$

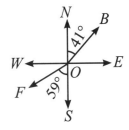

5E *Strategy: Find the total of the unshaded areas.*

The sum of the areas of the 3 circles, $4\pi + 9\pi + 16\pi = 29\pi$, includes each interior region in the picture. However, it includes regions B and C twice, since each is part of two circles. The sum of the areas of B and C is then $(29\pi - 17\pi) \div 2 = 6\pi$. The largest circle, whose area is 16π, consists of regions A, B, and C, so **the area of region A alone is** $16\pi - 6\pi = \mathbf{10\pi.}$

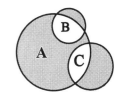

Set 16　Olympiad 1

1A **METHOD 1:** *Strategy: Use the distributive property.*

$2013 \times 10,001 = 2013 \times (10,000 + 1) = 20130000 + 2013$. There are no carries in the addition of the two addends, so the sum of the digits in the sum is the same as the sum of the digits in the two numbers. **The sum of the digits in the product is** $6 + 6 = \mathbf{12.}$

METHOD 2: *Strategy: Do the multiplication.*

$2013 \times 10,001 = 20,132,013$. The sum of the digits in the product is 12.

SET 16   SOLUTIONS

1B   *Strategy*: *Consider the first 6 positive integers.*

The problem suggests that it doesn't matter which 6 consecutive integers are chosen, so choose small values, say, 1 through 6. (You may choose any set of 6 consecutive integers.) Divide each of the numbers 1, 2, 3, 4, 5, and 6 by 6 and get remainders 1, 2, 3, 4, 5, and 0. **The sum of the resulting 6 remainders is 15.**

> **FOLLOW-UP**: *Ari lists the integers from 31 through 50, inclusive, and then crosses out one of them. He divides each of the remaining numbers by 20 and adds the remainders. The sum of the remainders is 177. Which number did Ari cross out?* [33]

1C   **METHOD 1**: *Strategy: Draw a number line.*

Case 1: If P is between –2 and 7 and twice as far from 7 as from –2, divide the segment between them into 3 equal parts as shown below. $7 - (-2) = 9$, so each part is 3 units long. One number that works is $-2 + 3 = 1$.

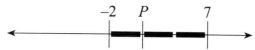

Case 2: If P is to the left of –2 and twice as far from 7 as from –2, then –2 is halfway between P and 7. Since 7 is 9 units to the right of –2, P is 9 units to the left of –2. Another number that works is $(-2) - 9 = -11$.

Note that no other number can be to the right of 7, as it would then be closer to 7 than to –2. **The two integers are 1 and –11.**

METHOD 2: *Strategy: Use algebra.*
Let P represent the number to be found.

Case 1: If P is between –2 and 7, then $7 - P = 2(P - (-2))$. That simplifies to $7 - P = 2(P + 2)$. Multiplying $P + 2$ by 2 results in $7 - P = 2P + 4$. Adding P to each side of the equation results in $7 = 3P + 4$. Subtracting 4 from each side results in $3 = 3P$. Then $P = 1$.

Case 2: However, if P is to the left of –2, then $7 - (-2) = -2 - P$. That simplifies to $9 = -2 - P$. Adding 2 to each side results in $11 = -P$. Multiplying both sides by –1 results in $P = -11$.

The two integers are 1 and –11.

1D   *Strategy*: *Start with five 30s, and adjust.*

The minimal values for the first two numbers are 1 and 1. To maximize the median make the other three numbers as nearly equal as possible. The mean is 30, so the sum of all five numbers is 150. If the first two are 1 and 1, the sum of the other three is 148. $148 \div 3 = 49$ R1. The three numbers can be 49, 49, and 50. **The greatest possible value of the median is 49.**

FOLLOW-UPS: *(1) What other set of 5 numbers would also satisfy the problem's conditions?* [1, 2, 49, 49, 49]   *(2) The mean of the set of numbers 35, 78, 54, 112 and x is 73. What is the median of the set?* [78]

1E   *Strategy: Examine each of the ten slices.*

Suppose the slices are made horizontally. The picture shows a view of all the slices. The top and bottom slices each have 9 blocks that have just one painted face. On each of the eight remaining slices there are 3 blocks with 1 painted face along each of the 4 horizontal sides. So, 3 blocks × 4 faces = 12 blocks painted per slice. **There is a total of** (2 × 9) + (8 × 12) = **114 blocks that have exactly one painted face.**

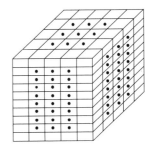

FOLLOW-UPS: *(1) How many of the 250 blocks have no faces painted?* [72]   *(2) How many have exactly 3 faces painted?* [8]   *(3) Suppose the original cube, after painting, is sliced into 25 pieces, each 10 × 10 × 0.4 and then each of these pieces is cut into 1 × 1 × 0.4 blocks. How many of these 2500 blocks have exactly 3 faces painted red?* [8]

Olympiad 2

2A   METHOD 1: *Strategy: Cast out weeks.*

After August 1st, there are 30 more days in August. There are 30 additional days in September and 25 more to October 25th. That is a total of 85 days. 85 ÷ 7 = 12, R1. Then October 25 is 1 day later in the week than August 1. October 25, 2018 is a Thursday, so **August 1, 2018 is Wednesday.**

METHOD 2: *Strategy: Count backward.*

October 25, 2018 is a Thursday. Then October 18, 11, 4, September 27, 20, 13, 6, August 30, 23, 16, 9, and 2 are also Thursdays. August 1, 2018 is a Wednesday.

METHOD 3: *Strategy: Count forward.*

August 1 is the same day of the week as August 8, 15, 22, 29, September 5, 12, 19, 26, October 3, 10, 17, and 24. October 25 is a Thursday, so August 1, 2018 is a Wednesday.

FOLLOW-UPS: *February 5, 2012 was a Sunday. On what day of the week is February 5, 2018?* [Monday]

2B **METHOD 1:** _Strategy: Split the region into more familiar shapes._
Draw $\overline{EF}$ to split the rectangle into 2 congruent squares. One-fourth of each square is shaded, and putting the squares together, one-fourth of rectangle *ABCD* is shaded. The area of *ABCD* is 128 sq cm, so **the area of the shaded region is 32 sq cm.**

METHOD 2: _Strategy: Draw a useful line segment._
Since $AE = EB = BC = CF = FD = DA = 8$, all acute angles in the figure measure 45° and all other angles are right angles. Draw $\overline{EF}$, which is also 8. Rectangle *ABCD* is now divided into 8 congruent isosceles right triangles. The area of *ABCD* is 128 sq cm, so the area of each of the smaller 8 triangles is 16 sq cm. The area of the shaded square, consisting of two such triangles, is 32 sq cm.

> **FOLLOW-UPS:** _(1) Suppose in the given problem, AB = 40 cm and BC = 7 cm. What is the area of the shaded region?_ [70 sq cm]   _(2) Suppose in the given problem, AB = x cm and BC = y cm. What is the area of the shaded region in terms of x and y?_ [$\frac{xy}{4}$ sq cm]

2C _Strategy: Start with the most restrictive condition._
There are fewer 2-digit perfect squares than 2-digit primes, so start with the squares.

$P + 3$	**16**	25	36	49	**64**	81
P	**13**	22	33	46	**61**	78
Is P prime?	**yes**	no	no	no	**yes**	no
$P + 6$	19				67	
Is $P = 6$ prime?	**yes**				**yes**	

19 and 67 are two-digit primes. However, 19 is not the next greater prime after 13; 17 is also prime. There are no primes between 61 and 67. **P is 61.**

2D **METHOD 1:** _Strategy: Simplify the problem by assuming the train is not moving._
The boy travels 3 mph faster than the train. Suppose the train is not moving and the boy travels at 3 mph. He will reach the front of the train in the same amount of time as he would in the given problem. Traveling at 3 mph is equivalent to traveling 1 mile in 20 minutes ($\frac{1}{3}$ of an hour), and thus $\frac{1}{4}$ of a mile in 5 minutes. Therefore, **M = 5.**

METHOD 2: *Strategy: Make a chart*

Using the information given, the train's speed is $\frac{8}{60}$ of a mile every minute, and the boy's speed is $\frac{11}{60}$ of a mile every minute, create the following chart:

Distances	At 1 minute	At 2 minutes	At 3 minutes	At 4 minutes	At 5 minutes
Train	$\frac{8}{60}$	$\frac{16}{60}$	$\frac{24}{60}$	$\frac{32}{60}$	$\frac{40}{60}$
Boy	$\frac{11}{60}$	$\frac{22}{60}$	$\frac{33}{60}$	$\frac{44}{60}$	$\frac{55}{60}$
From rear of train to boy	$\frac{3}{60}$	$\frac{6}{60}$	$\frac{9}{60}$	$\frac{12}{60}$	$\frac{15}{60}$

Since the train is $\frac{1}{4}$ of a mile long the distance between the boy and the rear of the train has to be $\frac{1}{4} = \frac{15}{60}$ of a mile. That occurs at 5 minutes.

> **FOLLOW-UP**: *Suppose the train travels at 12 mph and the boy starts at the front of the train and travels at 8 mph toward the rear of the train. How long will it take him to reach the rear of the train?* [45 seconds]

2E   *Strategy: Minimize the numerator and maximize the denominator.*

Divide: $\frac{a}{b} \div \frac{6}{25} = \frac{a}{b} \times \frac{25}{6}$. Because the result is a whole number, then 6 is a factor of a and b is a factor of 25. Likewise, $\frac{a}{b} \div \frac{8}{15} = \frac{a}{b} \times \frac{15}{8}$. Because this result is a whole number, then 8 is a factor of a and b is a factor of 15. Since 6 and 8 are both factors of a, the least possible value of a is 24. Also, since b is a factor of both 25 and 15, the greatest possible value of b is 5. **The least possible value of the fraction $\frac{a}{b}$ is $\frac{24}{5}$.**

Olympiad 3

3A   *Strategy: Use the 10 and 7 to find Y.*

Because $10 - Y = 7$, Y is 3. Then $8 - 3 = 5$ and $7 - 5 = 2$. Fill in 5 and 2.

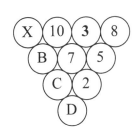

The remaining circles contain 1, 4, 6, and 9 in some order: because $C - 2 = D$, then C is 6 and D is 4. Fill in 6 and 4.

Since $|7 - B| = 6$, B is 1 or 13. Since 13 is not in the set, B is 1. Therefore, X is $10 - 1 = 9$. Thus **Y = 3 and X = 9.**

3B *Strategy: Represent the given information in algebraic form.*
The first 2 diagrams show that $2A + B = 17$ and $A + 2B = 13$. The third diagram shows that $A + B = C$. The question asks for the value of $A + B$.

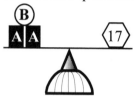 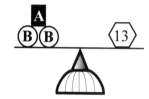 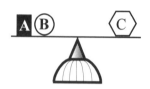

METHOD 1: Add the equations $2A + B = 17$ and $A + 2B = 13$ to get $3A + 3B = 30$. Divide both sides of $3A + 3B = 30$ by 3 to get $A + B = 10$. Because $A + B = C$, **C is 10.**

METHOD 2: Since $2A + B = 17$ and $A + 2B = 13$, the value of A is 4 more than that of B. Because $2A + B = 17$, $2A + A = 21$. Then $3A = 21$ and <u>A is 7</u>.

Now find B and then C: Since $2A + B = 17$, $14 + B = 17$ and <u>B is 3</u>. These values also check in $A + 2B = 13$. Since $A + B = 7 + 3$, <u>C is 10</u>.

> ***Follow Ups***: *(1) Find the value of $a + b + c$ in the system of equations: $a + b + 5c = 23$; $a + 5b + c = 19$; $5a + b + c = 35$. [11]   (2) Find the values of x, y, and z: $x + y - z = -2$; $x - y + z = 5$; $-x + y + z = -4$. [$x = \frac{3}{2}$, $y = -3$, $z = \frac{1}{2}$.]*

3C *Strategy: Seat the boys one at a time.*
Let the first boy pick any of the 8 available chairs. If the second boy is to sit in a chair next to the first boy, then he has only two choices out of the seven unoccupied chairs. So **the probability that the two boys are seated next to each other is $\frac{2}{7}$.** The girls may sit in any order without affecting the outcome.

> ***Follow-Up:*** *Suppose an empty chair is between the 2 boys at the table. What is the probability that one particular girl is <u>not</u> seated next to either boy? [$\frac{3}{6}$ or $\frac{1}{2}$]*

3D METHOD 1: *Strategy: Look for a pattern in the number of new trees each year.*
Each year the farmer plants 4 more trees than the previous year.

Year	1	2	3	4	...	9
Number of new trees planted	1	5	9	13	...	?
Total trees to date	1	6	15	28	...	?

3	3	3	3	3
3	2	2	2	3
3	2	1	2	3

The total number of trees is then $1 + 5 + 9 + 13 + 17 + 21 + 25 + 29 + 33 = 153$. Or, since the numbers in the second row of the table are equally spaced, their sum equals the median multiplied by the number of entries: $17 \times 9 = 153$. **By the end of the Year 9, he had planted 153 trees in all.**

METHOD 2: _Strategy_: _Find the dimensions of the rectangle at the end of each year._
Examine the diagram for each of the first three years. Starting with Year 2, each year he adds one more row and two more columns. Thus, the total number of trees at the end of two years is arrayed in 2 rows of 3 columns each for 6 trees, at the end of three years in 3 rows of 5 columns each for 15 trees, and at the end of four years, there were 4 rows of 7 columns each for a total of 28 trees (as shown in the table above). Following the pattern, at the end of nine years he had planted 9 rows of 17 columns each for a total of 153 trees.

3E   _Strategy_: _Express the area of triangle ABC in two ways._
Graph and label the figure, as shown. Counting boxes, $AB = 8$ and $BC = 6$. Express the area of triangle ABC two different ways: $\frac{1}{2} \times 6 \times 8$ and $\frac{1}{2} \times 10 \times h$. Then equate them since they represent the same area: $24 = 5 \times h$.

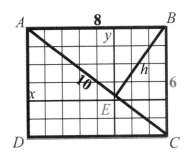

The length of $\overline{BE}$ is 4.8.

> **FOLLOW-UP:** _The lengths of the legs of a right triangle are represented by a units and b units, the hypotenuse by c units, and the altitude to the hypotenuse by h units. Express the value of h in terms of a, b, and c._ $[h = \frac{ab}{c}]$

Olympiad 4

4A   METHOD 1: _Strategy_: _Draw the diagram._
The shortest path occurs when each move is toward the goal. One possible path is shown. Count to find that **the shortest path is 21 units long.**

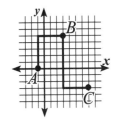

METHOD 2: _Strategy_: _Determine horizontal and vertical distances separately._
Horizontally, the distance from $A(-1, 0)$ to $B(3, 5)$ is 4 units, and then on to $C(7, -3)$ is also 4 units for a total of 8 units. Vertically, the distance from $A(-1, 0)$ to $B(3, 5)$ is 5 units, and then on to $C(7, -3)$ is 8 units for a total of 13 units. The length of the shortest path is $8 + 13 = 21$ units long.

4B _Strategy: Count in an organized way._

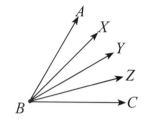

Consider each individual angle and each combination of adjacent individual angles.

One individual angle: $\angle ABX$, $\angle XBY$, $\angle YBZ$, $\angle ZBC$.
Two individual angles: $\angle ABY$, $\angle XBZ$, $\angle YBC$
Three individual angles: $\angle ABZ$, $\angle XBC$
Four individual angles: $\angle ABC$

Altogether, $4 + 3 + 2 + 1 = \textbf{10 acute angles are in the diagram.}$

> **Follow Ups:** _(1) A triangle is formed by connecting 3 vertices of a given pentagon. In how many ways can this be done? [10] (2) Why is this question equivalent to problem 4B? [Consider the vertices that are not used.] (3) How many different committees of 5 people can be chosen from a group of 7 people? [21]_

4C _Strategy: Minimize the number of ushers._

Group each 30 fans with 1 usher to form groups of 31. Then the 20,000 people are divided into 645 groups of 31 each, with 5 people left over. Those 5 people must contain at least 1 usher and at most 4 fans. There must be at least $645 + 1 = 646$ ushers. **There are at most** $20,000 - 646 = \textbf{19,354 fans that can be in attendance.}$

4D METHOD 1: _Strategy: Draw a useful line segment._

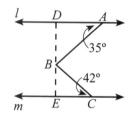

Through B draw a line segment ($\overline{DE}$) perpendicular to both line l and line m as shown. The acute angles in a right triangle are complementary. In right $\triangle DBA$, $\angle DBA$ contains $90 - 35 = 55°$. Similarly, in right $\triangle EBC$, $\angle EBC$ contains $90 - 42 = 48°$. $\angle DBE$ is a straight angle and it equals $180°$, **so** $\angle\textbf{ABC} = 180 - 55 - 48 = \textbf{77°.}$

METHOD 2: _Strategy: Draw a different useful line segment._

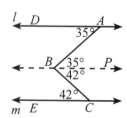

Through B draw line BP parallel to both line l and line m as shown. If a transversal cuts two parallel lines, the alternate interior angles are congruent. Then $\angle DAB$ contains the same number of degrees, 35, as $\angle ABP$ and $\angle PBC$ contains the same number of degrees, 42, as $\angle BCE$. Therefore $\angle ABC$ contains $35 + 42 = 77°$.

SET 16 SOLUTIONS

4E _Strategy: Convert the given fractions into decimals._
Counting the decimals is an easier process than counting fractions. Write the given fractions in decimal form using 3 decimal digits: $\frac{1}{4} = .250$ and $\frac{3}{8} = .375$. From .001 through .375, there are 375 three-place decimals, but 249 of them (.001 through .249) are not in the desired range. Thus there are $375 - 249 = 126$ decimals in the range that can be expressed using exactly three decimal places, and each of them is equivalent to a unique fraction in lowest terms. **There are 126 fractions between $\frac{1}{4}$ and $\frac{3}{8}$ inclusive that can be exactly represented using three-digit decimals.**

> **_Follow-Up:_** _There are exactly 13 fractions in lowest terms between $\frac{1}{5}$ and N, inclusive, that can be represented as a decimal numeral with exactly two decimal digits. $N > \frac{1}{5}$. Find N in lowest terms. $[\frac{8}{25}]$_

Olympiad 5

5A **METHOD 1:** _Strategy: Make a table comparing the faulty and actual distances._

Odometer Reading in Miles	4.6	9.2	...	46	92
Actual Miles Traveled	5	10	...	50	100

Acton and Bywater are 100 miles apart.

METHOD 2: _Strategy: Use proportional reasoning_
The ratio of registered miles to actual miles is always 4.6 to 5. Since 4.6 must be multiplied by 20 to get 92, multiply 5 by 20. Acton and Bywater are 100 miles apart.

METHOD 3: _Strategy: Use algebra._
  If x is the actual distance traveled, then: $\frac{4.6}{5} = \frac{92}{x}$
  Cross-multiply: $4.6x = (5)(92)$
  Simplify: $4.6x = 460$
  Divide each side of the equation by 4.6: $x = 100$
Therefore Acton and Bywater are 100 miles apart.

5B _Strategy: Look for a pattern in the partial sums._
Write the first term, the sum of the first two terms, the sum of the first three terms, and so on, to form a new sequence: 2, –1, –3, 0, then 2, –1, –3, 0, then 2, –1, –3, 0, ... These cumulative sums repeat in blocks of 4. 2012 is a multiple of 4, so the 2012th sum is 0. The 2013th sum is therefore 2. **The sum of the first 2013 terms of the sequence is 2.**

> **_FOLLOW-UPS:_** _(1) Suppose today is Wednesday. What day of the week is 1000 days from today? [Tuesday] (2) The first four terms of the series $2 - 3 - x + 3 + \ldots$ repeat endlessly. Find the value of x that will make the sum of the first 47 terms equal –87. [9]_

5C   METHOD 1: _Strategy: Select a convenient value for x._
There are infinitely many pairs of values of x and y that satisfy the given equation. Select any convenient value of y and use it to solve for x. For example, suppose y is 0. Then $5x - 2y = 30$ becomes $5x - 0 = 30$ and $x = 6$. Then $y - \frac{5}{2}x$ becomes $(0) - \frac{5}{2}(6) = 0 - 15$. Thus, $y - \frac{5}{2}x = -15$.

Check by using a few other values for x or y. The result will always be -15.

METHOD 2: _Strategy: Use algebraic procedures to transform the equation._

Start with the given equation:	$5x - 2y = 30$
Multiply both sides of equation by -1:	$-1(5x - 2y) = -30$
Distribute the negative sign on the left side of equation:	$-5x + 2y = -30$
Rearrange the terms on the left side of equation:	$2y - 5x = -30$
Divide each term by 2:	$y - \frac{5}{2}x = -15$:

5D   _Strategy: Use the meaning of percent._
The fraction of all adults starting a new business last year was $\frac{1}{N}$ and this year it was $\frac{1}{55}$. An increase of 20% means that the new rate is 120% of the old rate, or 1.2 times the old rate.

The old rate multiplied by 1.2 is the new rate:	$(1.2)\frac{1}{N} = \frac{1}{55}$
Multiply $\frac{1}{N}$ by 1.2:	$\frac{1.2}{N} = \frac{1}{55}$
Cross-multiply:	$(N)(1) = (1.2)(55)$
Simplify:	$N = 66$

The equation can be solved in several other ways but the result will always be $N = 66$.

5E   _Strategy: Start with simple cases and look for a pattern._
Start with a rectangle which has 4 "inside" corners and 0 "outside" corners. Then add one corner at a time by cutting right-angled pieces from it.

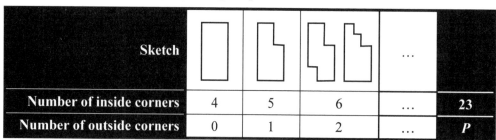

Sketch				...	
Number of inside corners	4	5	6	...	23
Number of outside corners	0	1	2	...	P

In each case there are 4 more inside corners than outside corners. In the complete floor plan, there are 23 inside corners and therefore 19 outside corners. **P = 19.**

HOST YOUR OWN TOURNAMENT

OUR TOURNAMENT PROGRAM

A TOURNAMENT IS A ONE-DAY LOCAL OR REGIONAL EVENT FOR STUDENTS IN GRADES 4 - 6 OR 6 - 8. IT PROVIDES A FACE-TO-FACE TEAM COMPETITION FOR AS MANY TEAMS AS YOUR VENUE CAN ACCOMMODATE, AND COULD PROVIDE AN EXCITING CULMINATION TO THE SCHOOL YEAR OR AN EXCITING KICK-OFF FOR A NEW YEAR.

THE TOURNAMENT YOU SET UP BEARS YOUR ORGANIZATION'S NAME - IT'S YOUR TOURNAMENT! RECENT TOURNAMENTS HAVE BEEN SPONSORED BY SCHOOL DISTRICTS, COLLEGES, PROFESSIONAL ORGANIZATIONS, AND AFTER-SCHOOL ENRICHMENT PROGRAMS.

A DETAILED TOURNAMENT HANDBOOK IS PROVIDED TO ENABLE YOUR SCHOOL, DISTRICT OR ORGANIZATION TO SUCCESSFULLY LAUNCH ONE OF THESE FAST-GROWING EVENTS.

PAYMENT OF THE ANNUAL FEE ENABLES YOU TO GIVE THE TOURNAMENT YOUR OWN NAME, DECIDE WHO WILL BE INVITED, AND WHEN IT WILL BE HELD!

FREQUENTLY ASKED QUESTIONS

How do I register for a Tournament?

Simply fill out a (Tournament Agreement form (available in this packet and also on line) and send it to our office for approval. Once it's approved (approval is based upon whether there is another Tournament running too close to the area you are requesting), you will be asked to submit fees and you will receive the Tournament Handbook. If you want to get an idea of the numbers of Math Olympiad teams in your proposed region, give us a call.

What information is contained in the handbook?

The handbook contains detailed instructions and valuable suggestions for running a successful event. Included are: schedules (for before the date and on the actual date), sample table arrangements, areas of responsibility and detailed instructions for your committee members (only 3 - 4 heads of committees make this endeavor work very well), and sample correspondence forms (including publicity letters for before and after the tournament, press releases, and team registration forms).

How is the tournament different from the monthly Mathematical Olympiad Contests?

Although the problems on the Tournaments are similar to those on the contests, there are some major differences. The competition is divided into three parts. Each team of 5 students will take a 10-question individual contest. That is followed up by another 10-question *team* event, where only one set of answers is submitted for each team. Finally, in the event of any ties (individuals or teams), there is a set of tiebreaker problems.

What does it mean when we say, "It's YOUR Tournament?"

The name that you give your tournament will appear in a 2-inch high masthead on top of every page (we provide the template for you to use). This tournament represents your group and provides many benefits, including promoting your reputation for excellence, strengthening your organization, generating publicity, or if desired, producing revenue.

What does the sponsoring organization have to do to get ready?

The sponsoring organization decides what fee (if any) to charge to teams, chooses a site, invites schools, prints and packages the contests, and buys awards. Our handbook will guide you through every step.

How will the teams get their results?

Every student and team will know where they stand in the Tournament by the end of the event. Scoring is done by a few volunteers during the event. An electronic spreadsheet is provided on which you will enter individuals' scores. That spreadsheet will rank the results, so that you will be able to have an awards program on the same day!

Are solutions to the problems included?

There is review time for all questions built into the suggested schedule. A set of Power Point® slides is included to use on that day, so that the person reviewing the answers has little to do, but explain strategies and answer questions.

Is it necessary that the students at the tournament have participated in the monthly Math Olympiad Contests?

No, in fact many sponsoring organizations use this as a way to get more schools in their area involved in Math Olympiads. Your tournament may be administered anytime from April through December of the same school year.

What if I still have other concerns or questions?

We are always available to help you or answer any other questions you may have. Just call or e-mail us.